The Economics of Tobacco Control

Towards an Optimal Policy Mix

Edited by

Iraj Abedian
Rowena van der Merwe
Nick Wilkins
Prabhat Jha

A publication of the
Applied Fiscal Research Centre, University of Cape Town

In collaboration with support by the Human Development Network of The
World Bank for the international conference on *The Economics of Tobacco
Control: Towards an Optimal Policy Mix*, Cape Town, 18-20 February 1998

Contents

Contributors

Iraj Abedian is Director of the Applied Fiscal Research Centre and Associate Professor in the School of Economics, University of Cape Town, Private Bag, Rondebosch 7700, Cape Town, South Africa.

Frank Chaloupka is Associate Professor at the Department of Economics, University of Illinois at Chicago, 601 South Morgan Street, Chicago, IL 60607-7121, USA.

David Collins is Associate Professor and Deputy Head of the School of Economic and Financial Studies at Macquarie University, Sydney, NSW 2109, Australia.

Neil Collishaw is the responsible officer on the Programme on Substance Abuse at the World Health Organisation, 20 Avenue Abbia, CH-1211, Geneva 27, Switzerland.

Michaelyn Corbett is a PhD Candidate at the Department of Economics, University of Illinois at Chicago, 601 South Morgan Street, Chicago, IL 60607-7121, USA.

Vera Luiza da Costa e Silva is a physician and Co-ordinator of Tobacco Control and Primary Cancer Prevention in the National Cancer Institute, Health Ministry of Brazil, Rua dos Inválidos 212/2a, Gr. 201 Centro, Rio de Janeiro, 20231-20, Brazil.

Brian Easton is an economist and Professorial Research Fellow at the Central Institute of Technology, 18 Talavera Terrace, Kelburn, Wellington, New Zealand.

Richard Feachem is the Director of Health, Nutrition and Population at the Human Development Network, The World Bank, 1818 H Street, NW, Washington, DC 20433, USA.

Helmut Geist is a geographer at the Institute of Geography at the University of Düsseldorf, D 40255, Düsseldorf, Germany.

Chee-Ruey Hsieh is an Associate Research Fellow at the Institute of Economics, Academia Sinica, Nankang, Taipei, Taiwan.

Teh-Wei Hu is a Professor of Health Economics at the School of Public Health at the University of California at Berkeley, 412 Warren Hall, Berkeley, CA 94720, USA.

Prabhat Jha is a Health Specialist at the Human Development Network, The World Bank, 1818 H Street, NW, Washington, DC 20433, USA.

Luk Joossens is a sociologist at the Research Department at the Centre of Research and Information of the Consumers' Organisation (CRIOC OIVO), Ridderstraat 18, 1050, Brussels, Belgium.

Kamal Kabra is a Professor of Economics at the Institute of Public Administration, Indraprastha Estate, Mahatma Gandhi Marg, New Delhi 110002, India.

Theodore Keeler is a Professor of Health Economics at the School of Public Health at the University of California at Berkeley, 412 Warren Hall, Berkeley, CA 94720, USA.

Pamphil H.M. Kweyuh is a journalist and Executive Co-ordinator of the Tobacco Control Commission, P.O. Box 12871, ATOM, Nairobi, Kenya.

Helen Lapsley is an economist and Senior Lecturer in Health Economics at the School of Health Services Management, Faculty of Medicine, University of New South Wales, Sydney 2052, Australia.

Yan-Shu Lin is an Associate Research Fellow at the Institute of Economics, Academia Sinica, Nankang, Taipei, Taiwan.

Judith Mackay is Director of the Asian Consultancy on Tobacco Control, Riftswood, 9th Milestone, DD 229, Lot 147 Clearwater Bay Road, Sai Kung, Kowloon HO, Hong Kong, China.

Edward Maravanyika is a researcher at the School of Economics at the University of Cape Town, Private Bag, Rondebosch 7700, Cape Town, South Africa.

Amy Marks is a Senior Lecturer at the Graduate School of Business at the University of Cape Town, Portswood Road, V&A Waterfront, Greenpoint 8060, Cape Town, South Africa.

Sergiusz Matusiak is Financial Manager for the Health Promotion Foundation, 5 Roentgen Street, 02-781 Warsaw, Poland.

Yumiko Mochizuki is a specialist at the Department of Community Health and Health Promotion at the Health Care Bureau, Ministry of Health and Welfare, 1-2-2, Kasumigaseki, Chiyoda-ku, Tokyo 100, Japan.

Toshitaka Nakahara is Director of the Department of Public Health at the School of Medicine, Sakyo-ku, Kyoto 606-01, Japan.

Thomas E. Novotny is the Centers for Disease Control (CDC) liaison to the Human Development Department at the World Bank, 1818 H Street, NW, Washington, DC 20433, USA.

Richard Peck is Associate Professor at the Department of Economics, University of Illinois at Chicago, 601 South Morgan Street, Chicago, IL 60607-7121, USA.

Krzysztof Przewozniak is Senior Researcher at the Cancer Epidemiology and Prevention Department of the Maria Skodowska-Curie Memorial Cancer Center and Institute of Oncology, 5 Roentgen Street, 02-781 Warsaw, Poland.

Joy Townsend is Professor and Director of the Centre for Research in Primary and Community Care, Hatfield Campus, College Lane, Hatfield, University of Hertfordshire, Herts AL 109 AB, United Kingdom.

Rowena van der Merwe is an economist and PhD candidate at the University of York, United Kingdom.

Kenneth Warner is Professor of Public Health in the Department of Health Management and Policy at the University of Michigan, 109 S. Observatory, Ann Arbor, MI 48 109-2029, USA.

Nick Wilkins is a Research Associate at the Applied Fiscal Research Centre of the School of Economics at the University of Cape Town, Private Bag, Rondebosch 7700, Cape Town, South Africa.

Xiao-peng Xu is a Post-Doctoral Fellow at the School of Public Health at the University of California at Berkeley, 412 Warren Hall, Berkeley, CA 94720, USA.

Derek Yach is responsible for Policy Action Co-ordination, CDG/WHO, at the World Health Organisation, 20 Avenue Abbia, CH-1211, Geneva 27, Switzerland.

Witold Zatonski is Director of the Cancer Epidemiology and Prevention Department of the Maria Skodowska-Curie Memorial Cancer Center and Institute of Oncology, 5 Roentgen Street, 02-781 Warsaw, Poland.

Preface

Iraj Abedian and Prabhat Jha

This book is a product of the international conference entitled *The Economics of Tobacco Control: Towards an Optimal Policy Mix*, held during 18-20 February 1998 in Cape Town, South Africa. The conference was hosted jointly by the University of Cape Town and the South African Medical Research Council, and was the first of its kind in the world to examine the economic issues pertaining to tobacco control across both developed and developing countries.

In some respects, the Conference was the culmination of the two-year research activities of the *Economics of Tobacco Control Project* (ETCP), based at the Applied Fiscal Research Centre (formerly The Budget Project) in the School of Economics of the University of Cape Town and financed by the International Tobacco Initiative (ITI). This project resulted in a variety of new economic analyses applied to South Africa and Zimbabwe; the former a key cigarette manufacturer and the latter a major tobacco producer in the region.

Concurrent with the activities of the ETCP, Prabhat Jha and others at the World Bank began a major review of the Bank's tobacco control policies. The Bank organised a consultation session at the *Tenth World Conference on Tobacco or Health* in Beijing, China in August 1997. There was a clear recognition at this meeting that insufficient global attention was being paid to the economics of tobacco control, and that for the most part, the methodological applications of economics at country level were of varying quality. The Applied Fiscal Research Centre of the University of Cape Town and the World Bank, in partnership with Fred Paccaud at the University of Lausanne and others, agreed to expand the February 1998 conference to involve a wider audience, and to disseminate the results of that meeting through this book.

Much more needs to be known about the various aspects of tobacco control in different settings. Increasingly those interested in control turn to economic analysis and methodology to guide public policy making. To this end, this book's audience is public policy-makers throughout the world, especially those in developing countries where the tobacco epidemic looms largest. The book is an attempt to collate the most recent economic research and analysis and to summarise directions for further work at the country level.

Note: The views represented in this book are those of the authors and not of the University of Cape Town or of the World Bank or its member countries.

Introduction

The Economics of Tobacco Control

Prabhat Jha and Iraj Abedian

There is no longer any doubt that prolonged smoking causes lung and other cancers, cardiovascular disease and respiratory disease. Smoking in pregnancy causes low birth weight, ectopic pregnancy and birth defects (Wald and Hackshaw, 1996). Direct evidence from large prospective (Thun *et al.*, 1997) and retrospective (Parish *et al.*, 1995) studies, and indirect evidence from use of the "smoking impact ratio" (Peto *et al.*, 1994) have improved the precision of estimates of tobacco-attributable mortality in developed countries over the last decade. Startlingly large hazards of smoking have emerged from these studies. One in two long-term smokers is killed by the habit, and half of these deaths occur in productive middle age (age 35-69). Among smokers four of five heart attacks in men aged 30 to 49 in the UK are due to smoking. On current smoking patterns, about half a billion people living today will be killed by their habit, and half of these will be today's children and teenagers.

Although epidemiological evidence on smoking has improved over the last 40 years, uncertainty remains on the relative and absolute hazards of prolonged smoking among different age groups in populations with differing underlying risks of chronic degenerative disease. Direct epidemiological evidence is urgently required in developing countries, where the tobacco epidemic is large and growing. Already, smoking causes about one in eight of Chinese male deaths and the percentage is rising quickly (Liu *et al.*, 1998). Richard Peto and Alan Lopez are updating estimates of tobacco-attributable mortality by region for the next World Conference on Tobacco or Health in 2000. Their estimates will likely confirm that the tobacco epidemic is now common to all regions of the world, and growing most rapidly among men in low- and middle-income countries and among women in most parts of the world.

Key debates in economics

While epidemiologists are certain of the health hazards of smoking, there are many debates among economists and policy-makers about public responses to smoking. The debate focuses on three questions:

1. Is smoking a social problem demanding societal or government action?
2. What are the economic benefits and costs of tobacco consumption?
3. What are economically efficient and equitable methods of reducing tobacco consumption?

All three issues have raised serious debate with no consensus. The lack of consensus is partly because economists have only recently addressed smoking,

1

and partly because economic methodologies to understand smoking are more complex ˉand more variable in their application than are epidemiological analyses of tobacco-attributable diseases.

With regard to the first issue, some economists argue that smoking does not constitute an important social problem. They believe smokers know the risks and bear the costs of their habit, and that tolerant societies ought therefore to do little to reduce smoking (*The Economist*, 1997). Such assumptions have been vigorously challenged. Ample evidence points to underestimation of risks of smoking, especially by children and teenagers. Nicotine addiction also alters perceived risks and benefits (Kessler, 1995). Recent estimates of the hazards of smoking in a 'mature' tobacco epidemic also suggest that any past estimates of risk may have been falsely low.

There is also ample debate on the net social costs of tobacco. Smoking accounts for a substantial percentage of health care costs in developed countries, but could reduce future health care costs or public pension payments. Despite these arguments, it is uncertain whether most societies do, in fact, save money from dead smokers (Warner *et al.*, 1995; Barendregt *et al.*, 1997). Such comparisons, of course, cause much concern to many in public health: the goal of public health policy is improved health and not financial savings. Most economists, policy-makers and public health officials would agree that societies value avoiding premature deaths and disability, and that healthy lives contribute to economic growth (World Bank, 1993). No doubt, the debate on smoking as a social issue will continue. This book contributes to that debate (see Chapters 1, 5, 6, 13 and 14). Partly, the answer to this question depends on one's underlying convictions about individual choice and about the role of the state. But perhaps more importantly, such debate has not yet benefited from sufficiently detailed and quantitative examination of risks and costs in developed or developing countries. Empirical estimates from a range of countries with varying income, education and public expenditure levels are needed to estimate actual, perceived and internalised risks of tobacco use. Better delineation of short-term and long-term social costs also requires additional empirical work prior to accepting the suggestion that smokers do "pay their way".

The second area of debate involves the benefits to governments, societies and economic growth from output and employment in tobacco farming and the manufacture of tobacco products, revenues from taxes on tobacco products, and jobs in advertising and promotion. Such arguments are not new. In the 1950s, the British Chancellor of the Exchequer warned of "the enormous contribution to the Exchequer from tobacco duties and the serious effect on the Commonwealth . . . that a campaign against smoking would have" (Pollock, 1996). Basic economics suggests that if people do not spend their money on tobacco products, they would spend it on other goods. Nonetheless, given that job losses are immediate, while both employment creation in other sectors and the consequences of tobacco use are longer-term, most governments have had difficulty applying such basic principles. Empirical analysis in the US, the UK and South Africa suggests that the net contribution of tobacco jobs to their economies is minimal at best (Warner and Fulton, 1994; Economics of Tobacco Control Project, 1997c).

Many governments rely on tax revenue from tobacco products, and the tobacco industry often argues that increased taxation would lower revenue. Tobacco demand is price-inelastic and its demand curve is downward-sloping. Thus, not surprisingly, numerous empirical studies find that raising tobacco taxes both increases revenue and decreases consumption. This book contains useful data from countries which previously did not have such demand analyses such as Brazil (Chapter 26), South Africa (Chapter 20), Zimbabwe (Chapter 21), and Taiwan (Chapter 24). Finally, the actual or perceived benefits from the tobacco industry influence the political economy of tobacco control. One framework for understanding links between such actual or perceived benefits and control measures is provided in Chapter 1 in this book. This framework supports, for example, the good sense of aggressive domestic tobacco control policies in countries that largely export their tobacco.

The third area of debate involves choices of economically efficient and equitable interventions to reduce demand. Interventions to reduce demand for tobacco vary considerably, including health promotion programmes, youth access restrictions, nicotine replacement policies, advertising and promotion bans, and price increases. There is increasing recognition that price, information and income largely determine demand for tobacco. Surprisingly, only recently has taxation entered the realm of tobacco control policies, as noted in Chapter 7 of this book. Although multiple strategies appear necessary, there is little doubt that tobacco taxation is the single most effective measure to reduce demand, especially among children and lower income groups. Tax increases are now the cornerstone of proposed tobacco control policies of several developed countries. These policies arose because of sufficient analyses to justify such tax increases (National Cancer Board, 1997). Analysis from Brazil, China, Japan, Taiwan, South Africa and Zimbabwe in this book supports the primacy of tax increases to reduce demand in developed and developing countries.

This book also discusses smuggling (Chapter 12) and trade (Chapter 11), two relatively newly identified areas that potentially affect optimal tax levels. As yet there are no comprehensive cost-effectiveness analyses of control interventions in developed or developing countries. Nor have public economics approaches or examination of the impact on the poor been applied widely to control interventions. Understanding impacts on poverty is increasingly important, given that smoking and tobacco-attributable diseases occur much more frequently in lower income groups (Townsend, 1996). Forthcoming analyses in the UK suggest that smoking may account for more than half of the mortality excess among lower social class middle-aged men, versus upper social class middle-aged men. This book underlines the fact that tax increases reduce smoking more among the poor than among the rich, and that the relative tax burden among the poor may be less than previously suggested. In contrast, the poor respond less to information than do the rich (see Chapter 8).

The structure of this book

This book has three distinct sections. Section 1 describes public policies and tobacco control, examining the overall systemic issues of tobacco control. Chapter 1 outlines a conceptual framework for a general economic analysis of an optimal policy mix for tobacco control. This is followed in Chapter 2 by an analysis of tobacco control within the context of the new global health policy. Chapter 3 underscores the significance of current policies *vis-à-vis* their impact on the global incidence of smoking and the burden of the smoking epidemic across the nations over the next two decades. The future pattern of smoking prevalence is, however, closely linked to our current vision of tobacco in the future; these interrelated issues are reviewed in Chapter 4. Given the central role of public policies, Chapter 5 focuses on the role of governments in tobacco control.

Section 2 concentrates on specific issues related to the economics of tobacco control, concerning aspects of production, distribution, and consumption. The section is composed of 13 chapters, which together cover nearly all the major economic issues that commonly arise in considering policy alternatives towards tobacco. Salient among them are the significance of government revenue from tobacco, earmarked taxation of tobacco, trade and smuggling, the social costs of tobacco, and the employment issue. Section 3 contains seven country case studies in tobacco control, mostly from the developing nations.

References

Barendregt, J. *et al.* (1997), "The health care costs of smoking", *New England Journal of Medicine*, 337:1052-7.

Economics of Tobacco Control Project (1997c), *The Output and Employment Effects of Reducing Tobacco Consumption in South Africa*, Update 6 (Van der Merwe, R.), Cape Town: University of Cape Town.

The Economist (1997), "Tobacco and tolerance", 20 December, pp.59-61.

Kessler, D.A. (1995), "Nicotine addiction in young people", *New England Journal of Medicine*, 333:186-9.

Liu, B., R. Peto, Z. Chen *et al.* (1998), "Tobacco hazards in China: proportional mortality study of 1 000 000 deaths", *British Medical Journal* (in press).

National Cancer Policy Board (1998), *Taking action to reduce tobacco use*, Institute of Medicine Commission on Life Sciences, National Research Council, Washington, DC: National Academy Press.

Parish, S., R. Collins, R. Peto *et al.* (1995), "Cigarette smoking, tar yields, and non-fatal myocardial infarction: 14 000 cases and 32 000 controls in the United Kingdom: the International Studies of Infarct Survival (ISIS) Collaborators", *British Medical Journal*, 311:471-7.

Peto, R., A.D. Lopez, J. Boreham, M. Thun and C. Heath Jr (1994), *Mortality from Smoking in Developed Countries 1950-2000*, New York: Oxford University Press.

Pollock, D. (1996), "Forty years on: a war to recognise and win (How the tobacco industry has survived the revelations on smoking and health)", *British Medical Bulletin*, 52:174-82.

Thun, M.J., R. Peto, A.D. Lopez *et al.* (1997), "Alcohol consumption and mortality among middle-aged and elderly US adults", *New England Journal of Medicine*, 337:1705-14.

Townsend, J. (1996), "Price and consumption of tobacco", *British Medical Bulletin*, 52:132-42.

Wald, N.J., A.K. Hackshaw (1996), "Cigarette smoking: an epidemiological overview", *British Medical Bulletin*, 52:3-9.

Warner, K., F. Chaloupka, P. Cook *et al.* (1995), "Criteria for determining an optional cigarette tax: the economist's perspective", *Tobacco Control*, 4:380-86.

Warner, K.E. and G.A. Fulton (1994), "The economic implications of tobacco product sales in a nontobacco state", *Journal of the American Medical Association*, 271:771-6.

World Bank (1993), *The World Development Report 1993: Investing in Health*, New York: Oxford University Press.

Section 1

Public Policies and Tobacco Control

Chapter 1

The Optimal Policy Mix for Tobacco Control: a Proposed Framework

Iraj Abedian

The economics of tobacco control concerns analysis of the demand and supply issues of tobacco production and consumption. Towards controlling tobacco consumption, there are a variety of policy instruments available to governments. Each of these policy instruments has its own strengths and limitations.

The notion of 'optimal policy mix' is based on two empirical observations. On the supply side, the role of the tobacco industry differs from economy to economy. On the demand side, tobacco consumption is affected by a series of factors ranging from price to the addictive nature of the substance itself. Despite fundamental similarities, there are sizeable differences amongst the arguments of the consumption function of various societies. These supply and demand variations have direct bearings on the choice of the policy mix. This chapter discusses the various components of the supply of and the demand for tobacco. The next section provides a taxonomy of the economic structures and the potential location of the tobacco industry, while the following section sketches the arguments of the consumption function in a generic form. Then the chapter briefly discusses the range of the anti-tobacco policy instruments available to governments, followed by the proposal of a framework for establishing an 'optimal policy mix' to deal with economics of tobacco control.

Tobacco and economic structure

The economic significance of tobacco differs from country to country. The differences pertain to the nature of supply and demand with respect to tobacco. Technically, there is an important difference between tobacco and cigarette manufacturing. A country may be a major (relatively speaking) producer of tobacco but not a significant manufacturer of cigarettes, or *vice versa*. In what follows this distinction is overlooked. This is because the taxonomy of countries as outlined below would not be affected in any significant manner either way.

In general there are five possible structural configurations with respect to tobacco/cigarette manufacturing:
1. the country does not produce tobacco but consumes it, i.e. it is a full importer of the product;
2. the country produces less than what it consumes, i.e. it is a net importer;
3. the country produces and consumes the same amount of tobacco. This is a

case of a 'closed economy' with respect to tobacco;

4. the country produces more tobacco than it consumes; i.e. it is a net exporter;
5. the country produces but does not consume tobacco, making it a full exporter.

Our approach, and policy mix towards economics of tobacco control, would differ in each of these cases. The last case, Category 5, is a theoretical possibility but in practice rare: countries by and large fall into one of the first four cases. In general, as one moves from Category 1 to Category 5 the economics of tobacco control becomes increasingly complex. This is because the real or structural adjustment costs of tobacco control rise. For instance, for a full importer economy, there is no production loss (and associated employment loss) when effective tobacco control policies are introduced. The full burden of adjustment falls on the consumption side and its related elements including import taxes, sales taxes, and trade-related employment. The political economy of this case largely concerns loss of fiscal revenues. Dealing with the fiscal revenue issues is much simpler and more feasible than cases involving potential large-scale job losses and widespread short-term disruptions to the income flows of numerous families.

A large number of countries fall into Category 2, because there are only a few major exporters of tobacco such as USA, Zimbabwe and Malawi (which fall into Category 4). The number of countries falling into Category 3 is also relatively limited; two prominent members are China and South Africa.

The consumption function

The generic consumption function of an individual is expressed as follows:
C = C (p, y, t, i, n, e)
where:
C = consumption;
p = price;
y = disposable income;
t = taste;
i = information;
n = nature of the product;
e = all other factors.

Consumption of 'smoking', therefore, is influenced by the following factors:

p: Price, which in turn is affected *inter alia* by production cost, profit margin, and taxes. Different taxes have different effects on the price. Price elasticity is one of the most important elements of the industry's pricing strategy, and is just as important for the taxation of tobacco products.

y: Disposable income, and the associated income elasticity of demand, are the next most important economic factors affecting the consumption of smoking. As income rises, it is expected that consumption would rise.

t: Taste is a factor that encompasses the subjective aspect of personal preferences. Since smoking is not a basic need, taste is an acquired factor in the consumption function, and is affected *inter alia* by advertising and promotion.

i: Information: this is critical for rational and sound decision-making. Herein lies the role of advertising, promotion, information disclosure, and education about smoking.

n: The nature of the product is important insofar as tobacco is an addictive substance. Repeat consumption would therefore tend to lead to a rise in consumption over time. Depending on the income level of the consumer, the consumption increase may be at the expense of other goods and services. Further, tobacco is cheap and relatively simple to manufacture, making supply-side restrictions more difficult to implement effectively.

e: All other factors: it is recognised that in addition to the factors identified, there are a whole host of factors, both general and person-specific, that influence demand. Among them is the 'social acceptability' factor.

A clear identification of the relative significance of the various arguments of the consumption function is critical for the choice of an optimal policy mix for curtailing consumption, either within a given period or over time.

There are likely to be differences in consumption behaviour between various categories of consumer during any given time period. Extreme cases of addiction aside, economic theory suggests that lower-income consumers would be more price-sensitive than their richer counterparts. Price increases within a given period would thus decrease smoking by the poor more than by the rich. However, anti-smoking campaigns based on general education, via information dissemination, are more likely to reach the rich than the poor. So, within the same period, the policy mix for different categories of consumer would vary. In aggregate, therefore, an optimal tobacco control policy would constitute a basket of targeted optimal policy mixes for a given period.

Over time, however, the relative dominance of the various categories of consumer changes, depending on the rate of economic growth and patterns of income distribution. The national optimal policy mix thus has to change accordingly. In general, price and income effects would have a larger short-term weighting in the mix of optimal policy, whereas attempts to influence 'taste' and 'information' are longer-term factors in curtailing smoking.

In the light of the various arguments of the consumption function, the challenge is to establish the marginal efficiency of the various policy instruments. A similar argument applies to the supply function. These policy instruments are further discussed next.

Tobacco control policy instruments

Tobacco control policies may target the supply or the demand side of the industry. Table 1 provides a taxonomy of these instruments. The choice of instruments and their combination would vary from country to country. For example, countries with either no or a small tobacco industry would have little to do with substitute crop development, or policy co-ordination around production subsidies and taxation. In these countries, supply-side policies would relate to trade, both domestic and international. On the demand side, however, nearly all countries would have to deal with all the above-mentioned policy instruments. In assessing the relative impact of supply and demand policy instruments, two observations are most apt.

Firstly, supply and demand policy instruments should be consistent and co-ordinated. In many countries, limited public resources are often used on one or more of the demand-side policies such as general public education, or various sponsorships whilst at the same time on the supply side the government provides tax breaks or subsidies to tobacco growers or manufacturers of cigarettes. Such policy inconsistencies are fiscally unsustainable and lead to inefficacy of tobacco control policies.

Secondly, some of these factors have immediate effect whilst others are effective over the medium- to long-term. An optimal policy would have to pay attention to the balance as well as the sequencing of the various policy instruments on the supply and demand sides.

Table 1. A taxonomy of tobacco control policy instruments

Supply-side instruments	*Demand-side instruments*
Substitute crop development	Taxation leading to price increases
Taxation/subsidisation of production	Education: information disclosure
Trade-related issues	Advertising regulation
	Sponsorship regulation
	Property rights assignment in favour of non-smokers
	Awareness campaigns
	General incentives
	Social acceptability

Two of the policy instruments mentioned in Table 1 merit special discussion. These are related to the assignment of property rights and the question of taxation. In the remainder of this section, these two issues are discussed in some detail.

(i) Public choice and the assignment of property rights

At the heart of the ongoing world-wide debate on the economics of tobacco control is a key issue of political economy, namely the assignment of 'property rights' on uncontaminated air. Much of the controversy persists because of the lack of clarity in this regard. In practice, however, this vagueness has led to two phenomena.

One is that almost inevitably, and by default, the actual assignment of property rights is in favour of the smoking addicts. The onus has thus fallen on the non-smokers to re-claim their rights, and in the process bear the 'burden of the proof'; i.e. costs of generating the required evidence, lobby expenses, and the like. Within an alternative constitutional framework with clearly defined property rights, it could well be the addicts who not only bear the burden of the proof but also they may be required to compensate the non-smokers for the disutility and social discomfort caused. Second, in the political economy discourse, in an attempt to conduct anti-smoking campaigns different interest groups have invoked all other constitutional rights in pursuit of their own self-interest. This is clearly ineffective and wasteful of scarce resources.

In terms of economic theory the Coasian hypothesis has long argued that a clear assignment, or re-assignment, of property rights would not necessarily affect the optimality of resource allocation, but would entail material consequences for the distribution of income or benefits. For the issue under consideration, it means the optimal resource use within an economy would not be affected by whether or not the constitution assigns the right for clean air to the non-smokers or permits the addicts to pollute the air. What will be affected, however, is the distribution of losses and gains amongst competing groups within the society. If the right to pollute the air is given to smokers, the income distribution in the society would favour those who smoke. For in such a society, not only do smokers derive utility from smoking, but they are under no obligation to compensate non-smokers for the pecuniary or non-pecuniary costs imposed on them. In fact, the non-smokers would technically have to bribe the smokers if they want them to abstain from smoking. If, however, entitlement to clean air is a constitutional right, then the distribution system would favour the non-smokers. Now, the smokers might well face a situation where they are expected to compensate the affected non-smokers for the associated externality costs.

Ultimately, therefore, it is the value system of the society that needs to determine which way property rights should be assigned. Clear articulation of rights assignment is needed in order to minimise wasteful resource use by contending claimants to capture the potential gains from property rights. In this way, the society also reveals its preference for the attendant income distribution consequences of the constitutional ruling.

(ii) Tobacco taxes and government's contesting objectives

With respect to tobacco taxation, government faces competing objectives. One is to optimise revenue from this source of income. A second is to use the tax as a policy tool (deterrent factor) to contain the consumption of a good that has evident short- and medium-term negative externalities. These objectives overlap to some extent and diverge otherwise. Within a certain range, as the tax rises government increases its revenue and achieves its goal of containing consumption, hence the two objectives converge. It is, however, possible that the tax rate which is optimal as a deterrent factor does not necessarily generate maximum revenue for the state.

The broader social objectives of government are also affected by tobacco taxation. Job creation (maintenance of employment) is one, particularly in countries where unemployment is relatively high. South Africa is a case in point: with an unemployment rate in excess of 30%, any tax policy leading to even temporary job displacement is hard to justify in socio-political terms. Meanwhile, the promotion of basic health in the society, particularly that of mothers and children, is another equally desirable government social objective. To this end, containing tobacco smoking is a well documented and effective policy measure.

The above illustrative cases highlight the inherent inability of a single policy tool (taxation) to achieve several diverse policy objectives simultaneously. It also underscores the need for general, as opposed to partial, equilibrium analysis of tobacco taxation. Much of the political economic discourse on tobacco taxation is based essentially on partial equilibrium analysis, which is unhelpful for arriving at a socially optimal policy conclusion.

Tobacco control: an optimal policy mix

The notion of 'optimality' may be interpreted in different ways. Without specifying the objective, it is difficult to define optimality. Clearly, optimality from the perspective of the industry would be very different from that of the public health authority, or from that of the government. Strictly speaking, an optimal mix of policies is either:
- a mix of policies such that at the margin each has the same effect in the reduction of tobacco consumption (definition 1); or, more accurately,
- a mix of policies such that after adjustment for costs each has the same marginal efficacy in reducing tobacco consumption (definition 2).

Either of these definitions has an underlying connotation of trade-offs in the choice over policies or over the relative cost of interventions.

The reality of tobacco control strategies world-wide is such that it is almost impractical to search for an analysis of optimal policy mix in line with the above-mentioned definitions. A less strict definition of optimality, however, may be expressed as a notion that complies with the following conditions:
1. for each 'argument' of either tobacco supply or demand there should be a matching policy instrument that is effective. In other words, no single policy instrument can be expected to solve as complex a problem as tobacco control;
2. there is inter-temporal and contemporaneous compatibility amongst the mix of policy instruments at any point in time;
3. there is maximum synergy amongst the components of the policy mix.

Within such a framework, the notion of optimal policy mix for tobacco control takes two critical categories. One is at the international level, at which there are both short-term and long-term policy mixes that could be considered. Whilst a full analysis of such mixes and their governing principles are beyond the scope of this paper, some of their possible components would be:
- the World Health Organisation (WHO) and the World Bank-International Monetary Fund partnership;
- the role of WHO in World Trade Organisation (WTO) negotiations;
- the global monitoring of and reporting on smuggling;
- a global search for products substituting tobacco in the future; and,
- the role of trans-national advertising and promotion.

It is increasingly evident that in a rapidly integrating world economic order, a great deal of policy co-ordination and harmonisation is needed in areas such as tobacco control. Increasingly, the systemic requirements of the globalised economy require policy co-ordination and possibly policy convergence.[1] At the regional level, this is particularly significant. Neighbouring countries need to establish effective policy co-ordination so as to ensure efficacy in tobacco control, while at the same time preventing potential fiscal revenue losses.

At the national level, the notion of optimal policy mix would imply that countries would be divided into the five categories described above. For each category a mix of policy instruments would be chosen based on the country-specific behavioural parameters. Table 2 presents the matrix of possibilities that would then emerge.

Table 2. Matrix of policy instrument combination by country category

Country category	Supply-focused policies	Demand-focused policies
1. Full importer	n/a	T, AC, PC, HE, ID, PR, SC, etc.
2. Net importer	SCD	T, AC, PC, HE, ID, PR, SC, etc.
3. Closed economy/ self-sufficient	SCD	T, AC, PC, HE, ID, PR, SC, etc.
4. Net exporter	SCD	T, AC, PC, HE, ID, PR, SC, etc.
5. Full exporter	SCD	n/a

Notes: n/a: Not applicable
  T: Taxation
  AC: Advertising control
  PC: Promotion control
  HE: Health education
  ID: Information disclosure
  PR: Property rights assignment
  SC: Smuggling control
  SCD: Substitute crop development

Having chosen the components of the policy mix, the question then is the relative weighting of each component. The empirical behavioural parameters of each country under consideration would determine the relative weighting of each policy component. For example, on the demand side, given the elasticity of demand and the extent of current taxation on tobacco, one could determine the scope of the use of this particular policy instrument. Consider the estimates of the price elasticity of demand for cigarettes presented in Table 3.

---

1. For a detailed analysis of systemic issues of a globalising society, see Commission on Global Governance (1996).

Table 3. Comparison of price elasticity estimates for cigarette consumption for selected countries

Date	Reference	Country studied	Elasticity estimate	Comments
1980	Fujii	USA	-0.45	1929-73 Time-series
1982	Lewit and Coate	USA	-0.42	1976 Health Interview Survey gives elasticity by age and sex
1984	Leu	Switzerland	-0.50	1954-81 Sales data
1985	Bishop and Yoo	USA	-0.45	1954-80 Time-series aggregate data
1985	Radfar	UK	-0.23 (SR) / -0.39 (LR)	1965-80 Quarterly aggregate sales data
1988	Godfrey and Maynard	UK	-0.56	1956-84 Aggregated sales data
1990	Chapman and Richardson	Papua New Guinea	-0.71 / -0.50	1973-86 Excise elasticity for cigarettes/non-cigarette tobacco
1993	Keeler, Hu, Barnett and Manning	California	-0.3 to -0.5 (SR) / -0.5 to -0.6 (LR)	1980-90 Monthly time-series consumption data
1994	Sung, Hu and Keeler	11 US states	-0.40 (SR) / -0.48 (LR)	1967-90 Panel data
1994	Reekie	SA	-0.877	1970-89 Time-series consumption data
1995	Tremblay and Tremblay	USA	-0.4	1955-90 Time-series
1996	Van Walbeek	SA	-0.32 (SR) / -0.53 (LR) / -0.66 (SR) / -1.52 (LR)	1972-90 Tobacco Board data / 1971-89 Reekie's data
1996b	Economics of Tobacco Control Project	SA	-0.57	1970-95 Time-series consumption data, integrated supply and demand
1997a	Abedian and Annett	SA	-0.59 (SR) / -0.69 (LR)	1970-95 Time-series consumption data

Source: Economics of Tobacco Control Project (1997a)

As Table 3 illustrates, the developed countries have a more inelastic demand function, whereas the opposite is true in the case of the developing nations. In general, the more inelastic the demand for cigarettes, the less likely that taxation *per se* would reduce the level and prevalence of smoking. This is mostly true in the developed countries. In such societies, in order to reduce consumption of tobacco, the other arguments of the demand function (see the above section on the consumption function) need to be emphasised. These arguments, *inter alia*, include 'information'. Thus in such cases, advertising and general education about the hazards of smoking are more likely to decrease consumption. It is noteworthy that inelasticity of demand implies that government in these societies could raise tobacco taxes substantially without fear of loss in fiscal revenues. Such revenues could then be utilised to pay for the cost of raising public awareness and general education about tobacco consumption.

On the other hand, in cases where demand is relatively elastic — and this is generally true in the less developed countries — taxation is a powerful tool for reducing smoking prevalence. As a corollary, elastic demand means that raising tobacco taxes would lead to lower fiscal revenues from this source. This is the trade-off that faces many developing countries. The more substantial the fiscal revenues from tobacco taxes, the more significant this trade-off would become. It is thus critical that governments define their policy objectives. If revenue maximisation is the goal, the taxation of tobacco would remain relatively low, hence tobacco consumption would stay high, leading to poorer public health. The political economy of dealing with such trade-offs is relatively complex. What compounds the problem to a significant extent is the time lag between costs and benefits. It is generally acknowledged that reducing tobacco consumption has medium- to long-term social and fiscal benefits, whilst the lowering of fiscal revenue has immediate effects on government's ability to carry out its functions.

A similar argument applies to the other policy instruments available to government. In general, government has to take a policy position that is based on trans-generational maximisation of social welfare within a general equilibrium framework. In other words, any partial equilibrium analysis of the total effects of a given policy instrument, such as taxation, advertising campaign, or trade restrictions is bound to be inadequate as a guide for social policy-making.

Concluding remarks

This chapter has attempted to highlight the need for an optimal policy framework for containing tobacco consumption. It has argued that optimality, first and foremost, requires clarity of policy objectives. With that in place, the next task is to establish the relative marginal efficacy of various policy options and instruments. The current reality is that the existing data on policy experiments world-wide does not provide details of the relative marginal costs and marginal benefits of anti-tobacco campaigns. A technical analysis of a representative optimal policy mix is constrained by this lack of empirical information.

Meanwhile, a less strict notion of optimality would suggest that governments should structure their anti-smoking strategies around a policy mix composed of effective policy instruments aimed at the arguments of the supply and demand sides of tobacco consumption. To this end, optimal policy would have both an international and a national component. Specific policy instruments would have to be identified dealing with the factors causing or reinforcing smoking addiction.

References

Commission on Global Governance (1996), *Our Global Neighbourhood (the Report of the Commission on Global Governance)*, Oxford University Press.
Economics of Tobacco Control Project (1997a), *An International Comparison of Tobacco Control Policies: Taxation, Pricing, and the Control of Advertising*, Update 4 (Van der Merwe, R.), Cape Town: University of Cape Town.

Chapter 2

The Importance of Tobacco Control to "Health for All in the 21st Century"

Derek Yach

The World Health Organisation (WHO) has completed a major global consultative process, which culminated in May 1998 in the adoption by the World Health Assembly of a new global health policy, "Health for All in the 21st Century". This global health policy updates the output of the WHO's Alma Ata conference in 1978, and sets the course for policy and strategy development in health for the first twenty years of the next century. Within that context, it is clear that tobacco use and its impact threaten the attainment of the goals of health for all and challenge many of the core values. Tobacco control should be regarded as integral to attempts by health professionals to ensure that health becomes central to human development. This chapter outlines the importance of tobacco control as vital to many of the functions required in building sustainable health systems. Further, the chapter emphasises the importance of complementary global and national actions, emerging hallmarks of the overall health and development policies of the 21st century, and directly applicable to tobacco control.

The consultative process was spread over two and a half years and drew upon the insights of member states, non-governmental organisations (NGOs), academics and researchers, United Nations agencies, development banks, and the private sector. Further, these more qualitative consultations were strongly supported and underpinned by quantitative analyses. The latter aimed at assessing likely trends in the major determinants of health and their subsequent impact on trends in health status, as well as their distribution by social class, geographic location, sex and age.

Goals of health for all and trends in tobacco use

The new policy emphasises the need to continue to support measures aimed at improving life expectancy. Particular attention needs to be given to closing the gap between the poorest sectors of society and those that have achieved life expectancy in excess of 80 years at birth. Tobacco use directly threatens attainment of these goals by increasing mortality across the lifespan. Detailed data and information with regard to the extent of tobacco's impact on life expectancy now come from prospective studies in developed and developing countries, and show increasing consistency in terms of the overall relationship between tobacco use and several major causes of death (such as lung cancer, for example). Other chapters in this book provide detailed information on this subject.

The policy does not only emphasise increasing life expectancy, but also gives explicit attention to the need to improve the quality of life. Here, tobacco use again threatens attainment of healthy ageing in populations, by increasing morbidity and disability across the lifespan. For example, children born to mothers who smoke during pregnancy are already compromised with regard to their birth weight, which is a major determinant of later cognitive development. Such children are also at greater risk of acute respiratory infections, placing them at increased risk in early and later adulthood of chronic obstructive airway disease. Adolescents who smoke find it difficult to break the habit, and typically become lifelong smokers. Their early exposure to the health risks of smoking translate into premature morbidity and increased disability during their productive years. Emerging research shows that *smoke-free cohorts not only attain a longer lifespan, but are also able to attain a healthier lifespan.* Thus, ageing need not be associated with an increasing prevalence of chronic diseases and disabilities — one of the most potent independent factors that could minimise this prevalence would be the elimination of tobacco use.

"Health for All" values

Before emphasising a number of technical solutions that form the heart of the policy, a set of values that have been distilled from the cumulative wisdom and inputs of the consultative process are outlined with specific reference given to their implications for tobacco control. Already at Alma Ata, the importance of an *equity-based policy* that gave emphasis to social justice was strongly endorsed. Support for equity as the cornerstone of Health for All policies remains an enduring value, and one that now requires greater oper-ationalisation if it is to be truly attained in its fullest respect.

Equity in health starts not by actions within the health system, but through a range of macro-economic and political actions aimed at reducing unfair differences between groups, differences that are amenable to intervention. There are many examples of how the marketing and use of tobacco lead to increasing gaps in well-being by social class, sex and geographic region. For example, in developed countries it is the poorest who smoke the most, who have the least access to information about the hazards of tobacco, and who are targeted and reached most poorly by health education programmes. In developing countries, the issue is more complex. While it is initially the trend-setters or groups in society experiencing increases in income who start smoking earliest, eventually these people become more aware of and sensitive to the impact of their habit on health, and they are more likely to have incentives and support to quit (or never to start in the first place). Thus, over the long-run one can expect, even in developing countries, that it is the poor who will have persistently higher rates of tobacco use and tobacco-related death and disease.

It follows that equity-oriented tobacco control policies are urgently needed. These include careful consideration of the levying of excise taxes, and the use of some of this revenue to ensure that health education and information reach the poorest communities and are able to counter the impact of tobacco advertising and marketing.

A second core value is the need to develop *gender-sensitive policies and strategies.* These highlight the need to involve women to a greater extent in decision-making with regard to health. Further, there is also a need to ensure that interventions and approaches to tobacco control are gender-sensitive, i.e. that they consider the specific needs of both women and men and ensure that policies are developed with a specific target gender group in mind. The tobacco industry, realising that one of the potential gains for them would come through increased tobacco use among women on a world-wide basis, have increasingly targeted their product marketing at women. This has been the case in advanced industrialised countries such as Sweden, the United Kingdom, the USA, and more recently is starting to occur in South Africa, China and other Asian countries. A gender-sensitive tobacco control policy needs to be explicitly developed if these trends are to be countered.

A third value is enshrined in the WHO Constitution. It states clearly that *the achievement of the highest possible level of health is a fundamental human right.* In recent decades, a number of international instruments (including, for example, the Convention on the Rights of the Child and the Convention on the Elimination of All Forms of Discrimination Against Women) contain provisions requiring governments to protect their populations against all forms of substance abuse, including tobacco. By signing such conventions, governments assume obligations that can be contested by individuals and groups in the courts of their countries. Thus, failure to protect people against the hazards of tobacco, or failure to provide information necessary for children to grow up smoke-free, could be challenged under the provisions of the Convention on the Rights of the Child. The use of "rights instruments" to promote public health has been well developed with regard to HIV/AIDS, but has not yet been developed with regard to tobacco control. It is thus an area requiring serious consideration.

The fourth value is the need to develop research policy and technologies in an *ethically sound* way. Ethics in health and medicine also apply at the international level with regard to corporate responsibility. Increasingly, ethical codes of conduct for multinationals are being developed. Consumers' groups are recommending to the general population that companies that do not subscribe to basic ethical principles should not be supported. This is the basis of the work of INFACT, a US-based NGO that lobbies for a boycott of all Philip Morris and RJR products. It is likely that there will be an increased growth of such attempts to strengthen corporate responsibility through NGO action. Obviously, *tobacco companies are regarded as inherently unethical because of the nature of the product they sell,* and more specifically are regarded as unethical in the ways they market to children and poorer communities.

Tobacco control as integral to human development

Several general approaches to ensuring that health is made central to human development are outlined in the policy and apply directly to tobacco control. For example, efforts to *combat poverty* through the direct and indirect efforts of health professionals need to consider the implications of tobacco use for poverty alleviation. As mentioned earlier with regard to equity, there is a strong relationship between poverty and tobacco use, encouraged by multinational marketing. Further, high levels of illiteracy blocks the use of information required to make fully informed choices. An added complication is that in the presence of massive marketing, with rising incomes, and under circumstances where the pricing of cigarettes makes them affordable to the poor, the absence of information about health risks results in the poor showing the fastest rate of increase in tobacco use. Thus there is a need, simultaneous with efforts to combat poverty, for holistic approaches to tobacco control — including an emphasis on pricing, tax and information policies designed explicitly to enable poor people to emerge from their poverty, and to avoid increased risk from tobacco use.

A second general approach for making health central to human development is the need to *promote health in all settings.* Here, the work of WHO in developing the "healthy cities" and "healthy villages" movements are particularly important. Various agencies and organisations in a particular setting (which could be a city or a village) are brought together to identify priority health-related issues and concerns that need attention. Health promotion in this sense implies not only the use of health education pamphlets, posters or media announcements, but is actively related to community mobilisation, and includes building strong NGOs at the local level capable of tackling priority health problems. Clearly, tobacco control has historically followed many of these approaches. The weakness, however, has been that NGOs involved in tobacco control have not forged strong enough links with NGOs involved in broader aspects of development, or with the health of women and environmental issues. *The opportunities for synergies in such interaction exist.* Settings appropriate to such action do not apply only to where people live, but also to where they gather to learn, receive health care, and participate in sport. Each one of these settings provides unique opportunities for tobacco control. For example, smoke-free schools, smoke-free recreation areas and certainly smoke-free health facilities are already well described by WHO, and have been established in many countries.

The third general approach relates to the need to *align the policies of all development sectors towards health.* It is known that trade, agriculture, education, sport and finance policies often have a more profound impact on the course of the tobacco epidemic than do the policies of the health systems themselves. In this context, it is interesting to note that in her latest report on eliminating world poverty, the United Kingdom's Secretary of State for International Development in November 1997 highlighted the fact that "we are working with other governments towards a global ban on tobacco advertising.

In the meantime, we will support the international code of conduct for trans-national companies advertising tobacco products, covering the content and exposure of children to advertising and the use of health warnings". This issue will be discussed in more detail below, particularly with regard to the need for stronger alignment between trade and health policies.

Tobacco control should be a fundamental part of all health systems functions

The new policy highlights *seven key functions of all health systems.* All of these are described in the policy in general terms. The challenge for tobacco control policy-makers and advocates is to indicate the specific tobacco control component for all seven functions.

The first function, *making quality health care available across the lifespan,* emphasises interventions with a preventive potential that extend from birth to death. It is based on evidence of intergenerational effects and on linking early factors, present before birth to childhood, with health in adolescence and in later life. From a practical and operational point of view, it requires that health systems incorporate the appropriate tobacco control interventions at the appropriate time of a person's life. For most developing countries, there is a particularly urgent need to develop strong tobacco control programmes having an impact during the antenatal period. Further, consideration should be given to providing both preventive and cessation programmes for young adults through the public health service. This raises the important question of whether nicotine replacement therapy should be included on the essential drugs list. These are only a few of the key questions that should be asked if tobacco control is to become incorporated into lifespan care.

The second function, *preventing and controlling disease and protecting health,* relates particularly in respect of tobacco control to the need to reduce exposure of non-smokers to tobacco smoke and restrict access by children to tobacco products. The first issue is receiving considerable attention from the South African government, and is likely to result in expanded legislation banning or restricting smoking in public places. The public health impact of this will be relatively minimal compared to that of excise taxation. However, it will reduce irritation and some health effects, and most importantly sends out a clear signal to the general public regarding the social unacceptability of smoking.

With regard to reducing child access to tobacco products, there is legislation in this regard which is poorly enforced in most countries. The challenge is to work with the appropriate health professionals, usually environmental health officers, to strengthen compliance with the legislation. The commissioning of NGOs to be the watchdog over enforcement of this legislation should be seriously considered. In addition, innovative approaches will be needed to reduce child access to street-side cigarette hawkers. If South Africa could find a solution to this particular problem, it would have wide application throughout the developing world.

The third function, *promoting legislation and regulation* is also well-applied and well-known with regard to tobacco control. Here, a wide range of legislative measures at national level is already in place or is being planned. The legislation should be sufficiently enabling to allow sub-national structures to introduce appropriate regulations relating in particular to enforcement of smoke-free areas, restriction of children's access to tobacco, and banning promotion and advertising.

The fourth function, *developing health information systems and ensuring active surveillance* is usually considered in relation to infectious diseases. However, it is vital to develop specific tobacco control targets and indicators as a means of assessing the effectiveness of legislation and other control measures. In Chapter 15, Joy Townsend highlights the United Kingdom's approach to the setting of targets and indicators. On a global basis, it is becoming increasingly recognised that health information systems should move from their current focus solely on infectious diseases, and include indicators with regard to non-communicable diseases and the determinants of tobacco use.

The fifth function, *fostering the use of science and technology* relates particularly to building a research culture that allows for evidence-based policies to be developed. The main thrust of this book highlights the benefits of multi-disciplinary research. Funding for tobacco control research on a world-wide basis has been minimal, and certainly does not match the extent of the current and projected burden of ill-health caused by tobacco use. For that reason, it is essential that all governments and the global research community accelerate funding for research likely to result in the development of effective interventions and policies. Funding in regard to the economics of tobacco has traditionally fallen between many agencies, and rarely been taken up fully by any particular one. That is why the International Tobacco Initiative, initially funded by a number of Canadian agencies and now likely to be supported by other countries, constitutes a particularly important and innovative approach to move the tobacco control agenda ahead. Additional complementary approaches should be formulated within developing countries.

The sixth important function relates to the need to *build and maintain human resources for health*. It has been found that even if money were available for tobacco control advocacy and research, human and institutional capacity to execute appropriate research and advocacy programmes is extremely weak in the vast majority of developing countries. Often there are no full-time tobacco control health professionals. Rather, people steal time from their official full-time job to work on tobacco control because of their concern about the public health impact of its use. This should not be so. It would be unthinkable not to have dedicated immunisation health professionals, or health professionals involved in almost any other aspect of public health. Strengthening capacity to execute research and advocate for appropriate tobacco control policies and action needs to be given higher priority on a world-wide basis. Failure to do so will mean that many of the above functions are unlikely to be carried out.

Finally, the seventh function, *sustainable financing* has unique and positive attributes in the area of tobacco control. The main theme of this book relates to many aspects of the economics of tobacco. Several chapters highlight the benefits of tobacco taxation and how it is one of those rare interventions which not only does not cost money, but in fact brings in extra revenue. Thus, it is a ready and sustainable source of financing for tobacco control. Governments need to have the will to tap it appropriately and to earmark a small proportion for essential tobacco control measures. Concerns about earmarking can be overcome in a number of ways that are discussed in Chapter 9. Suffice to say that one of the best ways of addressing concerns about the regressivity of tobacco tax is to differentially target health promotion towards the poor, as was discussed under the equity section.

Complementary Global and National Actions for Tobacco Control

It is important to acknowledge the need for global action to support national health. The new global health policy acknowledges that *the health of the world's citizens is inextricably linked*. The dramatic growth in trade, travel and migration, together with developments in technology, communications and marketing, have resulted in substantial gains for some groups and severe marginalisation of others. There is concern that increased trade in products harmful to health threatens the well-being of the global population, and particularly people in low-income countries.

Chapters 22 and 24 highlight the consequences of trade liberalisation for tobacco use. While the evidence is not yet in, it would appear that trade liberalisation need not necessarily lead to increased tobacco use, provided countries were able to develop strong national control policies in advance of liberalising. However, the reality is that few countries have the inherent capacity to develop such policies, nor do they have the political will to do so. In fact, those countries likely to be undergoing trade liberalisation would be most subject to the harsh marketing and advocacy efforts of the trans-national tobacco corporations. Thus, at the point of liberalising they would have weak tobacco control policies, and under such circumstances trade liberalisation is likely to increase tobacco use within their country.

The solution lies in working at the national and global levels simultaneously. At the global level, WHO is developing an *International Framework Convention* for tobacco control that aims particularly to reduce the marketing, trade and distribution of tobacco products. Its success depends, however, upon national legislation and action being in place. Simultaneously, the role of the World Trade Organisation is being carefully considered. At this stage it appears to be a promoter of the tobacco trade, since it regards tobacco as a "normal good" not subject to any other formal controls; the health consequences of tobacco use are ignored when considering its impact.

Tobacco industry representatives remind one continually that their trade is lawful and so is their product. But they now acknowledge that their product is addictive and kills people who use it the way the industry recommends. This raises fundamental questions about how one should deal with tobacco, particularly in relation to other products that are indeed normal. Tables 1 and 2 show the trade in un-manufactured and manufactured tobacco, listing the top ten importing and exporting countries. These data are from the World Trade Organisation's official statistics.

Importantly, there has been a significant shift in US tobacco trade policy. Eighteen months ago the then US trade representative, Mickey Kantor, said that planned regulation of nicotine and tobacco products by the US Food and Drug Administration would not affect his efforts to promote trade in tobacco produced by American farmers. However, a provision in the 1998 Appropriations Act of the US Department of Commerce recommends that tobacco-related dealings of the US trade representative should include consultations with the Department of Health and Human Services: *"US actions that conflict with credible tobacco control efforts in other countries are regarded as inappropriate"*. This raises the first chance for regarding tobacco not as a normal good, but as one that causes substantial death and disease world-wide.

Table 1. Trade in un-manufactured tobacco: top ten importing and exporting countries (% of world total)

Importers		Exporters	
Germany	13.2	USA	28.2
USA	10.3	Brazil	15.4
Japan	10.3	Zimbabwe	9.7
UK	7.6	Turkey	4.9
Spain	4.6	Italy	3.8
Belgium/Luxembourg	3.1	Malawi	3.7
Switzerland	2.7	China	2.0
Egypt	2.4	Argentina	2.0
France	2.1	Thailand	1.1

Table 2. Trade in manufactured tobacco: top ten importing and exporting countries (% of world total)

Importers		Exporters	
Japan	14.9	USA	28.4
France	10.8	Netherlands	14.9
Hong Kong	8.9	UK	9.5
Italy	7.0	Hong Kong	7.9
Singapore	5.2	Germany	7.2
Germany	4.4	Singapore	5.4
Russian Fed.	4.2	China	4.9
Iran	3.9	Switzerland	2.0
Netherlands	3.5	Belgium/Luxembourg	1.8
USA	1.3	Canada	0.4

Conclusion

It is important to recognise that this book is not developing a blueprint for tobacco control, but rather the appropriate policy mix. Such a mix should consider first of all, what is the appropriate emphasis for tobacco control in a global policy for sustainable human development? Within a global health policy, what proportion should focus on tobacco? Within a national health policy, what proportion should focus on tobacco? And then the major theme of this book, what should be the appropriate proportion of specific interventions in a national control policy? This approach thus emphasises that one needs to position tobacco control within the broader aspects of global health policy and, wherever possible, seek opportunities for synergy and interaction. This is particularly important under conditions of scarcity.

Tobacco control features as a strong component of the new global health policy. It is there because of the major public health impact it causes in the 1990s, and the even greater impact it will cause in the decades ahead. Failure to give high priority to tobacco control would simply mean that attempts to achieve health for all in the next century would go up in smoke. With that in mind, specific targets and indicators for tobacco control, initially on a world-wide basis and later at a regional, national and local level, should be developed. It is hoped that the development of such targets will signal the importance of tobacco use as a major public health threat to all countries. The strategies outlined above indicate how tobacco control needs to be incorporated into all aspects of health systems and services, and into global policies and actions, if the aim of achieving health for all in the next century is to succeed.

Chapter 3

Updating the Global Predictions for 2020: the Impact of Current Policies

Neil Collishaw

How hazardous is tobacco?

Most people know that tobacco is hazardous, but few people, even among the ranks of health professionals, appreciate how hazardous it really is. Recent estimates for the United States indicate that in a cohort of American boys 15 years of age, tobacco can be expected to kill *three times more* of them before the age of 70 than drug abuse, murder, suicide, AIDS, traffic accidents and alcohol *combined* (see Table 1). In Canada, among a group of 1 000 20-year-old smokers who continue to smoke throughout their lives, it can be expected that, before age 70, one will be murdered, nine will die in traffic accidents, and 250 will be killed by smoking. Those 250 dying from smoking before age 70 will lose about 22 years of life expectancy. And another 250 will die from tobacco-caused illnesses after age 70. American estimates show smoking to cause 13 times more fatalities among exposed persons than the next most risky activity — alcohol consumption. Even passive smoking carries considerable risk. In Canada, the United States, and everywhere else, smoking will kill about half of smokers who start in adolescence and continue to smoke throughout their lives.

Table 1. Risks of premature death before age 70 in a cohort of 100 000 United States males aged 15, 1990

Drug abuse	250
Homicide (excluding alcohol-attributable deaths)	300
Suicide (excluding alcohol-attributable deaths)	660
AIDS	750
Motor vehicle accidents (excluding alcohol-attributable deaths)	770
Alcohol	2 200
Tobacco	11 700

Source: WHO Programme on Substance Abuse (PSA) estimates

The situation is scarcely rosier in developing countries. The World Bank (1993) has recently concluded that "unless smoking behaviour changes, three decades from now premature deaths caused by tobacco in the developing world will exceed the expected deaths from AIDS, tuberculosis, and complications of childbirth *combined*." Similarly, a group of international experts meeting in Bellagio, Italy, recently concluded that: "world-wide, there are only two major underlying causes of premature death that are increasing substantially — HIV and tobacco. Tobacco consumption is a major threat to sustainable and equitable development . . .. In the developing world, tobacco poses a major challenge, not just to health, but also to social and economic development and to environmental sustainability" (Bellagio Statement, 1995).

A model of the tobacco epidemic

The hazards of tobacco are so great that many people simply do not believe it. The reason for this is that smoking is commonplace, and the everyday observation is that there are quite a lot of smokers around who appear more or less healthy. Many of them have been smoking quite a long time and are not dead — yet. So everyday observation apparently does not conform with statements of scientific facts. Unfortunately, many people are more likely to discount scientific facts than their own conclusions based on their own everyday observations. Yet the scientific facts and people's everyday observations are both true. The reason for the confusion lies in the slow-acting nature of the tobacco epidemic.

The model of the cigarette epidemic presented in Figure 1 helps to clarify the source of the confusion. This model shows that the rise in tobacco mortality mirrors almost exactly the rise in smoking prevalence — three to four decades earlier. The same pattern holds true for both men and women, although in most countries, fewer women take up smoking than men and the epidemic has generally started later for women than men.

So, many people smoke for three decades or more before contracting a smoking-related disease. Moreover, again because of the long lag times, it is

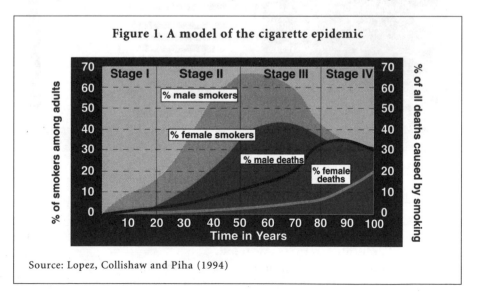

Figure 1. A model of the cigarette epidemic

Source: Lopez, Collishaw and Piha (1994)

perfectly possible, indeed expected, that smoking-related mortality will be increasing at the same time that smoking prevalence is decreasing. This is most evident in Stage III of the model, and it is because tobacco-related mortality is determined mainly by *previous* tobacco consumption, not current levels of consumption.

WHO estimates that there are 1.1 billion cigarette and *bidi* smokers in the world, and that most of these, 800 million, are in developing countries (Table 2). Already, half the men in developing countries smoke (Figure 2). If the experience of developed countries is repeated in developing countries, the latter may soon see a rapid increase in smoking prevalence among women.

Table 2. Estimated number of smokers in the world, early 1990s (million people)

	Women	Men	Total
Developed countries	100	200	300
Developing countries	100	700	800
Total	200	900	1 100

Source: WHO (1996b)

Figure 2. Daily smoking prevalence among men and women aged 15 and over in selected regions, early 1990s (%)

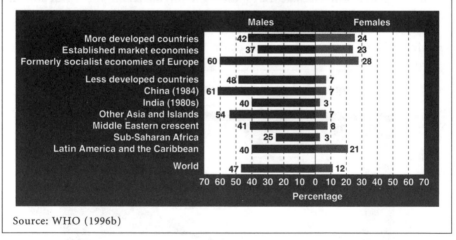

Source: WHO (1996b)

The number of cigarettes smoked per day per smoker is higher in developed countries than in developing countries (Table 3). However, as the smoking population ages in developing countries their intake will likely increase; rising incomes will probably accelerate this trend.

There has been a marked shift in the distribution of the epidemic of tobacco consumption in the last two decades (Table 4). Declining consumption in

Table 3. Number of cigarettes smoked per smoker per day by region

Region	Cigarettes per day
World	15
WHO regions:	
African	10
American	18
Eastern Mediterranean	13
European	18
South-East Asian	14
Western Pacific	16
More developed countries:	22
Established market economies	24
Formerly socialist economies of Europe	17
Less developed countries:	14
China	15
India	18
Other Asia and islands	11
Middle Eastern crescent	13
Sub-Saharan Africa	10
Latin America and the Caribbean	12

Source: WHO (1996b)

Table 4. Relative cigarette consumption in developed and developing countries, 1970-92

	1970-72	*1980-82*	*1990-92*
Ratio of cigarette consumption per adult in developed to that in developing countries	3.33	2.44	1.84
Cigarettes consumption per adult per year:			
World	1 400	1 650	1 700
More developed countries	2 850	2 950	2 590
Less developed countries	850	1 225	1 400
China	750	1 300	1 900

Source: WHO (1996b)

developed countries has been counterbalanced by increasing consumption in developing countries. Apparent success in tobacco control in some countries has been negated by growth in tobacco use in others. Globally, there was no net progress in reducing tobacco consumption. World consumption has remained constant at about 1 650 cigarettes per adult per year since the early 1980s (Table 5).

Forty years of epidemiological observations in a few countries have revealed that smoking kills about half of persistent smokers who take up the habit in adolescence, and half of these before the age of 70.

Table 5. Annual consumption of cigarettes per adult 15 years of age and over by region, 1990-92

Region	Cigarettes per year
World	1 660
WHO regions:	
African	590
American	1 900
Eastern Mediterranean	930
European	2 340
South-East Asian	1 230
Western Pacific	2 010
More developed countries:	2 590
Established market economies	2 570
Formerly socialist economies of Europe	2 770
Less developed countries:	1 410
China	1 900
India	1 370
Other Asia and islands	1 190
Middle Eastern crescent	1 200
Sub-Saharan Africa	500
Latin America and the Caribbean	1 310

Source: WHO (1996b)

Figure 3. Selected leading causes of death, 1990 and 2020 (number of deaths, % of all deaths)

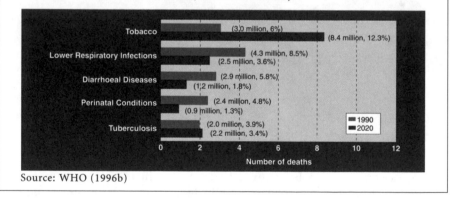

Source: WHO (1996b)

New studies of tobacco mortality in China estimate that there are about 750 000 deaths per year caused by tobacco in China, more than in any other country. Largely on the basis of this new information, WHO has updated its estimate of the number of deaths caused per year by tobacco in the early 1990s from about 3 million per year to 3.5 million per year. WHO estimates that this total will rise to about 8 million by 2020, and to 10 million per year in three to four decades, if current smoking trends persist (Figure 3). Most of this increase will occur in developing countries, where the annual number of deaths caused by tobacco is expected to increase rapidly from about 1.5 million per year at present to 7 million per year. If current trends persist, about 500 million people alive today — nearly 9 per cent of the world's population — will eventually be killed by tobacco.

Currently, the tobacco pandemic is at its worst in Southern, Central and Eastern Europe, and in the Western Pacific Region. For 1995, WHO estimated that there were about 700 000 deaths caused by tobacco in Central and Eastern Europe. Moreover, in marked contrast to countries of Western Europe or North America where half or less of these deaths occur to people under 70, two-thirds to four-fifths are deaths in middle age throughout Central and Eastern Europe. And the situation is getting worse instead of better. Trends and forecasts of per adult tobacco consumption show consumption in these countries to be among the highest in the world, approximately twice the world average in some cases, and still increasing.

Efforts to slow the epidemic are often frustrated because tobacco users are very strongly dependent on their drug. Some addiction experts have rated tobacco as the worst dependence-producing drug, worse than heroin or cocaine. The 1988 Report of the United States Surgeon General, called *Nicotine Addiction*, concluded that: "The pharmacologic and behavioural processes that determine tobacco addiction are similar to those that determine addiction to drugs such as heroin and cocaine" (US Department of Health and Human Services, 1988).

The Tenth Revision of the *International Statistical Classification of Diseases and Related Health Problems* (WHO, 1992) reserves classification F17 for "Mental and behavioural disorders due to use of tobacco". Included under this title is subclassification F17.2, Dependence Syndrome: "A cluster of behavioural, cognitive and physiological phenomena that develop after repeated substance use and that typically include a strong desire to take the drug, difficulties in controlling its use, persisting in use despite harmful consequences, a higher priority given to drug use than to other activities and obligations, increased tolerance, and sometimes a physical withdrawal state."

The tobacco epidemic can be documented, but can it be stopped, or even slowed down? This chapter will now discuss the steps being taken by WHO to help stem the epidemic's progress.

Resolutions of the World Health Assembly

WHO's governing body, the World Health Assembly, has repeatedly expressed its concern about the tobacco pandemic since 1970. Since that time it has adopted sixteen resolutions on various tobacco or health issues. Taken together, they add up to very strong encouragement to Member States to adopt comprehensive multisectoral tobacco control policies and programmes. The resolutions deal with many aspects of comprehensive tobacco control strategies, some of them several times over. Table 6 summarises ten of the most important

Table 6. A ten-point programme for successful tobacco control

1. Protection for children from becoming addicted to tobacco.
2. Use of fiscal policies to discourage the use of tobacco, such as tobacco taxes that increase faster than the growth in prices and income.
3. Use a portion of the money raised from tobacco to finance other tobacco control and health promotion measures.
4. Health promotion, health education and smoking cessation programmes. Health workers and institutions set an example by being smoke-free.
5. Protection from involuntary exposure to environmental tobacco smoke.
6. Elimination of socio-economic, behavioural and other incentives which maintain and promote use of tobacco.
7. Elimination of direct and indirect tobacco advertising, promotion and sponsorship.
8. Controls on tobacco products, including prominent health warnings on tobacco products and any remaining advertisements; limits on and mandatory reporting of toxic constituents in tobacco products and tobacco smoke.
9. Promotion of economic alternatives to tobacco growing and manufacturing.
10. Effective management, monitoring and evaluation of tobacco issues.

elements of comprehensive tobacco control strategies that have been requested by the World Health Assembly. All 16 resolutions were adopted without dissent, meaning that there is a most remarkable global consensus of all the Health Ministers of all 191 WHO Member States in favour of comprehensive tobacco control policies.

Despite this consensus, only a handful of WHO Member States have actually implemented the comprehensive tobacco control strategies called for in the World Health Assembly resolutions. While there is a global consensus on *what* needs to be done to control the tobacco pandemic, public health agencies around the world experience a great deal of difficulty in knowing *how* this is to be done.

WHO's Tobacco or Health Programme

A large part of WHO's efforts in its Tobacco or Health Programme is designed to provide Member States and others with the information, advice and assistance that is needed to answer the "*how*" question — how can comprehensive tobacco control policies actually be implemented? WHO's Tobacco or Health Programme is necessarily strategic in nature. With a very small staff, and in a world where six trillion cigarettes are smoked every year, over 9 000 people die every day from tobacco use, and the world's largest tobacco company has annual operating revenues approximately equal to the GNP of Portugal, the Programme could not be anything but strategic. The Programme's activities are concentrated in three main areas:

1. the WHO data centre on Tobacco or Health;
2. promotion, public information and education; and
3. strengthening national and international tobacco control programmes.

(i) WHO data centre on Tobacco or Health

The activities of the Tobacco or Health data centre are oriented in four main directions:

1. *global epidemiological surveillance* via a computerised database routinely updated with valuable information on tobacco or health to help Member States develop policy options for national programmes of tobacco control;

2. *dissemination of information* on tobacco use and health effects, including the preparation of a comprehensive tobacco or health atlas;

3. *preparation of guidelines* on how to estimate tobacco consumption, the prevalence of tobacco use, and mortality and morbidity attributable to tobacco use;

4. *promotion of research* into the health effects of tobacco use in different epidemiological environments through the establishment of global research networks.

Drawing on the computerised database mentioned above, the Tobacco or Health Programme has produced estimates of indicators of tobacco consumption and mortality caused by tobacco use, some of which are presented in the tables and figures in this chapter. Much more detailed information will be available in the WHO *Tobacco or Health Atlas*, currently in preparation.

(ii) Promotion, public information and education

World No-Tobacco Day has proven itself to be a highly successful vehicle for focusing public and media attention and discussion on important tobacco or health issues. Besides official celebrations of World No-Tobacco Day, the Programme prepares a variety of materials including posters, advisory kits, press kits, and press releases, all in support of celebrations of World No-Tobacco Day. The Programme publishes numerous articles in scholarly journals, and draws attention to the tobacco epidemic as far as possible through attendance at conferences and meetings.

(iii) Strengthening national and international tobacco control programmes

The Programme's work on strengthening tobacco control includes the preparation of guidelines, and working to strengthen tobacco control at the international, regional and national levels. At the international level, notable successes have been achieved in work with the World Bank, the International Civil Aviation Organisation and in the creation of the new United Nations Focal Point on Tobacco in the United Nations Conference on Trade and Development.

The World Bank no longer provides loans for tobacco growing and manufacturing projects. The International Civil Aviation Organisation has adopted a resolution which called for a ban on smoking on all international flights and, in October 1996, reaffirmed their commitment to implement this resolution.

WHO has provided direct on-site assistance to over 30 Member States since

1991 in helping them to strengthen their national tobacco control programmes. Now, with some encouragement from WHO, comprehensive tobacco control strategies are being phased in in developing countries like China, South Africa and Nepal, and in countries of Central and Eastern Europe like Slovenia, Lithuania, the Czech Republic and Poland.

Conclusion

WHO is doing what it can to encourage the development of global action to control tobacco. But the international tobacco control problem is great, and the resources are few. It is also clear that the tobacco pandemic will not be effectively addressed unless public health agencies around the world work closely together on solutions to the problem.

It has been predicted that, if current smoking trends continue, 250 million children alive today will eventually be killed by tobacco. WHO's Tobacco or Health Programme will be working hard to ensure that this prediction never comes true, but needs partners to help it achieve this goal. The Programme hopes that it can count on the support of people around the world concerned with tobacco control as active partners to contribute in ways both large and small to the global solution to the global tobacco pandemic. The future good health of 250 million children demands nothing less. Let's do it for the children.

References

Bellagio Statement (1995), *Bellagio Statement on Tobacco and Sustainable Development*, Rockefeller Foundation Study and Conference Centre, Bellagio, Italy.

Lopez, A.D., N.E. Collishaw and T. Piha (1994), "A descriptive model of the cigarette epidemic in developed countries", *Tobacco Control*, 3:242-7.

Murray, C.J.L. and A.D. Lopez (1996), *The Global Burden of Disease*, Cambridge, Mass: Harvard University Press.

Peto, R., A.D. Lopez, J. Boreham, M. Thun and C. Heath Jr (1994), *Mortality from Smoking in Developed Countries 1950-2000: Indirect Estimates from National Vital Statistics*, New York: Oxford University Press.

US Department of Health and Human Services (1988), *The Health Consequences of Smoking: Nicotine Addiction: a Report of the Surgeon General*, DHHS Publication No. (CDC) 88-8406, Rockville, MD: Centers for Disease Control.

World Bank (1993), *World Development Report 1993: Investing in Health*, New York: Oxford University Press.

World Health Organisation (1992), *The ICD-10 Classification of Mental and Behavioural Disorders: Clinical Descriptions and Diagnostic Guidelines*, Geneva: World Health Organisation.

World Health Organisation (1996a), *Investing in Health Research and Development*, Report of the Ad Hoc Committee on Health Research Relating to Future Intervention Options (Document TDR/Gen/96.1), Geneva: World Health Organisation.

World Health Organisation (1996b), *Tobacco Alert Special Issue: the Tobacco Epidemic: a Global Public Health Emergency*, Geneva: World Health Organisation.

World Health Organisation, (1997), *Tobacco or Health: a Global Status Report*, Geneva: World Health Organisation.

Chapter 4

The Tobacco Scenario: a Vision for the Future

Judith Mackay

The vision of where one would *like* the world to be and the reality of where the world *will* be in the future are very different scenarios. Globally, one would *like* there to be:
1. a reduction in tobacco use;
2. a reduction in tobacco-attributable mortality;
3. robust tobacco control measures firmly established;
4. strict regulation of the tobacco industry.

By 2025, there seems virtually no possibility of realising the first and second objectives, but perhaps a glimmer of hope for the last two goals.

A reduction in tobacco use

The reality is that the total numbers of smokers will go up. There are 1.1 billion smokers in the world today, and this will increase to over 1.64 billion by 2025 — because:
- the world's population will rise (from the current 6 billion to 8.5 billion);
- people will live longer (United Nations, 1991); and
- more women will be smoking.

(i) Women

In developing countries, prevalence of smoking among women will rise from 8 per cent to about 20 per cent by 2025. The good news is that the prevalence of smoking among men will fall to 25 per cent in developed countries (possibly even as low as 15 per cent in some) and from 60 per cent to 45 per cent in developing countries by 2025 (personal communications, Dr Alan Lopez, 1997). But this decrease in male prevalence is offset by the huge increase in the number of women smokers — which will have enormous consequences on health, income, the foetus and the family.

The Tenth World Conference on Tobacco or Health in Beijing in August 1997 made an unprecedented effort to involve women at all levels — on committees, as chairs, speakers, discussants and funded delegates. Every invited speaker was asked to include a perspective on tobacco and women in their presentation. And perhaps when women are involved at core decision-making level in tobacco control efforts (in future conferences, on the WHO Expert Panel) the issues of women and tobacco will be properly addressed.

(ii) Developing countries

By 2025, the transfer of the tobacco epidemic from rich to poor countries will be well advanced, with only 15 per cent of the world's smokers living in the rich countries. Health care facilities will be hopelessly inadequate to cope with this epidemic. However, even in the USA, the number of smokers will be approximately the same as today, as any reduction in prevalence will be offset by an increase in population of about 40 million.

A reduction in tobacco-attributable mortality

The reality is that three times as many people will die from tobacco in 2025. Tobacco-attributable deaths will continue to rise from today's 3 million to 10 million a year by 2025 (Peto, Lopez, and Liu, 1997). China will be the leading country for these deaths. Passive smoking will continue to harm a significant number of non-smokers. The limited good news is that tobacco-attributable deaths will continue to fall among males in the small-population developed countries.

(i) Treatment and care

There are possibilities of spectacular advances in diagnosis, investigation and treatment of tobacco-attributable diseases, for example in genetics, surgery, nanotechnology, telemedicine, targeted pharmaceuticals and radiotherapy. In 2025, individuals genetically prone to tobacco-attributable diseases could be identified early in life. Secondary cancers, currently untreatable, could be treated. Most of this technology will be expensive but some, for example, automated sputum cytology, could be cheaper. Medical advances will have almost no impact on global mortality statistics, but will help individual smokers, especially in the rich countries.

Robust tobacco control measures firmly established

(i) Globally

By 2025, the WHO International Framework Convention on Tobacco Control should have been adopted, ratified and implemented. WHO may have a major department on Tobacco Control (TC) at headquarters in Geneva, appropriately staffed and financed, with a Tobacco Control staff member in each regional office. All other UN agencies and relevant international health and other organisations may recognise their responsibilities. There will be the need for:
- global policies and legislation on issues such as supra-national tobacco advertising via satellite and Internet, tar and nicotine yields, additives, tax, and smuggling;
- greater regional co-ordination, such as in the European Union and ASEAN (Association of South East Asian Nations);

- restriction on trade pressures related to tobacco from one government to another;
- electronic networking, such as Globalink.

(ii) Nationally

Tobacco control is clearly a low priority for most governments, illustrated by general lack of action appropriate to the magnitude of the tobacco epidemic, and negligible funding and staffing. Currently, there are less than 10 full-time people working on tobacco control in the whole Asia-Pacific region, covering more than half the world's smokers.

Economics

By 2025, national governments may finally understand that tobacco control is good for the economy, that no tobacco farmers, retailers or tobacco workers will be out of a job because of tobacco control measures, and that tax increases will not reduce government revenue. They should all agree with the World Bank statement that tobacco control efforts could contribute to economic development in low- and middle-income countries.

The tobacco industry is increasingly using economic arguments to prevent governments from taking tobacco control measures; thus the forthcoming World Bank economic analyses and this book are of crucial important.

National tobacco control measures

In future, a major distinction will evolve between nations which have or have not made the "transition" to committed and vigorous preventive health measures and practices (Koplan, 1997). By 2025:
1. "Post-transition" nations will have robust health education programmes and extremely restrictive tobacco policies, along with active promotion of, and increased support for, physical activity and a low-fat, high-fibre, high-fruit and mainly vegetarian diet.
2. "Pre-transition" nations will be grappling with deteriorating health status, and unabated epidemics of lung cancer, heart disease, obesity, and industrial and road accidents. They will struggle with deeply entrenched tobacco interests that manipulate their governments, the media and public opinion. They will have made an extremely costly mistake by missing the opportunity to build significant barriers to tobacco in the late 20th and early 21st century, and will then find it very difficult to expel the powerful foreign tobacco companies and their domestic allies. They will be doomed to repeat the painful and costly experience of the "post-transition" nations who laboured for 30-50 years to achieve significant gains over tobacco peddlers.

The following will have been attained in nations that take serious tobacco control action now:
- Establishment of a National Office to co-ordinate tobacco control efforts.

- Licensing of nicotine as an addictive drug with manufacture, promotion and sale under regulatory control by agencies such as the Food and Drug Administration in the USA.
- Smoke-free areas in workplaces, indoor public areas and public transport.
- Bans on all tobacco promotion. Sports and arts bodies will look back with amazement at the time in history when their predecessors accepted tobacco money.
- Cigarette packets will be plain black and white and contain only brand name, tar and nicotine levels and health warnings.
- Tar levels will be below 15 mg all over the world, and 10 mgs in "post-transition" countries.
- Health education will be carried out by all nations, in some more effectively than in others. The failure of school programmes in the 20th century will force health educators to turn to social marketers for professional help.
- Cessation: If efforts concentrate only on preventing children from smoking, there will be no reduction in the up to 200 million smoking-related deaths expected to occur before 2025 in already-smokers. Few countries, especially developing countries, are sufficiently energetic at present about assisting cessation.
- Medical education: By 2025, medical and allied health schools will have systematically incorporated tobacco issues into the curriculum, and health professionals will be competent and effective in advising patients on quitting smoking.
- Prices will be higher in real terms by comparison with today. 'Duty Free' tobacco will have long disappeared. Smuggling (which currently constitutes 30 per cent of all traded cigarettes) will continue to undermine price policy. As this smuggling trade expands, tobacco will have become a predominantly illegal product in many markets. The tobacco industry may have been hit by several spectacular legal cases concerning the involvement of tobacco companies in the smuggling of their own cigarettes.
- Core funding for tobacco control and health promotion will come from tobacco tax and other government revenue, although it will become fashionable in future for big business to contribute, in the same way it is beginning to contribute to environmental issues today.
- Partners in fighting the tobacco epidemic will include a wide range of youth leaders, environmentalists, religious leaders, consumer pressure groups, sports bodies, and many others. But despite these efforts, by 2025 smoking will still be firmly entrenched among rebellious youth.

Strict regulation of the tobacco industry

Currently, the commercial, transnational companies come under few regulations, while they expand their empires, deny the health evidence against tobacco use, advertise and promote their products in every corner of the earth, obstruct government action, overpower national monopolies, and sell more and more cigarettes. Their grip on the big markets in developing countries will become stronger as they move their growing and manufacturing processes out of the USA; by 2025 there may be no tobacco grown in the USA.

An ex-tobacco industry executive has made the interesting prediction that tobacco production could be reduced by the global demand for food, brought about by population increase and a century of ecological abuse and mismanagement of the planet's food and water supply. He pointed out that as many of the tobacco companies are involved with the transnational food business, their corporate and personal pockets, previously lined with tobacco gold, will now likewise be lined with gold from wheat, corn and rice.

The 20th World Conference on Tobacco or Health in 2025 may be discussing the domination of the world tobacco market by the largest exporters — China and Japan — and the reversal of the fortunes of the American and British tobacco companies.

The litigation flurry will have run its course. Much of the developed world will have moved to a managed tobacco industry, with liability automatically paid for tobacco-attributable health care costs and to individual smokers who have been harmed by tobacco.

The proposed Settlement Agreement with the tobacco industry in the United States was the first, imperfect and painful step in this process. Who would have imagined 30 years ago that the tobacco companies would engage in such talks today?

In the next few years, many nations will be examining the applicability of this type of agreement to their own countries, in particular, the other large exporting countries such as Great Britain, Japan, Indonesia and, less likely, China.

Conclusion

The global tobacco epidemic is worse today than it was 30 years ago. The extraordinary effort needed to prevent the epidemic being even worse in another 30 years is not being made.

Several countries have already shown that smoking rates can be reduced. These successes can be reproduced by any responsible nation only by determined, immediate and sustained governmental and community action. Action that they will only be prepared to take once they are convinced that the resulting economic benefit is as real as the health benefit.

References

Bellagio Statement (1995), *The Bellagio Statement on Tobacco and Sustainable Development*, Rockefeller Foundation Study and Conference Centre, 26-30 June, Bellagio, Italy.

Koplan, J. (1997), "Global trends in health and health care", paper presented at *Healthcare — the Next Millennium*, 12 March, London.

Personal communications, Dr Alan Lopez (1997), Programme on Substance Abuse, Geneva: World Health Organisation.

Peto, R., A.D. Lopez and B. Liu (1997), "Global tobacco mortality", paper presented at *Tenth World Conference on Tobacco or Health*, 24-28 August, Beijing.

United Nations (1991), *World Population Prospects 1990*, Population Studies No. 120, Department of International Economic and Social Affairs, New York: United Nations.

Chapter 5

The Role of Governments in Global Tobacco Control

Prabhat Jha, Thomas E. Novotny and Richard Feachem[1]

Human health has improved more in this century than in all previous centuries combined. In the past, reductions in communicable, maternal, and perinatal diseases have contributed most to improved health (World Bank, 1993). Today, governments and developmental agencies face several challenges in sustaining these health gains. These include the large and unfinished agenda of childhood and maternal diseases, threats from re-emerging infections such as tuberculosis and malaria, increases in infection with human immunodeficiency virus (HIV), and the growing burden of death and disability from non-communicable diseases (World Health Organisation, 1996a). Tobacco control is the leading intervention to reduce the burden of non-communicable diseases.

Over the last 20 to 30 years, age-specific death rates for most diseases have fallen because of lower incidence and lower case-fatality rates. Over the last few decades and over the next few decades, the only large and growing causes of death in the world are tobacco use and HIV (World Health Organisation, 1996a; Murray and Lopez, 1996). For both diseases, non-governmental organisations (NGOs) and academic institutions have implemented many targeted activities. In addition, governments (and developmental agencies) have responded to HIV with considerable attention, including substantial fiscal and human resources (World Bank, 1997). What should be government's response to tobacco? Using economics and public policy and public health theories, this chapter reviews the reasons why governments should intervene to control tobacco, and what governments should do.

Why should governments intervene to reduce tobacco consumption?

Governments have several responsibilities (Stiglitz, 1989; Musgrove, 1996), including increasing information, taking actions that others (individuals, or the voluntary and private sectors) cannot or will not take, and protecting the poor. Governments also have the responsibility to promote good health — both because it is important in itself, and because it contributes to economic development (World Bank, 1993). Within these roles, the enormous health

---

1. This work was supported in part by the World Bank's Research Support Board (Grant No. 681-95). The opinions expressed are those of the authors, and not the World Bank or its member countries.

impact of tobacco is the main reason for governments to intervene to reduce tobacco consumption.

(i) Tobacco use is incompatible with good health

Tobacco use is one of the largest risks to maintaining the major health gains of the last century. Over the past forty years, global life expectancy has improved more than in the previous 4 000 years. Similarly, infant mortality in 1990 in the developing world approaches the levels of developed countries[2] in the 1950s (World Bank, 1993). Model-based projections suggest that non-communicable diseases will dominate mortality world-wide by 2020, with much of this increase driven by tobacco use. Murray and Lopez (1996) estimate that the proportion of total deaths in developing countries due to non-communicable disease will increase from 47 to 69 per cent, while the proportion due to communicable, maternal, and perinatal diseases will fall from 42 to 18 per cent. Thus, developing countries will fast approach the non-communicable disease burdens of developed countries in 1990 (86 per cent of total deaths).

Despite the uncertainty inherent in model-based projections, little doubt exists that tobacco will become the leading cause of death in the world within two or three decades. The numbers of tobacco deaths expected on current smoking patterns are staggering. It is estimated that about 500 million people alive in 1990 will die from tobacco-related causes such as heart attacks, strokes, lung cancer, chronic respiratory disease, and other cancers (Peto *et al.*, 1994). Of these, about 200-300 million are today's children and teenagers. Over the next 20 years alone, there will be about 100 million tobacco deaths, mostly among adults. It is estimated that by 2020 tobacco use will cause about one in eight of all deaths, up from one in 16 deaths in 1990 (Murray and Lopez, 1996). Tobacco deaths by the year 2030 are expected to reach or exceed 10 million per year, with 70 per cent of these deaths occurring in developing countries. This total will exceed deaths from malaria, tuberculosis, childhood diarrhoea, and maternal conditions combined (World Bank, 1993). Of great relevance to developing countries is the fact that at least one half of these deaths occur in middle age (35-69), a time of great productivity and social importance in all societies.

The rates of tobacco-attributable mortality and resulting years of life lost should be compared to those among non-smokers. In most developed countries, age-standardised rates for non-tobacco-attributable mortality from various causes (total, cardiovascular and cancers), have fallen over the last 30 or so years (Peto *et al.*, 1994). In the United Kingdom, the Doctors Longitudinal Health Study found that four in five of non-smokers could expect to reach age 70, but only one in two of smokers would do so (Doll *et al.*, 1994). In developed and developing countries, most major causes of death that could compete with

---

2. Unless otherwise noted in this paper, "developed countries" refer to established market economies and those of former socialist economies. Developing countries refer to demographically developing countries, such as China, India, Brazil etc. This classification is given in the *World Development Report 1993* (World Bank, 1993).

tobacco-attributable deaths in middle-age (such as maternal and some communicable causes) have decreased in significance, and are expected to further decline over the next three decades (Murray and Lopez, 1996; Over *et al.*, 1992).

(ii) The economics of tobacco use

On purely economic criteria, there would be little reason for governments to intervene to reduce tobacco consumption if tobacco users knew all of the risks of their addictive habit and assumed all of its costs. There is strong evidence of underestimation of risks, but unclear evidence on the net costs of tobacco use (Warner, Chaloupka, Cook *et al.*, 1995).

It could be argued that smokers are informed and have made a choice that reflects their preferences. However, most smokers start early in life, as teenagers or children, have imperfect information on risks, and lose some (but not all) of their ability to quit because of addiction. Most adult smokers state that they wish they never started (US Department of Health and Human Services, 1989). For several reasons people and governments seriously underestimate the risks of tobacco use (see Chapter 3 for an explanation of this phenomenon). Even among highly-educated populations such as in the United States and Poland, there is surprisingly low valuation of the health impact of smoking (see Table 1). Children and teenagers are even less informed than adults of the risks of tobacco use, and tend to discount the future more than adults. One particular survey has suggested that US smokers may overestimate the probability that

Table 1. Low valuation of risks of tobacco use in the United States and Poland

US Survey[+]			*Poland Survey*[*]
Rank	Habit	%	Habit
1	Never drive after drinking	62	Environment
2	Air quality	55	Dietary habits
3	Water quality	45	Stress, hectic lifestyle
4	Domestic fire detectors	27	*Tobacco smoking*
5	Body weight	25	Genetics
6	Annual blood pressure	24	Sport, physical activity
7	Control stress		
8	Vitamins and minerals		
9	Exercise		
10	*Not smoking*		
11	Have friends		
12	Good genes		

Sources: + (Harris and Associates, 1989): A 1983 Harris poll of 1 254 US adults asking what "helps people in general to live a long and healthy life" (1 = most, 12 = least perceived importance).
* (Zatonski, 1996): A 1995 representative poll of 1 391 Polish people aged 15 years and above who were asked "the most important factors influencing human health".

they will develop lung cancer (Viscusi, 1989), but this survey did not refer to risks other than lung cancer, did not cover the consumer's estimate of the economic costs of tobacco consumption, and did not refer to the risks of death in middle or in older age.

Thus, it is no surprise that even respectable journals such as *The Economist* (1997) mistakenly state that "most smokers (two-thirds or more) do not die of smoking-related disease. They gamble and win. Moreover, the years lost to smoking come from the end of life, when people are most likely to die of something else anyway". In fact, epidemiology suggests that one in two of long-term smokers are eventually killed by tobacco (Peto *et al.*, 1994), with half of these dying during the ages 35-69. Information on the hazards of tobacco use has increased in many Western countries over the last 20 to 30 years. However, developing countries have even lower awareness of the hazards of tobacco because of lower education levels, the lag effects of increased consumption and tobacco-attributable mortality, less availability of information on the hazards of tobacco, and the strong social, political, and economic influence of the tobacco industry.

Several studies from middle and high-income countries suggest that tobacco-related diseases already create considerable and avoidable costs. As a percentage of gross domestic product (GDP), these losses range from 0.7 to 2.0 per cent (see Table 2). The uncertainty in the methods used to measure costs partly explains this variation. In low-income countries, a rising incidence of tobacco-attributable disease will likely contribute to cost-escalation, including pressures for publicly-funded curative tertiary services (World Bank, 1990; 1992; 1994a), similarly to the expected impact of the growth of HIV infection (World Bank, 1997). Many developing countries face dual burdens of communicable, maternal and perinatal disease and non-communicable disease. Without suitable tobacco control, these diseases may displace limited public funding from other priority public health programmes such as communicable disease control, immunisation, and child health.

Table 2. Economic studies of tobacco-attributable costs (% of GDP)

Country (reference)	% of GDP
Australia (Robson and Single, 1995)	1.4
Canada (Robson and Single, 1995)	1.9
China (World Bank unpublished data)	1.5
Japan (Goto and Watanabe, 1995)	1.1
South Africa (Yach, McIntyre and Saloojee, 1992)	0.7
United States (Robson and Single, 1995)	2.0

Various economists have pointed out that smokers in developed countries may "pay their own way" by not consuming pensions or health care costs in older age, although this finding is not consistent (Warner, Chaloupka, Cook *et al.*, 1995; Hodgson, 1998). These analyses have several limitations. First, and most important, they ignore the value of human life. Non-smokers spend their health care dollars over a longer, healthier life. The present authors calculate that the one billion life years lost from tobacco-related deaths at ages 35-69 over the next 20 years have a total value of $146 billion dollars (or $81 billion dollars discounted at 3 per cent; see Table 3). This assumes a value of life of only US$1 a day (the World Bank's approximate definition of the level of absolute poverty, and about the annual *per capita* GDP of India), and assumes that one-half of smokers make an informed decision to start and to continue smoking. This suggests that the more human life is worth, the higher the loss will be from current patterns of tobacco use. It also suggests that if all smokers were perfectly informed of the risks, or if human life had no value, then the value of life lost from tobacco would be zero. Estimates of economic externalities and pricing decisions should be examined in the context of such losses.

Table 3. Value of life lost during ages 35-69 from tobacco deaths over the next 20 years, under different discount rates

	Value of life per year in US$			
	200	*365*	*700*	*1 000*
Billions of years of life lost during ages 35-69 (A)	1.1	1.1	1.1	1.1
Percentage not informed of risks (B)	50	50	50	50
Number of years over which deaths occur (C)	20	20	20	20
Undiscounted value in US$ bn (= A*B*C)	80	146	280	400
Discounted value in US$ bn: 3% discount rate	44	81	155	221
5% discount rate	30	55	106	151
10% discount rate	12	22	42	59

Source: Authors' estimates: to arrive at (A), it is assumed that there are 100 million deaths over the next 20 years, of which one half during ages 35-69 (Peto *et al.*, 1994; Slama, 1995). The average loss of life from tobacco deaths during ages 35-69 is about 20-25 years when compared to non-smoker life expectancy (Peto *et al.*, 1994). The discounted value is the un-discounted value divided by the discount value (which is the discount rate, raised to the power of years or (C)).

There are other problems with the analyses suggesting that smokers pay their own way. These analyses ignore the fact that in developing countries, the death of an adult imposes economic losses on other household members (World Bank, 1993; Over *et al.*, 1992). In addition, household income transfers may be as important as formal transfers — public pensions total only 0.7 per cent of GDP in the low-income economies of developing countries, compared with 8.2 per cent in developed countries (World Bank, 1994b). In addition, *per capita* costs of health care expenditure are lower without smoking (Warner, Chaloupka, Cook *et al.*, 1995; Barendregt *et al.*, 1997). Finally, such analyses have not yet evaluated the economic costs of involuntary or "passive" smoking. A meta-analysis of epidemiological studies suggests that the risks of involuntary smoking are real (Law, Morris and Wald, 1997; Hackshaw, Law and Wald, 1997), but markedly small in comparison to risks to smokers.

(iii) Equity issues

Tobacco burdens are highest among the poor in most countries of the world. Tobacco consumption rises as incomes rise in low- and middle-income countries, but this increase is influenced by the maturity of the tobacco epidemic and by the types of tobacco products available. In established market economies rates have widened between rich and poor. In Norway, smoking prevalence among high-income and low-income males was 75 and 60 per cent respectively in 1955, and by 1990 had fallen to 28 and 40 per cent respectively (Lund, Roenneberg and Hafstad, 1995). In the United States, the odds of smoking for persons below the poverty level were significantly higher than for those above that level in a series of national surveys since 1983, after controlling for sex, race, age, education, region, and employment status (Flint and Novotny, 1997). In Brazil, China, and India, the prevalence of tobacco use is already higher among the poor (see Table 4). Across countries, the poor have higher death rates from tobacco-attributable diseases, lower access to and use of preventive information, and fewer curative health services. Finally, tobacco-attributable adult deaths cause adverse outcomes in children, especially those in poor households, by increasing household poverty (World Bank, 1993; Over *et al.*, 1992).

Table 4. Tobacco use in different social groups in developing countries

Place (reference)	Risk factor	Difference	Comparisons
Brazil (World Bank, 1990)	Smoking	5-fold	uneducated vs. secondary schooled adult
China (World Bank, 1992)	Smoking	2.5-fold	lowest vs. highest education sextile
India (Jha, Jamison & Habayeb, 1998)	Tobacco use	2-fold	rural vs. urban

What should governments do to reduce tobacco consumption?

To reduce demand for tobacco, governments must fulfil roles that individuals will not or cannot do, and they must protect the poor. Government actions should aim to create an environment where tobacco users fully understand the risks involved, and where they pay a sufficient price for their use. The principle tools for this are information, price and regulation. Governments need to adopt a package of interventions, because no single measure is effective alone (Novotny *et al.*, 1992; Laugesen and Meads, 1991).

(i) Increase information on tobacco use

Information, price and income are the key determinants of the uptake of tobacco use. Many established market economies, such as the United Kingdom and Canada, show a declining proportion of tobacco-attributable mortality, including among the middle-aged. In the United Kingdom, tobacco-attributable mortality rates in middle-age have halved since the 1950s (Peto *et al.*, 1994). The United Kingdom has experienced a 23 per cent decline in cigarettes consumed per adult from 1976 to 1988: regression analysis suggests that real price increases lowered consumption by about 17 per cent, while rising income increased consumption by about 12 per cent. The residual reduction of 18 per cent (i.e. 23-17+12) was due to health promotion influences, and decreases in advertising and promotion (Townsend, 1993). An analysis of several developed countries suggests that combinations of price increases, restrictions on advertising and promotion, and strong and varied health warnings on tobacco products have reduced consumption by about 13 per cent (Laugesen and Meads, 1991).

Income increases in developing countries would be expected to increase consumption. But information can powerfully mitigate increases in income. World Bank data suggest that *per capita* cigarette consumption rose with income in 1970 in both established market economies and demographically developing countries, but more so in the former. By 1990, however, *per capita* consumption *fell* with rising income in established market economies, but rose in demographically developing countries. This reversal is not random: better information on the hazards of tobacco appears largely responsible for the reversal in direction of income elasticity in established market economies (World Bank, unpublished data). A likely interpretation of these data by the tobacco industry would be that in the absence of information and early price increases, increased consumption and profit would arise from encouraging access to cheaper tobacco products in low-income countries, and then increasing price as incomes rise and product loyalty is built up from addiction, advertising and promotion (Ensor, 1992).

Information needs to be in three forms (US Department of Health and Human Services, 1989):
- complete bans on advertising and promotion of tobacco products, trademarks, logos, or associated symbols;
- research on causes, consequences and costs of tobacco use; and
- public information campaigns, including serious health warnings on tobacco products.

Advertising and promotion bans are justified on several grounds, much of which has been reviewed elsewhere. Several recent studies comparing countries with partial or full bans on tobacco advertising or promotion conclude that complete bans produce significant reductions in smoking prevalence and overall cigarette consumption. A 10 per cent increase in advertising and promotion raises consumption by about 1-2 per cent (Laugesen and Meads, 1991; Tye, Warner and Glantz, 1987; Economics of Tobacco Control Project, 1996c). In contrast, partial bans are relatively ineffective given substitution toward other types of media. Secondly, advertising and promotion targets children, who are least informed about the risks of tobacco use. In the United States, "Joe Camel" advertisements helped increase RJ Reynolds tobacco company's market share of under-18 smokers from 0.5 per cent to 33 per cent, without touching the adult market (Difranza *et al.*, 1991). In the United Kingdom, boys aged 12-13 who can name a tobacco-sponsored motor-racing sport are twice as likely to smoke than boys who cannot name such a sport (about the same difference as if the father smoked; Charlton, While and Kelly, 1997). Bans on promotion are also needed as spending has shifted from advertising. In 1983, US cigarette companies spent about US$1.4 billion (in 1993 US dollars) on promotion and an equal amount on advertising. By 1993, they spent US$5.5 billion on promotion and only US$0.8 billion on advertising (Federal Trade Commission, 1995).

Research on the causes, consequences and costs of tobacco use has contributed to a social climate where effective tobacco control can occur. The lack of such information in most low- and middle-income countries may cause governments and health officials to dismiss evidence that is not local or regional. For example, the regions in the world where the tobacco-attributable mortality will be highest in absolute numbers in the next few decades lack direct evidence on the absolute and relative health risks from tobacco used in those regions (see Table 5). India is expected to have about one-fifth of all world-wide tobacco deaths by 2020, but vital registration and cause-of-death data are complete for less than 0.5 per cent of the population (Murray and Lopez, 1996). In addition, only a limited number of epidemiological studies exist on the contribution of manufactured cigarettes, *bidis,* and other types of tobacco to premature mortality (Gupta, 1996).

Table 5. Gaps in data sources necessary for estimating tobacco-attributable mortality

Region	Tobacco-attributable mortality in 2020 (% of world total)	Vital registration in 1990 (% coverage in 1997)	Representative epidemiological evidence on tobacco
China	27	Limited[+]	Limited retrospective and prospective
India	18	Limited[*]	Limited and ongoing prospective
Established market economies	15	99	Retrospective and prospective
Former socialist economies	13	99	Indirect, ongoing retrospective
Middle East crescent	10	22	None
Other Asia and Islands	8	10	None
Latin America	5	43	None
Sub-Saharan Africa	4	1	None

Notes: + Data for China is based on a sample registration system covering 10 million people.
         * Data for India is based on an urban registration system and a survey of rural causes of death.
Source: Murray and Lopez, 1996; Liu *et al.,* 1998; Gupta, 1996; Richard Peto, personal communication.

Examination of the abstracts of papers presented to the *Ninth World Conference on Tobacco or Health* held in Paris in 1994 is telling with regard to the paucity of information from developing countries that could guide public health policy or inform individual risks. Most presentations were on advocacy efforts modelled from developed countries (see Table 6). A reasonable goal for the next *World Conference on Tobacco or Health* in 2000 would be to substantially increase the quantity and quality of analytical studies coming from developing countries.

Table 6. Abstracts of papers presented to the *Ninth World Conference on Tobacco or Health* by type and region of origin (% of total)

Topic	Established market economies	Former socialist economies	Demo- graphically developing countries
Advocacy and broad policy	47	4	9
Epidemiology/causes and consequences	24	4	4
Economics/Taxation/Trade/Employment	6	1	1

Source: Slama (1995)

Priority research is required in the world's major regions to support advocacy and action on tobacco control. Priority research includes investigation of the causes, consequences, and costs of tobacco use. Better understanding of causes includes studies of the determinants of tobacco use or reduction (information, income and price, including taxation), and impact on consumption of advertising and promotion, smuggling, trade, and tobacco industry lobbying. Better information on health consequences results from studies of tobacco-attributable mortality in local or regional settings. Better information on costs involves studies of cost-escalation in the health sector, tobacco and household expenditures, and costs of involuntary smoking. Research is needed to shed more critical light on claims of the tobacco industry regarding the economic benefits from tobacco use (Warner, 1994).

These studies need to be done at local levels while following international standards. Examples include the review of epidemiological studies of tobacco led by the World Health Organisation (WHO) and Oxford University, and the World Bank's ongoing Economic Survey of Tobacco Use (prices, spending, taxes, tariffs, revenues, subsidies and smuggling; *http://www.worldbank.org/html/ hcovp/heal/tobacco.html.*) Other examples include development of methods to estimate economic costs of tobacco use (Single *et al.*, 1996; US Centers for Disease Control and Prevention, 1994), but these must be expanded to include some value of human life — even a conservative measure such as *per capita* gross domestic product.

Such research will require funding from governments, but because the information generated is a global public good, international developmental agencies and governments of established market economies should more actively support research in low- and middle-income countries. Over the last few years, investment in research and development in tobacco control amounted to US$50 per 1990 death (a total of US$148 million-US$164 million). In contrast, HIV research and development received about US$3 000 per 1990 death (a total of US$919 million-US$985 million). Spending on both diseases is primarily in developed countries (World Health Organisation, 1996a).

Promoting public information and media campaigns involves both mass counter-advertising efforts and serious warning labels on tobacco products. In the US, there is early evidence based on the anti-smoking advertising campaign in the US during the late-1960s (US Department of Health and Human Services, 1989). More recent evidence comes from counter-advertising campaigns in California, Massachusetts, and elsewhere that are financed by earmarked cigarette taxes (Goldman and Glantz, 1998). Health warnings on tobacco products need to inform the smoker of the true hazards of tobacco. Such warnings need to be large in size, strong and varied in message, and written in local languages. Local language warnings may also help to control smuggling. Canadian-type warning labels are the prototype for such labels (Mahood, 1995).

(ii) Raise the costs of smoking

Taxation is arguably the most effective tool of any type to control tobacco use. A 10 per cent increase in tobacco prices will reduce consumption in the short-term by 3 to 5 per cent, and more so in the longer term. Reductions are largest in children and lower-income groups (Townsend, 1996). What should be the optimal tax? Economic models have been unable to conclusively establish the ideal cost of smoking, because of difficulties in establishing the externalities associated with tobacco and the costs of smoking (Warner, Chaloupka, Cook *et al.*, 1995). Reviews of taxation based on the minimal distortion of consumer behaviour, bearing the cost of consumption choices, or equity, have not led to any definitive recommendations (Warner, Chaloupka, Cook *et al.*, 1995). The estimates of an economically efficient tax in the United States by Manning *et al.* (1991) are several hundred fold greater than the wholesale price of the tobacco content in a pack of cigarettes. Taxation based on targets to reduce smoking is easier to quantify: Townsend (1993) suggests that a 63 per cent increase in cigarette price by the year 2000 in the United Kingdom would decrease cigarette consumption per adult by about 34 per cent. The proposal by the US Institute of Medicine to increase taxes by US$2 per pack would reduce overall smoking prevalence by about 40 per cent, and youth smoking by about two-thirds (National Cancer Policy Board, 1998).

Price increases and information are synergistic, in that consumers will value more information to purchase higher-priced goods. Newer analyses suggest that advertising and promotion restrictions are similar in effect to raising taxes on smoking (Economics of Tobacco Control Project, 1996c). From the perspective of a smoker or potential smoker, it can be seen from Table 3 that if smokers had perfect information, the value of human life lost would be zero. Perfect information does not exist anywhere in the world today (and may not be achievable).

Because of the hazardous nature of smoking, governments could consider taxation based on the "tobacco product" (P), which sums the production, manufacturing and marketing cost of tobacco (T), the economic cost of information (I), and any conventional externalities (E) such as involuntary smoking and net use of public funds for health expenditures and income transfers. Currently, with low levels of awareness of tobacco hazards, the addictive nature of nicotine, and because of advertising and promotion, "I" is likely to be very high, and critical to taxation decisions. In contrast, "E" is likely to be low, and not important for taxation decisions. Each of the costs could be based on willingness-to-pay, which may also take into account differing social norms of involuntary smoking and present social mobilisation. Of note, taxation aimed at revenue generation would have very different assumptions, and could, arguably, call for *less* information.

Governments must also consider several other issues in tobacco taxation. First, to discourage consumption over time, taxation structures within a country need to be effective over time. Many countries, including the United States and South Africa, have allowed tax rates to erode with inflation, thus reducing their effect on health outcomes. In the United States, tobacco tax rates in 1990 fell to 51 per cent of rates in 1955 in real terms (Tobacco Institute, 1995). In South Africa, tobacco tax rates in 1990 fell to 44 per cent of rates in 1970 (Economics of Tobacco Control Project, 1996b). Second, governments need to use a combination of specific taxes and *ad valorem* taxes to discourage consumption across various types of tobacco products, and not to simply encourage switching to lower-priced brands (Townsend, 1996). Third, governments should aim to remove tobacco products from standard cost of living indices. Such removal is not likely to be inflationary (Longfield, 1994). Fourth, as noted earlier the poor are more responsive to price increases than the rich, and are also least likely to use information on tobacco's health hazards. Thus, tax increases will decrease the inequality in consumption between poor and rich, although they may impose a higher tax burden (taxes in relation to personal income) on the poor (Townsend, 1993; 1996). Such a burden needs to be considered in the context of health gains among the poor, and how other public services are targeted to the poor.

Increasing tax rates reduces consumption and, in the short- to medium-term, increases government revenue. China is perhaps the best recent example of the potential health and revenue benefit of appropriate taxation. In China, tobacco taxation has been a major revenue source for many years. In 1983, nearly 15 per cent of government revenue came from the cigarette tax, but this fell to 9 per cent by 1992, suggesting that there is room to increase the tax. A recent World Bank report on financing health services suggested that a 10 per cent additional tax on tobacco could decrease consumption by 5 per cent while generating an additional 4.5 per cent increase in revenue. This extra revenue would cover more than a third of the incremental funds needed for provision of basic health services to China's poorest 100 million inhabitants (World Bank, 1996).

Reducing the cost of smoking cessation is an emerging area of study — particularly as it may involve only public regulation and not finance. Nicotine replacement products (NRP) are effective as part of a smoking cessation programme (Silagy et al., 1994), although their cost-effectiveness is not well established in low- and middle-income countries. De facto, NRP could end the monopoly of the tobacco industry in the nicotine addiction market. In some countries, NRP manufacturers have generated publicity for smoking cessation. The regulation of NRP is a complex issue, and government action could range from symmetrical restrictions on all types of nicotine products, to complete liberalisation of NRP, including removal of non-tariff barriers to NRP imports and permitting adults to self-subscribe. Ideally, government policies need to discourage use of the most harmful products, while allowing adults to access the least harmful products (Warner, Slade and Sweanor, 1997).

There are other methods to raise the cost of smoking, such as banning smoking in the workplace or public places. Such instruments are rather blunt, and in many developing countries may not yet be socially acceptable because of an absence of suitable information and advocacy. Including the estimated costs of involuntary smoking in consideration of taxation increases is reasonable but, as noted above, such analyses are less robust than those dealing with active smoking.

(iii) Spend public tobacco control funds on the most effective and cost-effective interventions

Public funds are limited, and thus policy-makers must ask: is tobacco control a good investment? What about other competing disease priorities? These decisions rely partly on epidemiology and partly on cost-effectiveness analysis, which compares a unit of health outcome to the costs of the intervention.

There are two key epidemiological considerations. First, small reductions in risk across large populations reduce death and disability far more than large reductions in risk across small populations. Second, control measures need to consider the implications of past, current, and future tobacco use. Thus, over the next two decades, effective tobacco control will require focus on quitting smoking as well as preventing smoking initiation. Over 800 million of the world's 1.1 billion smokers live in developing countries, and many of these individuals are in their 20s and 30s. Results from the Doctors Longitudinal Health Study in the United Kingdom show that smokers who quit before age 35 have risks of dying close to those of people who never smoked (Doll et al., 1994). Considerable attention has been focused on protection of children from starting smoking by education and restricting their access to tobacco. Yet even among teenagers, an effective strategy would be to increase the quit rate through price increases and counter-advertising. The present authors examined smoking prevalence for males and females in countries with more than 10 million teenagers (totalling over 700 million teenagers). It is estimated that a 10 per cent increase in quit rate among teenage smokers before middle among (i.e., quit rate increases from 50 to 60 per cent in males and from 70 to 80 per cent in females) would avoid over 13 million tobacco deaths, assuming that only one in three of long-term smokers starting in their teens would die from tobacco (World Bank, unpublished data).

In addition, a recent analysis suggests that much of the mortality burden over the next 20 years from smoking will arise from current smokers and not from future new smokers (Peto *et al.*, 1994; Dr Alan Lopez, personal communication). Thus, depending on the time frame involved, a narrow focus of tobacco control on reducing uptake by children would have minimal impact on the tobacco epidemic of the next two to three decades. Fortunately, the key interventions of price increases and advertising and promotion bans are also the major interventions to reduce smoking in children (National Cancer Policy Board, 1998).

Tobacco control is a highly cost-effective choice for governments. Policy-based control efforts (comprising price increases, advertising and promotion bans, and mass media counter-advertising) is a highly cost-effective health intervention, comparable to the range of cost-effectiveness values for childhood immunisation (see Table 7). Existing cost-effectiveness studies suggest that policy-based programmes cost about US$20-US$80 per discounted year of life saved (Barnum and Greenberg, 1993; Jha, Ranson and Bangoura, 1998; Tengs *et al.*, 1995). The World Bank's 1993 *World Development Report: Investing in Health* suggested that tobacco control policies be included in a minimum package of publicly-financed health services (World Bank, 1993). In contrast, individual smoking cessation programmes are less cost-effective. The cost-effectiveness of implementing such policies at different stages of the tobacco epidemic is not well known, but deserves much study, especially as addiction may influence receptivity to health warnings on tobacco products (Kessler, 1995).

(iv) Develop global and regional taxation and regulatory approaches

There are several reasons to develop regional approaches. First, tobacco is a traded good, and effective control requires harmonised taxation, regulation,

---

Table 7. Cost-effectiveness of tobacco control and other interventions

Place (reference)	Intervention	Cost per life year saved (US$)
Low-income country (Barnum & Greenberg, 1993)	Tax increases, ban advertising and promotion, mass campaigns	20-40
India (Jha, Jamison & Habayeb, 1998)	Tax increases, ban advertising and promotion, mass campaigns	50-70
Guinea, Africa (Jha, Ranson & Bangoura, 1998)	Legislation, warnings, tax increases	77
United States (Tengs et al., 1995)	Smoke-cessation advice to middle-age adults	600-1000
Low-income country (World Bank, 1993)	Childhood immunisation	20-40

and trade strategies. There is already evidence that the United States' trade pressure on East Asian countries has increased tobacco consumption, largely from increased advertising and promotion (Chaloupka and Laixuthai, 1996). Second, with increasing communication and more global access to advertising and promotion mediums, tobacco control must also adopt trans-national approaches. Third, common markets often imply that common standards (such as product liability) for many commercial products are possible. Fourth, the European Union has adopted a partial ban on advertising and promotion. This ban, along with proposed advertising restrictions as part of the US legislation on tobacco, could help establish new minimal global standards for tobacco control.

Taxation efforts need to ensure that tax structures between countries discourage smuggling by minimising price differentials. Unfortunately, the absence of regional tax structures contributes to smuggling, a significant barrier to maintaining tax increases (Joossens and Raw, 1995; Non-Smokers' Rights Association, 1994; Sweanor, 1997). Even with adjustment for purchasing power parity, variation in tax structures in Europe encourages high consumption and smuggling (see Figure 1). Smuggling is a major problem, equivalent to 5 per cent of global cigarette production and 30 per cent of global cigarette trade. The tobacco industry knows this very well and has argued effectively for reduced tax rates to decrease smuggling (*Financial Express*, 1997). Smuggling also exerts pressure on governments to lower tax rates; as seen in Canada (Non-Smokers' Rights Association, 1994) and South Asia (World Bank, unpublished data), which can lead to increased consumption. The proper response to smuggling should be to harmonise prices and to improve enforcement by customs and tax officials, including use of prominent warning labels and tax stamps in local languages.

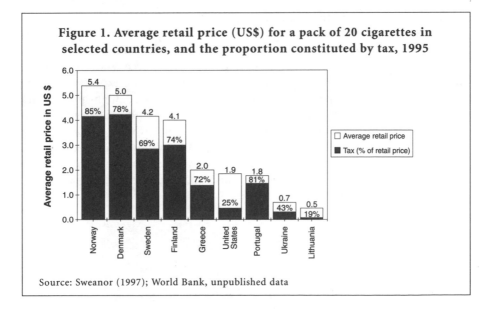

Figure 1. Average retail price (US$) for a pack of 20 cigarettes in selected countries, and the proportion constituted by tax, 1995

Source: Sweanor (1997); World Bank, unpublished data

Other aspects of tobacco regulation that require further study include: regulation of nicotine and other tobacco additives as a drug by an appropriate agency; and using World Trade Organisation agreements or other agreements to establish 'international best practice' for tobacco trade and manufacture. Finally, world-wide reductions in tar and nicotine content of manufactured cigarettes are desirable, and are occurring in any case to some extent (Parish *et al.*, 1995).

Symmetrical regulation mandates policies that apply to all types of tobacco products without prejudice to source of production. The United States, China, Germany, and Japan account for one-half of global cigarette production. Limiting one country's supply abroad may not reduce demand, as smokers may switch to different brands. Brazil and China have sharply increased cigarette exports in recent years, for example. In some countries, such as China and France, state-owned tobacco companies generate substantial revenues (World Health Organisation, 1996b).

Regulation also involves policy co-ordination among various developmental agencies, with stronger public health leadership at the WHO. One key tool for co-ordination is the Framework Convention on Tobacco Control (Collishaw, 1996). Policies of developmental agencies such as the World Bank and European Union should support the Framework Convention. Current World Bank support for tobacco control includes:
- country-specific lending on health promotion and capacity building;
- providing global economic and taxation analyses;
- collaborating in epidemiological studies of tobacco-attributable mortality (China, India and Poland);
- supporting country-specific economic and policy studies on tobacco; and
- working with WHO and various other developmental agencies and NGOs.

Current World Bank's policy advice to countries, and its operational policy on tobacco, are given in the box below.

Finally, it is imperative to target tobacco control efforts where the problem is largest. This involves investment in capacity in low- and middle-income countries to study and monitor the epidemic of tobacco and to promote effective control. Tobacco research can learn much from the experience of the Tropical Disease Research Programme that has supported high-quality and peer-reviewed research in developing countries (Godal, 1996). Governments of established market economies should identify ways of providing financial and technical resources to such research in low- and middle-income countries. "Tobacco or Health" units in every country are needed, and these should have expertise in fiscal, trade, and regulatory polices, along with a strong analytical and policy-oriented public health capacity.

World Bank policies on tobacco, 1997

In recognition of the harmful effects of tobacco on individuals and societies, the World Bank has since 1991 maintained a formal policy of not lending for tobacco production, processing, or marketing. In addition, the Bank encourages tobacco control through lending, policy and research support. The *key policy recommendations* by the World Bank to client governments were discussed as part of the Sector Strategy Paper, Health Nutrition and Population, in 1997. The Bank recommends that governments:
* adopt significant price and tax increases — with adjustment for inflation;
* implement complete bans on tobacco advertising and promotion of tobacco goods, trademarks or logos;
* disseminate information on health risks that is clearly understood, e.g., Canadian labelling laws and media-based public information campaigns;
* research the causes, consequences, and costs of tobacco use — including better direct estimates of deaths and disability from tobacco — and conduct research on fiscal, trade, and marketing policies that effect consumption; and
* increase funding and expertise for tobacco control units.

The World Bank's operational policy (No 4.76) on tobacco states:
* World Bank activities in the health sector — including sector work, policy dialogue, and lending — discourage the use of tobacco products;
* The World Bank does not lend directly for, invest in, or guarantee investments or loans for tobacco production, processing, or marketing. Exceptions may be allowed for countries that are heavily dependent on tobacco as a source of income (especially for poor farmers and farm workers) and foreign exchange earnings (i.e., those where tobacco accounts for more than 10 per cent of exports). The World Bank seeks to help these countries diversify away from tobacco;
* To the extent practicable, the World Bank does not lend indirectly for tobacco production activities, although some indirect support of the tobacco economy may occur as an inseparable part of a project that has a broader set of objectives and outcomes (e.g. rural roads);
* Un-manufactured and manufactured tobacco, tobacco processing machinery and equipment, and related services are included in the negative list of imports in World Bank Loan Agreements;
* Tobacco and tobacco-related producer or consumer imports may be exempt from borrowers' agreements with the World Bank to liberalise trade and reduce tariff levels.

Conclusion

The challenge of tobacco control is as great as any facing public health and development. Tobacco use is harmful to health and to the welfare of societies, especially to the poor. Governments should reduce demand for tobacco by:
* increasing information for individuals on tobacco by adopting serious warning labels on tobacco products, by banning tobacco advertising and promotion, and by increasing research on the causes, consequences and costs of tobacco products;
* raising the cost of smoking through taxation and regulation;
* spending public funds on the most effective and cost-effective tobacco control interventions; and
* developing global and regional taxation and regulatory approaches, including control of smuggling.
Governments also need to make selected cost-effective investments in

capacities to develop and implement these polices, and should adopt a package of interventions, because no single measure will work alone. Taken together, these interventions could significantly reduce global consumption and subsequently the disease burden caused by tobacco.

References

Barendregt, J. *et al.* (1997), "The health care costs of smoking", *New England Journal of Medicine*, 337:1052-1057.

Barnum, H. and R.E. Greenberg (1993), "Cancers", in Jamison, D.T., H.W. Mosley, A.R. Measham and J.L. Bobadilla (eds.), *Disease Control Priorities in Developing Countries*, New York: Oxford Medical Publications.

Chaloupka, F.J. and A. Laixuthai (1996), *US Trade Policy and Cigarette Smoking in Asia*, NBER Working Paper 5543, Cambridge, Mass.: National Bureau of Economic Research.

Charlton, A., D. While and S. Kelly (1997), "Boys' smoking and cigarette-brand-sponsored motor racing", *Lancet*, 350:1474.

Collishaw, N. (1996), "An international framework convention for tobacco control", *Heart Beat*, 2:11.

DiFranza, J.R., J.W. Richards *et al.* (1991), "Nabisco's cartoon camel promotes Camel cigarettes to children", *Journal of the American Medical Association*, 266:3149-53.

Doll, R., R. Peto, K. Wheatley, R. Gray and I. Sutherland (1994), "Mortality in relation to smoking: 40 years' observations on male British doctors", *British Medical Journal*, 309:901-11.

Economics of Tobacco Control Project, (1996b), *An Econometric Estimation of Actual and Potential Government Revenue from Cigarette Taxation in South Africa: 1970-1995*, Update 2 (Annett, N.), Cape Town: University of Cape Town.

Economics of Tobacco Control Project, (1996c), *An Econometric Analysis of the Effect of Advertising on Cigarette Consumption in South Africa: 1970-1995*, Update 3 (Annett, N.), Cape Town: University of Cape Town.

The Economist (1997) "Tobacco and tolerance", 20 December, pp.59-61.

Ensor, T. (1992), "Regulating tobacco consumption in developing countries", *Health Policy and Planning*, 7:375-81.

Federal Trade Commission (1995), "Cigarette advertising and promotion in the United Sates, 1993: a report of the Federal Trade Commission", *Tobacco Control*, 4:310-3.

Financial Express (India) (1997), "Tobacco industry for broadening of tax base", 26 Feb, p.15.

Flint, A.J. and T.E. Novotny (1997), "Poverty status and cigarette smoking prevalence and cessation in the United States, 1983-1993: the independent risk of being poor", *Tobacco Control*, 6:14-8.

Godal, T. (1996), "Tropical disease: from investigation to eradication", in World Health Organisation (eds.), *Investing in Health Research and Development*, report of the Ad Hoc Committee on Health Research Relating to Future Intervention Options (Document TDR/Gen/96.1), Geneva: World Health Organisation.

Goldman, L.K. and S.A. Glantz (1998), "Evaluation of anti-smoking advertising campaigns", *Journal of the American Medical Association*, 279:772-77.

Goto, K. and S. Watanabe (1995), "Social cost of smoking for the 21st Century", *Journal of Epidemiology*, 5:113-5.

Gupta, P.C. (1996), "Survey of sociodemographic characteristics of tobacco use among 99 598 individuals in Bombay, India using handheld computers", *Tobacco Control*, 5:114-20.

Hackshaw, A.K., M.R. Law and N.J. Wald (1997), "The accumulated evidence of lung cancer and environmental tobacco smoke", *British Medical Journal*, 315:980-8X.

Harris and Associates (1989), *Prevention in America: Steps People Take — or Fail to Take — For Better Health*, cited in US Department of Health and Human Services (1989), *Reducing the Health Consequences of Smoking: 25 Years of Progress: a Report of the Surgeon General*, DHHS Publication No. (CDC) 89-8411, Office on Smoking and Health, Center for Chronic Disease Prevention and Health Promotion, Centers for Disease Control, Public Health Service, Washington, DC: US Department of Human and Health Services.

Hodgson, T.A. (1998), "The health care costs of smoking", *New England Journal of Medicine*, 338:470.

Jha, P., K. Ranson and O. Bangoura (1998), "The cost-effectiveness of forty health interventions in Guinea", *Health Policy and Planning* (in press).

Jha, P., D.T. Jamison and S. Habayeb (1998), *Approaches to the Control of Non-communicable Disease in India*, World Bank Background Paper, Washington, DC: World Bank.

Joossens, L. and M. Raw (1995), "Smuggling and cross-border shopping of tobacco in Europe", *British Medical Journal*, 310:1393-7.

Kessler, D.A. (1995), "Nicotine addiction in young people", *New England Journal of Medicine*, 333:186-9.

Laugesen, M. and C. Meads (1991), "Tobacco advertising restrictions, price, income and tobacco consumption in OECD countries, 1960-1986", *British Journal of Addiction*, 86:1343-54.

Law, M.R., J.K. Morris and N.J. Wald (1997), "Environmental tobacco smoke exposure and ischemic heart disease: an evaluation of the evidence", *British Medical Journal*, 315:973-80X.

Liu, B., R. Peto, Z. Chen et al. (1998), "Tobacco hazards in China: proportional mortality study of 1 000 000 deaths", British Medical Journal (in press).

Longfield, J. (1994), Tobacco Taxes in the European Union: How to Make Them Work for Health, London: UICC and Health Education Authority.

Lund, K.E., A. Roennebcrg and A. Hafstad (1995), "The social and demographic diffusion of the tobacco epidemic in Norway", in Slama, K. (ed), Tobacco and Health, New York: Plenum Press.

Mahood, G. (1995), "Canadian tobacco package warning system", Tobacco Control, 4:10-4.

Manning, W.G., E.B. Keeler, J.P. Newhouse, E.M. Sloss and J. Wasserman (1991), The Costs of Poor Health Habits, Cambridge, Mass.: Harvard University Press.

Murray, C.J.L. and A.D. Lopez (1996), The Global Burden of Disease, Cambridge, Mass.: Harvard University Press.

Musgrove, P. (1996), Public and Private Roles in Health, Discussion Paper No. 339, Washington, D.C.: World Bank.

National Cancer Policy Board (1998), Taking Action to Reduce Tobacco Use, Institute of Medicine Commission on Life Sciences, National Research Council, Washington, DC: National Academy Press.

Non-Smokers' Rights Association/Smoking and Health Action Foundation (Canada) (1994), The Smuggling of Tobacco Products: Lessons from Canada, Ottawa: NSRA/SHAF.

Novotny, T.E., R.A. Romano, R.M. Davis and S.L. Mills (1992), "The public health practice of tobacco control: lessons learned and directions for the states in the 1990s", Annual Review of Public Health, 13:287-318.

Over, M., R.P. Ellis, J.H. Huber and O. Solon (1992), "The consequences of adult ill-health", in Feachem, G.A., T. Kjellstrom, J.L. Murray, M. Over and M.A. Phillips (eds.), The Health of Adults in the Developing World, New York, NY: Oxford University Press.

Parish, S., R. Collins, R. Peto et al. (1995), "Cigarette smoking, tar yields, and non-fatal myocardial infarction: 14 000 cases and 32 000 controls in the United Kingdom", The International Studies of Infarct Survival (ISIS) Collaborators, British Medical Journal, 311:471-77.

Peto, R., A.D. Lopez, J. Boreham, M. Thun and C. Heath Jr. (1994), Mortality from Smoking in Developed Countries 1950-2000, New York, NY: Oxford University Press.

Robson, L. and E. Single (1995), Literature Review of Studies of the Economic Costs of Substance Abuse, Ottawa: Canadian Center on Substance Abuse.

Schelling, T.C. (1986), "Economics and cigarettes", Prev. Med., 15:549-60.

Silagy, C., D. Mant, G. Fowler and M. Lodge (1994), "Meta-analysis on efficacy of nicotine replacement therapies in smoking cessation", Lancet, 343:139-42.

Single, E., D. Collins, B. Easton, H. Harwood, H. Lapsley and A. Maynard (1996), International Guidelines for Estimating the Costs of Substance Abuse, Ottawa: Canadian Center on Substance Abuse.

Slama, K. (1995), Tobacco and Health, New York, NY: Plenum Press.

Stiglitz, J. (1989), "On the economic role of the state", in A. Heertje (ed.), The Economic Role of the State, Cambridge, Mass: Basil Blackwell in association with Bank Insinger de Beauford NV.

Sweanor, D. (1997), Global Cigarette Taxes and Prices, Ottawa: Non-Smokers' Rights Association.

Tengs, T.O., M.E. Adams, J.S. Pliskin et al. (1995), "Five-hundred life-saving interventions and their cost effectiveness", Risk Analysis, 15:369-90.

Tobacco Institute (1995), The Tax Burden on Tobacco, Washington, DC: The Tobacco Institute.

Townsend, J. (1993), "Policies to halve smoking deaths", Addiction, 88:37-46.

Townsend, J. (1996), "Price and consumption of tobacco", British Medical Bulletin, 52:132-42.

Tye, J.B., K.E. Warner and S.A. Glantz (1987), "Tobacco advertising and consumption: evidence of a causal relationship", Journal of Public Health Policy, 8:492-508.

US Department of Health and Human Services (1989), Reducing the Health Consequences of Smoking: 25 Years of Progress: a Report of the Surgeon General, DHHS Publication No. (CDC) 89-8411, Office on Smoking and Health, Center for Chronic Disease Prevention and Health Promotion, Centers for Disease Control, Public Health Service, Washington, DC: US Department of Human and Health Services.

US Centers for Disease Control and Prevention (1994), "Medical-care expenditures attributable to cigarette smoking — United States, 1993", Morbidity and Mortality Weekly Report, 43:469-72.

Viscusi, K. (1989), "Do smokers underestimate risks?", Journal of Political Economy, 98:1253-69.

Warner, K., F. Chaloupka, P. Cook et al. (1995), "Criteria for determining an optional cigarette tax: the economist's perspective", Tobacco Control, 4:380-86.

Warner, K.E. (1994), "Health and economic implications of a tobacco-free society", Journal of the American Medical Association, 258:2080-86.

Warner, K.E., J. Slade and D.T. Sweanor (1997), "The emerging market for long-term nicotine maintenance", Journal of the American Medical Association, 278:1087-92.

World Bank (1990), Brazil: the New Challenge of Adult Health, Washington, DC: World Bank.

World Bank (1992), China: Long-Term Issues and Options in the Health Transition, Washington, DC: World Bank.

World Bank (1993), The World Development Report 1993: Investing in Health, New York, NY: Oxford University Press.

World Bank (1994a), Chile: the New Adult Health Policy Challenge, Washington, DC: World Bank, 1994.

World Bank (1994b), *Averting the Old Age Crisis*, Washington, DC: World Bank.
World Bank (1996), *China: Issues and Options in Health Financing*, Report No. 15278-CHA, Washington, DC: World Bank.
World Bank (1997), *Confronting AIDS: Public Priorities in a Global Epidemic*, World Bank Policy Report, Washington, DC: World Bank.
World Health Organisation (1996a), *Investing in Health Research and Development*, report of the Ad Hoc Committee on Health Research Relating to Future Intervention Options (Document TDR/Gen/96.1), Geneva: World Health Organisation.
World Health Organisation (1996b), *Tobacco Alert Special Issue: the Tobacco Epidemic: a Global Public Health Emergency*, Geneva: World Health Organisation.
Wright, V.B. (1986), "Will quitting smoking help Medicare solve its financial problems?", *Inquiry*, 23:76-82.
Yach, D., D.E. McIntyre and Y. Saloojee (1992), "Smoking in South Africa: the health and economic impact", *Tobacco Control*, 1:272-80.
Zatonski, W. (1996), *Evolution of Health in Poland Since 1988*, Warsaw: Marie Skeodowska-Curie Cancer Center and Institute of Oncology Department of Epidemiology and Cancer Prevention.

Section 2

Economic Issues Relating to Tobacco Control

Chapter 6

The Economics of Tobacco and Health: an Overview

Kenneth Warner

Although there are many products that enrich their purveyors while injuring their consumers, none approaches the dominance of tobacco and its derivative products in both domains. A major cash crop in scores of countries, tobacco is the principal raw ingredient in a manufactured product, cigarettes, that has created an international industrial and marketing behemoth. That same product is currently responsible for 3.5 million deaths world-wide each year, a figure projected to rise to 10 million by the year 2030 (Peto, Lopez and Liu, 1997). At that time, tobacco will lead all other causes of death in the developing world, as it does in the industrialised nations today.

Since ill-health and wealth represent the defining dimensions of tobacco, doctors and economists constitute two groups with a logical professional interest in tobacco. Innumerable physicians and medical scientists have investigated the relationship between tobacco and disease since the middle of this century. In contrast, only a handful of industrial organisation economists studied tobacco in the first half of this period, and they had virtually no interest in its health implications. Since the early 1980s, however, a growing cadre of health economists has tackled issues of economics and tobacco primarily in the hope of gaining understanding relevant to stemming the disease toll of tobacco (Chaloupka and Warner, 1998).

In some areas of policy, economic research has "delivered the goods", producing the essential findings needed to elucidate relationships between influences on smoking and their effects on consumption of cigarettes; the best example concerns the relationship between cigarette price and quantity demanded, and between cigarette excise taxation and cigarette pricing. In other areas of policy, economics has offered insights that complement those from other disciplines. More generally, economics offers a conceptual framework within which policy-makers can evaluate the desirability of different mixes of policies.

This chapter provides an overview of the contributions that economics can offer, and the methods economists employ in addressing tobacco policy questions. As such, it provides little detail, but rather identifies the broad themes covered by other contributions in this book.

The next section of the chapter describes the areas of policy interest that have captured the most attention of economists, reflecting both the innate importance of those policy measures and the anticipated contribution that economics can make toward understanding their implications. It identifies the principal research methods that economists have used in studying the issues identified in the preceding section. The contribution of economic analysis to the understanding of tobacco control policy is evaluated, considering the special insights that economics has produced and acknowledging the limitations of economic research. The chapter then introduces an economics-based conceptual approach to searching for an optimal tobacco control policy mix; although earlier discussion examines the use of specific analytical tools, this section's objective is to offer an evaluative perspective, to consider how it can guide consideration of optimal policy design. Finally, a few concluding remarks are offered on the strengths and limitations of the existing body of research, and on the need for and potential of future economic analysis of tobacco policy.

Substantive interests of economic research

(i) Effects of taxation, advertising, and restrictions on smoking in public places

Without a doubt, the area of greatest concentration of economic analysis effort, and consequent contribution to knowledge, has been the effects of price on the demand for cigarettes. The relationship between price and quantity demanded is a natural for economists to study. It lies at the heart of economics and is one of the very first concepts presented to students in introductory economics courses. Innumerable economists have made careers out of analysing this relationship, for one commodity and then another. Private sector industrial economists evaluate it to inform their companies' product pricing decisions. Academic economists study it to better understand market phenomena in general and, in some instances, such as the present one, to inform policy decision-making.

As excise taxation is the principal policy variable relevant to price, a subset of the economists interested in tobacco and health have studied the relationship between cigarette excise taxation and pricing, which is not as straightforward as one might expect. Research in the United States has found that the oligopolistic cigarette industry has taken advantage of tax increases by raising retail prices by more than the amount of the tax increase, primarily at the federal level (Harris, 1987) but also at the state level, although to a much smaller degree (Keeler *et al.*, 1996).

The main interest in this body of price-demand literature concerns how price changes (typically price increases) influence both the decision of whether or not to smoke (called "participation" in much of the literature; better known by the epidemiological term "prevalence") and the decision of how many cigarettes to smoke, given that one continues to smoke. Overall, there is a consensus that in the major industrialised nations in which most of this research has been performed, the price elasticity of demand for cigarettes is in the vicinity of −0.4 to −0.5 (Chaloupka and Warner, 1998). (In developing countries, demand is likely to be considerably more elastic (Chapman and Richardson, 1990; Warner,

1990)). There is less precise consensus on how much of the elasticity reflects price-induced decisions to quit (or start) smoking *versus* decisions to cut back (or increase) the number of cigarettes smoked.

An important subset of the literature has focused on differences in price-responsiveness by age, with a special interest in the price-responsiveness of teenagers compared with that of adults. Although one prominent study failed to find a difference (Wasserman *et al.*, 1991), the weight of the evidence supports the conclusion that children are substantially more price-responsive than adults, on the order of two to three times more responsive, and that young adults are more price-responsive than older adults (Lewit, Coate and Grossman, 1981; Lewit and Coate, 1982; Chaloupka and Grossman, 1996; Chaloupka and Wechsler, 1997).

Of great interest is a question that has been carefully explored only in the United Kingdom: are lower socio-economic status smokers more price-responsive than those in the upper socio-economic classes? Townsend and her colleagues confirmed this relationship in their analysis of smoking in the United Kingdom, concluding that in the lowest socio-economic status class, price elasticity of demand approached unity, while in the highest class, elasticity was not significantly different from zero (Townsend, Roderick and Cooper, 1994).

The number of contributions to the body of literature on the effects of cigarette price has grown steadily, with methodological refinements characterising much of the recent literature (Chaloupka and Warner, 1998). New models of how addiction influences demand have mingled with the more conventional demand models (Chaloupka and Warner, 1998; Becker, Grossman and Murphy, 1994).

If the quantity and quality of contributions to this literature have increased, so, too, has the sophistication of the questions asked. Recently, for example, Evans and Farrelly (1998) decided to examine whether price increases might have a different and subtle influence on smoking behaviour, specifically whether they would cause some smokers to switch from cigarettes with a lower tar and nicotine content to cigarettes with a higher tar and nicotine content. Such a phenomenon might diminish (but not eliminate) the expected health benefits from increasing a cigarette tax. The authors did find evidence of this relationship, with stronger effects indicated for younger smokers.

Knowledge gleaned from the body of literature on the tax-price-demand relationship has provided a solid basis for policy decision-making, and indeed has influenced policy around the world (Roemer, 1993). It has moved the issue of taxation from being a public health backwater, of little interest to public health professionals (who often viewed economic incentives with disdain), to the forefront of tobacco control policy. It seems safe to assert that the impact of tax policy on smoking behaviour is better understood than that of any other tobacco control policy. That this owes almost exclusively to the work of economists makes this the crowning achievement of economics tobacco policy research to date.

Economists have also devoted considerable effort to studying the relationship between cigarette advertising and consumption. The bulk of this research has focused on conventional (although often quite sophisticated) regression analysis of the relationship between total advertising expenditures and total cigarette consumption. The results of these studies have been mixed, with the weight of the evidence leaning modestly in the direction of finding a small but statistically significant relationship.

As has been pointed out (Warner *et al.*, 1986), however, regression analysis is designed to address the question of whether an independent variable (here, advertising expenditure) affects a dependent variable (cigarette consumption) *on the margin*; that is, these regressions can examine whether a small increase in advertising expenditures is associated with a (presumably small) change in cigarette consumption. As such, these studies do not address the essential policy question, namely whether a substantial decrease in advertising, generally a partial or complete ban, would significantly affect consumption. Only in recent years have regression studies been designed to evaluate this important policy question. The few studies performed to date tend to support the notion that advertising bans, partial or complete, do reduce smoking, although all concerned would concur that more research is needed (Chaloupka and Warner, 1998).

The controversy over the importance of advertising in the determination of the aggregate level of smoking has not been effectively addressed by the economic analyses published to date. This is due in part to measurement problems. Most notably, how does one measure the "quantity" of advertising when its nature is so variable over time — responding, as it has periodically, to the vagaries of societal knowledge about and attitudes toward smoking, as well as to changes in the "rules of the game" (for example, a ban on broadcast media advertising of cigarettes) (Warner *et al.*, 1986)? In part it owes to the inherent limitations of the economist's methodological bag of tricks, as suggested above: econometric analyses do not and cannot address all the complexities of this issue satisfactorily.

As a consequence, one may characterise the body of economic research on this subject as contributing insights toward an understanding that has developed from the work of scholars in multiple disciplines. Despite the efforts of many such scholars, understanding of the nature and extent of advertising's influence on consumption remains limited. The US Surgeon General has interpreted the weight of the evidence as strongly favouring the view that advertising does increase consumption (US Department of Health and Human Services, 1989). But unlike the case of price and consumption, there is no 'smoking gun' to prove this.

Economists have also made important contributions to knowledge in the relatively newer body of research concerning the effects of restrictions on smoking in public places. Addressed in both macro-level and micro-level studies, the relationship between such restrictions and smoking is a complicated one with multiple dimensions. Using macro-level data (e.g. indices of indoor-air smoking restrictions in the US states), economists have observed significant inverse relationships between the restrictiveness of state laws and state-specific consumption rates (Chaloupka and Warner, 1998). As has often been observed, however, the relationship could reflect a third variable operating on both the adoption and implementation of laws and citizens' smoking: a general social environment opposed to public smoking could persuade legislators to pass tough laws and, independently, it could encourage smokers to quit (Warner, 1981).

Micro-level data studies, comparing individuals' self-reports of their smoking with reports on their workplaces' smoking policies, tend to confirm the inverse relationship. Several of these have been produced by non-economists; the work of economists contributes to but does not dominate this literature. Unlike the case of advertising, this relationship should lend itself to reasonably definitive conclusions as the research increases in quantity and quality.

(ii) The social costs (and benefits) of smoking

Assessment of the burden that smoking imposes on a society typically focuses on two dimensions, its impact on health and its economic consequences. Epidemiologists have dominated the research on the former, producing the most important studies in a smoking-and-health literature that now exceeds 70 000 contributions in English alone (US Department of Health and Human Services, 1989). The work of economists has quite naturally dominated evaluation of the economic consequences of smoking. Analysis of the medical costs associated with smoking constitutes the principal interest of literature on the economic consequences of smoking, which is quite modest in terms of the number of contributions. The relevance of this work to policy has increased dramatically in recent years, however, as a result of lawsuits filed by the chief legal officers of the US states to recover publicly funded smoking-related medical expenditures from the tobacco companies. Research performed by US health economists (and others) has formed the basis for defining the economic burden imposed on the states (Bartlett *et al.*, 1994). Economic models are being used to estimate the specific burdens experienced by each of the individual states (Miller *et al.*, 1998).

Published studies on the medical costs of smoking have consistently found that smoking is responsible for approximately 6 per cent of US medical care expenditures. This consistency is attributable in large part to substantial similarity in the methods applied to develop estimates and even to considerable overlap in authorship of the published studies. Despite the consistency, however, there are several reasons to believe that 6 per cent underestimates the actual proportionate share, possibly very significantly (Warner, Hodgson and Carroll, 1998).

Owing to a variety of factors relating to the nature of different countries' health care systems and the stages of their smoking epidemics, the medical costs of smoking differ from one country to another. Further, those costs are likely to vary within countries over time as their medical sectors develop and their smoking epidemics intensify (Warner, 1998). With basic research methods well-established, once the underlying epidemiological and medical expenditure data become available, countries should be able to develop reliable minimum estimates of the economic burden of smoking using these widely-accepted methods.

At dispute, however, is the proper concept of economic burden. Since the early 1980s (Leu and Schaub, 1983), a number of economists have demonstrated that non-smokers' accrual of medical costs in the extra years of life they experience, compared to smokers, compensate in part or entirely for smokers' higher annual medical costs during the course of their (shortened) lives. The size and even the ultimate direction of the compensatory effect is unresolved, with some analysts concluding that the compensatory effect eventually outweighs non-smokers' lower annual costs (Barendregt, Bonneux and Van der Maas, 1997), while others find that smokers' higher annual costs outweigh the longer lives of non-smokers (Hodgson, 1992). If a recent review of the literature is correct in its conclusion that gross costs have been systematically underestimated (Warner, Hodgson and Carroll, 1998), the weight of the evidence may shift toward the finding that non-smokers' longer lives do not compensate for smokers' higher annual costs. In any case, further research will be needed to resolve this question.

For reasons similar to those discussed above concerning variability in the gross medical costs of smoking across countries, the bottom-line answer to whether smokers or non-smokers incur more lifetime medical costs may well vary from one country to another or from one time to another within a given country, depending on levels of public expenditure. The essential point, however, is beyond dispute: the longer lives of non-smokers do compensate at least in part for the higher annual costs of smokers while they are alive (Warner, Hodgson and Carroll, 1998).

The proper uses of the net *versus* gross measures of smoking's medical costs remain the subject of some debate (Warner, Hodgson and Carroll, 1998; Viscusi, 1995; Tollison and Wagner, 1992). There is a consensus among many economists, however, that the externality argument often cited by the public health community to support higher tobacco taxation, which relies on the gross-cost concept, is flawed. Even economists who strongly support higher tobacco taxation appeal to other considerations in doing so, such as the ability of higher prices to discourage children from embarking on a lifetime of addiction to nicotine (Warner *et al.*, 1995).

The "offset" argument (that non-smokers incur costs in their extra years of life) has two additional dimensions of interest that have been little explored to date. One concerns the implications of smoking for nursing home expenditures. Here, too, there are two counterbalancing forces: on the one hand, the greater numbers of elderly non-smokers suggest a non-smoking burden on nursing care; on the other hand, surviving smokers are sicker than non-smokers and more in need of nursing home care. Which force dominates the calculus has yet to be determined.

The second offset argument pertains to the implications of smoking for pensions. In one study, scholars at Stanford University concluded that, by virtue of dying earlier on average, smokers subsidise the Social Security benefits of

America's non-smokers (Shoven, Sundberg and Bunker, 1989). In another study evaluating the implications of smoking for the benefits package of a major US company, a team of non-economists concluded that the pension savings attributable to smokers' dying earlier swamped the extra medical costs they imposed on the company's health care plan. The study failed, however, to discount either medical or pension costs (Gori, Richter and Yu, 1984).

Clearly, this is an area of considerable interest that would benefit from careful economic research. As one economist has observed, even the Stanford study is tenuous, since the analysts did not consider a number of factors that might well diminish the subsidy by smokers of non-smokers' Social Security benefits (Michael Schoenbaum, personal communication). Specifically, he noted, in America smokers tend to be lower wage earners than non-smokers, thereby contributing less into the retirement system; and they tend to retire earlier than non-smokers, no doubt in part to being sicker. As such, smokers commence receiving their Social Security benefits earlier on average than do non-smokers.

This literature on the costs (and "benefits") of smoking thus represents a mix of consistent evidence on the gross medical costs of smoking and a much more controversial set of studies that raises interesting questions, more than answering them, about net costs. Economic research clearly has more to offer in this area of interest. In so doing, however, it will become increasingly important to pose questions, and conduct studies, within an explicit framework of values. Most notably, the literature on the costs (and "benefits") of smoking never addresses a very fundamental question: what is the value of human life? Medical costs and pension savings do not occur in a vacuum. Economists seem to be examining the tangible financial implications of smoking without considering the benefit that all societies attribute to the preservation and elongation of healthy life.

Another area of tobacco economics research closely parallels the gross *versus* net issue in evaluating the medical costs of smoking, although interestingly the political tables are reversed. Whereas the public health community relies on the gross medical cost of smoking to make the case that smoking imposes a burden on society, the tobacco industry relies on a gross analysis of its "contribution" to the economy to defend its societal importance. Conversely, supporters of the industry (Tollison and Wagner, 1992) and others (Manning *et al.*, 1989) net out the medical costs of smoking, which reduces the apparent economic burden of smoking, while health-oriented economists evaluate the net contribution of tobacco's economic activity to the society, which reduces the apparent benefit of tobacco industry activity.

Analysis of the gross economic contribution of the tobacco industry to a society is a time-honoured practice by the industry, dating back approximately 20 years. In an exercise carried out globally (Agro-economic Services Ltd. and Tabacosmos Ltd., 1987), as well as in several individual countries (and in smaller jurisdictions such as states and major cities in the United States), economics consulting firms estimate the amount of employment, by sector, that is attributable to the growing of tobacco and manufacture, distribution, and sale of tobacco products. In addition, they calculate the incomes associated with this employment, tax revenues generated by the sale of tobacco products, and, where relevant, the contribution to a country's balance of trade.

The purpose of this exercise is to convince policy influentials, especially government officials and journalists, that however they may feel about the health implications of tobacco, they should recognise the dependence of their constituents on tobacco for employment and incomes. The implicit message, occasionally made explicitly, is that anything that threatens tobacco sales, such as a tobacco control policy, will damage the economic vitality of their communities.

To economists, an essential ingredient of this analysis is obviously missing: in the absence of tobacco sales, consumers would spend their money on other goods and services which would thereby create other jobs and incomes. In general, for an entire country, the net difference in employment between the two expenditure patterns (with and without domestic tobacco sales) would be negligible. In at least two instances, the consultants hired by the tobacco industry acknowledged as much in their detailed reports to their clients (Chase Econometrics, 1985; American Economics Group, Inc., 1996).

However obvious this may be to economists, it is not necessarily clear to the lay public. Specifically to address what they viewed as the misleading impression the tobacco industry was creating through its use of its economic argument, economists in at least four countries have undertaken macroeconomic studies to evaluate the net employment implications of tobacco in their countries. The first analysis of the net implications of tobacco evaluated the issue qualitatively (Allen, 1993). The next employed a dynamic macroeconomic model, comparable to those used by the industries' consultants, to "complete" the analyses performed by the industry consultants (Warner and Fulton, 1994; Warner *et al.*, 1996). Economists in the United Kingdom (Buck *et al.*, 1995) and South Africa (Van der Merwe and Abedian, 1997) followed with similar analyses, using input-output models instead. The basic argument has been applied to the case of smoking in the Pacific Islands (Collins and Lapsley, 1997).

In all instances, the non-industry economists demonstrated that the absence of tobacco (or a decline in tobacco product consumption) would not harm the society's employment. In the first empirical analysis, Warner and Fulton showed that for a non-tobacco jurisdiction (in their case, a non-tobacco-producing state in the US), declining tobacco product consumption would actually increase employment within the jurisdiction, since a disproportionate percentage of expenditures on tobacco are "exported" to the tobacco-producing jurisdictions (Warner and Fulton, 1994).

These "counter" studies are few in number but important in demarcating an area of economic research on tobacco that has been highly visible of late.

(iii) Other topics

There are several other tobacco-related subjects that have received the attention of economist researchers, including the effect of tax-induced price differentials on cigarette smuggling (Galbraith and Kaiserman, 1997), trade issues (Chaloupka, 1998), the implications of public dissemination of information on the hazards of smoking (Viscusi, 1992), and, of course, tobacco agriculture (the subject of much research, but virtually none of it related to tobacco's health consequences). One of the most promising areas is the relationship between policy measures and ultimate health outcomes. To date, economists' contributions in this domain relate almost exclusively to the eventual health implications of increasing cigarette taxes (Harris, 1987; Moore, 1996; Warner, 1986).

This section of the chapter has covered the subjects that have captured the most time and attention of economists interested in tobacco as a source of ill-health. The next section provides a brief overview of the methods these scholars have employed in performing this research.

Economic methods used in research

Given the wide array of topics studied by economists interested in tobacco, it is hardly surprising to learn that scholars have exploited many of the standard methods in the economist's toolbox.

With studies of the relationship between cigarette price and demand dominating the literature, price elasticity calculations have derived from regression analyses employing both micro-level (survey) data and macro-level (aggregate) data. As described above, the models employed exhibit considerable variety in conception and execution. Given the unique attributes of smoking, the literature reveals several interesting means of addressing smoking-specific demand issues. For example, interstate smuggling of cigarettes in the US, attributable to tax-defined differences in state prices, creates a problem in estimating demand equations: smokers in high-tax states can cross state borders to buy their cigarettes in nearby low-tax states. Nowhere is this more evident than in state sales data that show *per capita* sales in New Hampshire, at 158.5 in 1995, 65 per cent above the national average. Neighbouring New Hampshire is Massachusetts, with a major population centre (the city of Boston) very near the New Hampshire border. New Hampshire's state tax in 1995 was 25 cents, while that of Massachusetts was 51 cents (Tobacco Institute, 1996).

Failure to take cross-border purchases of cigarettes into account will lead to mis-estimation of price elasticity, since border-residing smokers will not reduce smoking much (if at all) when their state's tax increases. Economists using survey data have handled this problem by restricting their analyses to data on respondents residing a considerable distance from lower-tax state borders (e.g. at least 20 miles). Note that to do so requires a detailed data set with access to respondents' precise geographical identifiers.

Innovative modelling has addressed the issue of how the addictiveness of smoking affects demand and the relationship between price and demand. Economists have recognised the issue for years, often including lagged consumption as an indicator of the stock of addicted smoking (Chaloupka and Warner, 1998). More recently, modelling of the relationship between price (and price expectations) and addictive demand has been formulated in the "rational addiction" model (Becker, Grossman and Murphy, 1994), an unfortunate name for a model that explicitly addresses how smokers' future price expectations affect their current smoking behaviour. (The model does not posit that becoming addicted is rational. Rather, it examines how being addicted influences the price-demand relationship.)

Analyses of the relationships between advertising and demand, and between smoking restrictions and consumption have also relied on regression analyses, again exhibiting increasing conceptual and technical sophistication over time. As with most microeconomic empirical work, regression analysis lies at the heart of this work.

Other issues have employed other techniques in addition to, or occasionally in lieu of, regression analysis. The literature on the medical costs of smoking, for example, relies heavily on cost-of-illness (COI) measurement techniques. This, in turn, demands an appreciation (and use) of epidemiological methods such as estimation of attributable risk. With various colleagues, Rice has played a seminal role in developing both the basic COI methods (Rice, 1966; Hodgson and Meiners, 1982) and in applying them to the case of the health consequences of smoking (Rice, Hodgson, Sinsheimer et al., 1986). A critique of this literature suggests that future research would benefit from refinements of the estimating techniques (Warner, Hodgson and Carroll, 1998).

If cost-of-illness analysis has played a central role in the economics of tobacco, a very common technique in economic evaluation, cost-effectiveness analysis (Gold et al., 1996) is less in evidence in this literature. There is one notable exception, a fairly sizeable (and growing) literature on cost-effectiveness analyses of various approaches to smoking cessation (Warner, 1997a; Cromwell et al., 1997). Although this literature has considerable policy relevance, it is worth noting that much of it does not pertain directly to governmental policy decision-making per se.

The macroeconomic studies of the contribution of tobacco to countries' economies employ elaborate multi-equation macro-level models. In some instances these are dynamic adjustment models (Warner and Fulton, 1994; Warner et al., 1996), while in others they are input-output models (Buck et al., 1995; Van der Merwe and Abedian, 1997). In all instances, they represent an innovative policy-analytical application of macro-level models. The developer of one of the most respected macro-level models in the United States, REMI (Treyz, 1993), considers the policy simulations performed with his model (Warner and Fulton, 1994; Warner et al., 1996) to represent a sensible and creative new way to employ macro-level models in the evaluation of potential government policies (George Treyz, personal communication).

Analyses of other subjects have employed other methods as well. In a technical review of the literature on the economics of smoking, Chaloupka and Warner (1998) describe in some detail the various analytical and econometric approaches applied to the major areas of interest in this literature.

The contribution of economic analysis to understanding tobacco control policy

Scholars from numerous disciplines devote their skills and analytical perspectives to the effort to understand, and thereby develop, a rational tobacco control policy strategy. Economists bring three unique attributes to this effort:
- a rigorous set of statistical methods with which relationships like that between cigarette price and quantity demanded can be thoroughly evaluated;
- a coherent theory and the rational modelling perspective that comes from years of studying it; as is discussed in the next section, this permits economists to offer a conceptualisation of how societies can allocate tobacco control resources to maximise their effectiveness; and
- a body of substantive knowledge directly germane to elucidating important relationships in tobacco control.

Economics, and economists, have much to offer the pursuit of optimal tobacco control policy. But tobacco use, like all other social phenomena, is not a discipline-specific problem. Rather, it is a multi- and inter-disciplinary problem, one demanding, in addition to that of economists, the thoughtful input of sociologists, political scientists, lawyers, philosophers and ethicists, and, of course, physicians and biomedical scientists. As such, it is important to reflect on the role of economics and economists in grappling with tobacco control policy: where are their strengths most applicable? Where can they be applied independently, and where (and when) can they be used most effectively in collaboration with other scholars? What are the domains in which economics has relatively little to offer?

There are domains within tobacco control in which economics is uniquely valuable. Analysis of the relationships between tobacco taxation and retail price, and price and the demand for tobacco, is perhaps the best example. Virtually all of the important knowledge gleaned from research on these relationships, both quantitative and qualitative, derives from economic analysis, specifically regression analysis from which price elasticities can be calculated.

Yet this example clarifies some of the limits of economics, as much as the strengths. Understanding how tax affects price, and how price affects consumption, does not instruct us as to how high taxes should be set. Ironically, a large number of non-economists have appealed to the negative externality argument to justify the imposition of relatively high taxes on cigarettes. Market failure theory in economics posits that product-specific taxation is often warranted when consumption (or production) of the good in question imposes significant burdens on third parties not involved in the consumption or production decisions. Non-economists often point to the medical costs of smoking, borne by non-smokers, as a justification for high cigarette taxes. Yet when economists examine the facts closely, they conclude that the externality argument is weak, reflecting in part cost offsets (described in the section above on social costs and benefits of smoking) and, in part, the notion that many of the costs are not truly "external" to the smokers (Viscusi, 1995; Tollison and Wagner, 1992). Rather, economists who support higher cigarette taxation often appeal to non-standard economic arguments, such as the ability of high prices to protect children from embarking on a lifetime of nicotine addiction (Warner *et al.*, 1995).

Another aspect of taxation policy relates to the distributional implications of taxation. Particularly in industrialised societies, in which smoking prevalence is inversely related to socio-economic status, cigarette taxes are regressive; that is, they impose a proportionately greater financial burden on the poor than on the rich. Economists can and do contribute to understanding this phenomenon by estimating the differential burdens by social class; but they cannot contribute anything unique to the debate over whether the regressive burden is defensible. That is a matter of philosophy, of ethics, of social policy more broadly construed. Economists can contribute their opinions to the debate as citizens only, not as scholars possessing relevant expertise.

There are other domains in tobacco control in which economists' contributions are uniquely valuable, if limited. Estimating the medical costs of smoking is one; analysing the employment implications of tobacco sales is another; a third is evaluation of the impacts of trade policies on smoking in other countries (Chaloupka, 1998). In all such domains, the tools and perspectives of economics can be applied to generate both quantitative findings and qualitative insights into the nature of tobacco-related policy issues that cannot be expected from practitioners of any other discipline. These are areas in which economic analysis greatly enriches understanding of tobacco control policy and, indeed, is essential to developing such understanding.

In some areas of tobacco control policy, economic analysis has a clear but decidedly limited role to play. Unlike the above subjects, in which economics possesses a near-monopoly on the expertise needed to develop a basic empirical understanding, several policy topics do not lend themselves quite so neatly to economic dissection. Determination of the effects of advertising and promotion constitutes a good example. As was discussed in the section above on substantive interests of economic research, economists' regression studies of the relationship between cigarette advertising expenditures and consumption have provided some guidance as to what can (or cannot) be expected of policies restricting advertising. The same is true of economic analyses of the smoking implications of clean indoor air laws. But in each case, limits on economists' ability to precisely capture the "right" phenomenon restrict the potential of economics to resolve the debates over the effectiveness of these policies.

One example of this problem is noted above: how to measure "advertising", when all that economists have available are dollar expenditures. In concept, dollar expenditures ought to capture the marginal value of advertising quite effectively. In practice, however, the value of a dollar of cigarette advertising almost certainly varies substantially from year to year (and from medium to medium within a given year), reflecting the oligopolistic nature of the industry and its often experimental responses to the extraordinary (and extraordinarily rapid) changes in the social environment surrounding smoking. Critics of the tobacco industry enjoy pointing to numerous occasions on which the industry's advertising campaigns may well have backfired, discouraging smoking rather than encouraging it (Calfee, 1986). Clearly, this would not represent rational, efficient advertising.

A similar if less challenging problem confronts economists who want to understand how effective are laws on clean indoor air in decreasing overall smoking. Such laws reflect changes in societal attitudes toward smoking, as much as shaping them. As such, concurrent passage of clean indoor air laws and decreases in smoking may both reflect independent responses to changes in the social environment. Accurately characterising the latter quantitatively is a challenge of the first order. This said, it is worth noting that through use of two-stage least squares and other econometric techniques, economists have contributed more insight into the complexity of this issue than have the practitioners of other disciplines.

If economics has been helpful regarding knowledge-building in several areas of tobacco control policy, it has fallen short in others. With notable exceptions (Viscusi, 1992; Hamilton, 1972; Warner, 1977), few economists have examined the consumption implications of cigarette labelling requirements and of other educational efforts, including school health education and broadcast media anti-smoking campaigns. These subjects have been examined by scholars in other fields. Economists have contributed little to the debate on product regulation. Even in areas in which the input of economists might appear to be a natural, one often finds little evidence of interest; a notable example is analysis of the implications of differential insurance rates on smoking behaviour (US Department of Health and Human Services, 1989).

Economics has offered tobacco control policy-makers some of the most important evidence produced to date on the implications of various policy measures. The *forte* of economists clearly lies in unravelling quantitative relationships that lend themselves to empirical analysis, particularly (but not exclusively) statistical analysis. Economists contribute the most at the "up-front end", the development of fundamental understanding of the nature and magnitude of relationships between policy variables and tobacco use outcomes. Economists possess, but have not frequently employed, the tools to carry this knowledge development to its extreme: linking policy interventions to ultimate health outcomes (Moore, 1996).

Economists also possess a conceptual perspective, combined with a bent toward formal modelling, which offers the field of tobacco control an opportunity to conceptualise, and eventually evaluate, how one combines tobacco control policy measures in an optimal fashion. The following section is a brief consideration of this important area of research.

Informing the search for an optimal mix of tobacco control policies

Although the number of existing and conceivable individual tobacco control policy measures is enormous, most interventions can be usefully categorised as falling under one of three headings (US Department of Health and Human Services, 1989; Warner *et al.*, 1990):
• policies pertaining to information and education;

- financial incentives; and
- direct restrictions on the manufacture and use of tobacco products.

The first category includes mandated education about the hazards of tobacco use, through school health education and media campaigns, disclosure of product constituents, the use of product warning labels, and restrictions on tobacco advertising and promotion. The second category focuses on the use of tax and other price-relevant policies, but also considers the incentives that derive from sometimes-mandated differential insurance rates for smokers and non-smokers (for health, life, and even property insurance). The third category consists of government-required limitations on smoking in public places and workplaces, restrictions on children's access to tobacco products, and governmental regulation of the composition and "performance" characteristics of tobacco products (e.g. fire safety).

Confronting such a wide array of policy options, how should policy-makers choose to allocate their scarce tobacco control resources? Obviously, one wants to identify those options that will be most cost-effective in reducing tobacco consumption, through both prevention of initiation and promotion of cessation. But assessing the cost-effectiveness of a multitude of possible interventions is exceedingly difficult, especially when one considers that both the cost and effectiveness of individual interventions will vary depending on what other tobacco control measures are in place, and to what degree. The issue of cost-effectiveness in doing "what" will also arise: is preventing smoking initiation equally as valuable as encouraging cessation of current use? Is it more valuable or less valuable? Under what circumstances does each answer obtain?

At the most simplistic level — itself far from simple — the task confronting policy-makers appears to be one of identifying the "average" cost-effectiveness of a variety of policy measures, identifying whom they benefit and how, and then selecting a mix that will attain policy objectives at a reasonable cost. Even achieving success in this endeavour would represent an almost heroic accomplishment, however, because for most policy options decision-makers do not possess even the rudimentary cost-effectiveness analyses that would be necessary to guide policy decisions. The origin of this problem lies not so much in economics as in the epidemiology of policy: there is a lack of good data on the basic effectiveness of most policy interventions.

This recognised, the fact remains that societies must choose how much of their scarce resources to devote to tobacco control, and how to do so. The discipline of economics has much to offer by way of a conceptual framework. Although it may be impossible to translate concept directly into rational action, the prospects for improving the efficiency of tobacco control policy seem likely to be enhanced by contemplating a design for optimal policy decision-making. The remainder of this section offers some thoughts pertinent to further consideration of optimal policy design.

Boiling down the pursuit of efficiency to its economic essence typically involves attempting to maximise an objective, itself a function of multiple variables, subject to one or more constraints, one of the latter being a constraint on resource availability. (Other constraints may relate to ethical or distributional considerations, etc.) In the grandest scheme, society strives to maximise a social welfare function, which incorporates the utilities of all members of the society (the utilities being a function of each individual's consumption of goods and services), subject to constrained resources of labour, capital, and land (natural resources).

Theoretically, the task in tobacco control ought to be to incorporate tobacco control into the utility functions of members of society and then to manipulate tobacco policies in accordance with the overall goal of maximising social welfare. This, of course, is impossible in practical terms. It is a useful point of departure for one reason, however: by co-mingling tobacco control with tobacco consumption in the consumers' utility functions, it emphasises that tobacco consumption produces utility for some members of society, and that this utility warrants recognition (and perhaps some respect) in planning optimal tobacco control policy.

Since formal maximisation of a societal welfare function is a practical impossibility, a more realistic approach is to define a tobacco control objective function, a "production function" of tobacco control, with the intention of considering how distributing resources across the different policy measures (the arguments of the function) might affect the ultimate tobacco control goals. This, itself, exceeds realistic abilities today, when policy-makers lack so much of the basic knowledge about single-variable relationships with tobacco control, much less interaction effects. But it structures the policy decision problem logically, and it necessarily forces policy-makers to contemplate trade-offs when proposing the adoption of specific policy measures.

The approach also forces social decision-makers to consider the basic objective of tobacco control. Is it to reduce tobacco use to the lowest possible level, which one presumes would be the goal of most public health professionals? Or is it, as economists would advocate, to reduce consumption to the level at which the marginal costs of further reductions exceed the marginal benefits? Marginal costs can exceed marginal benefits for two reasons, one purely pragmatic, the other more philosophical. Pragmatically, a point might be reached at which additional investments in tobacco control yielded too little change in consumption to warrant their expansion (the extra cost would not yield equivalent extra benefits). Philosophically, the marginal costs of tobacco control could rise as interventions impinge on the liberty of adults to consume tobacco products as and when they wish.

Contemplation of the objective of tobacco control sharply focuses attention on an issue too often ignored in health policy circles: the optimal national tobacco control policy may well not be one oriented toward minimising tobacco consumption. Indeed, certain tobacco control advocates, including this author (Warner, 1997b), have expressed respect for the notion that knowledgeable adults who are fully informed of the health risks involved should have the right to consume tobacco products in environments in which they are not imposing burdens on others.

How can one take these lofty principles and translate them into practical tools for decision-making? At one level, the answer is simply that it cannot be done. At a more down-to-business level, however, the answer is qualified: the task cannot be carried out to the theoretical ideal, but considerable room remains for sub-optimising. It is indeed possible to examine the relative contributions of different "quantities" of various tobacco control interventions in reducing tobacco product consumption. Several researchers have attempted to do precisely this. The literature now includes a number of contributions in which economists evaluate the impacts on cigarette consumption of two (or occasionally more) interventions. Most common are comparisons of taxes (the most well-studied policy) and clean indoor air laws (Wasserman *et al.*, 1991; Chaloupka and Saffer, 1992), and taxes and media anti-smoking campaigns (Warner, 1977; Hu *et al.*, 1995). A recent study examines the concurrent effects of taxation and advertising (Abedian and Annett, 1997). But efforts to consider concurrently the effects of three or more types of interventions do exist, demonstrating both the logic and potential of such comparisons (Warner, 1989; Townsend, 1993).

Studies such as these clarify the principles that underlie the search for an optimal configuration of policy measures, with a comparison of marginal costs and benefits implicit, if not explicit, in most such analyses. A careful reading of these studies also indicates the challenging problems that confront the would-be policy optimiser. Most notably, not only is it difficult to assess the effectiveness of many interventions; it verges on impossible to measure the "quantity" of many of them, or the cost or benefit, for that matter. How, for example, does one assess either the full costs or benefits of a ban on smoking in restaurants? How much utility does such a ban deprive smokers from experiencing? How much extra utility does clean air generate for non-smokers?

Conclusion

That much remains to be learned about the effects of tobacco control policies is self-evident to anyone who has perused the literature. Less obvious to the casual student of this literature is that quite a bit has been learned, and that economists have made a major contribution to developing the understanding that exists today. Clearly, the most important finding of all tobacco policy research to date — that taxation is a potent tobacco control weapon (with good estimates of the extent of its potency) — owes exclusively to the work of economists who have studied the relationships between taxation and price (Harris, 1987), price and demand (Chaloupka and Warner, 1998), and demand and health (Moore, 1996). The research on taxation and price serves as a model of the best that tobacco policy research has to offer, and a means by which economics can contribute to it.

Before economists declare victory and close up shop, however, there is a need to acknowledge again the limitations of economic research in untangling the relationships between numerous tobacco policy measures and tobacco consumption. That economists have much to offer in evaluating the individual relationships is demonstrated by the efforts put forth to date. That additional contributions will require substantial research creativity is evident as well. Even some of the seemingly more straightforward extensions of research, notably including evaluation of the price elasticity of demand for tobacco products in poor countries, may require creativity to surmount data problems that are far less challenging in developed nations where the bulk of the research has been performed to date (Chapman and Richardson, 1990; Warner, 1990). Certainly, research on all aspects of the economics of tobacco in developing countries must be considered a high priority on any tobacco policy research agenda, although it might prove a tall order to fill.

A fundamental purpose of this book is to see how far one can push the frontiers of analysis of an optimal policy mix. This is an area in which economists should lead the charge. If successful, this exercise would have important implications for a wide variety of policy issues, not just tobacco control.

References

Abedian, I. and N. Annett (1997), *An Empirical Analysis of Cigarette Taxes and Advertising in South Africa: 1970-1995*, working paper, Economics of Tobacco Control Project, Cape Town: University of Cape Town.

Agro-economic Services Ltd and Tabacosmos Ltd (1987), *The Employment, Tax Revenue and Wealth that the Tobacco Industry Creates.*

Allen, R.C. (1993), *The False Dilemma: the Impact of Tobacco Control Policy on Employment in Canada*, Ottawa: National Campaign for Action on Tobacco.

American Economics Group, Inc. (1996), *Economic Impact in the States of Proposed FDA Regulations Regarding the Advertising, Labeling and Sale of Tobacco Products*, Washington, DC: American Economics Group.

Barendregt, J.J., L. Bonneux and P.J. Van der Maas (1997), "The health care costs of smoking", *New England Journal of Medicine*, 337:1052-7.

Bartlett, J.C., L.S. Miller, D.P. Rice, W.B. Max and Office on Smoking and Health, CDC (1994), "Medical care expenditures attributable to cigarette smoking — United States, 1993", *MMWR*, 43:469-72.

Becker, G.S., M. Grossman, K.M. Murphy (1994), "An empirical analysis of cigarette addiction", *American Economic Review*, 84:396-418.

Buck, D., C. Godfrey, M. Raw and M. Sutton (1995), *Tobacco and Jobs*, York, England: Society for the Study of Addiction and the Centre for Health Economics, University of York.

Calfee, J.E. (1986), "The ghost of cigarette advertising past", *Regulation*, November-December:35-45.

Chaloupka, F.J. (1998), "Do trade pressures lead to market expansion?", in Lu, R., J. Mackay, S. Niu and R. Peto (eds.), *The Growing Epidemic*, proceedings of the *Tenth World Conference on Tobacco or Health*, Beijing, 24-28 August 1997, Singapore: Springer-Verlag (in press).

Chaloupka, F.J. and M. Grossman (1996), *Price, Tobacco Control Policies and Youth Smoking*, NBER Working Paper Series, Cambridge, Mass: National Bureau of Economic Research.

Chaloupka, F.J. and H. Saffer (1992), "Clean indoor air laws and the demand for cigarettes", *Contemporary Policy Issues*, 10:72-83.

Chaloupka, F.J. and K.E. Warner (1998), "Smoking", in Newhouse, J.P. and A. Culyer (eds.), *Handbook of Health Economics*, Amsterdam: North-Holland (in press).

Chaloupka, F.J. and H. Wechsler (1997), "Price, tobacco control policies and smoking among young adults", *Journal of Health Economics*, 16:359-73.

Chapman, S. and J. Richardson (1990), "Tobacco excise and declining tobacco consumption: the case of Papua New Guinea", *American Journal of Public Health*, 80:537-40.

Chase Econometrics (1985), *The Economic Impact of the Tobacco Industry on the United States Economy*, Bala Cynwyd, PA: Chase Econometrics.

Collins, D.J. and H.M. Lapsley (1997), *The Economic Impact of Tobacco Smoking in Pacific Islands*, Wahroonga, NSW, Australia: Pacific Tobacco and Health Project.

Cromwell, J., W.J. Bartosch, M.C. Fiore et al. (1997), "Cost-effectiveness of the clinical practice recommendations in the AHCPR guideline for smoking cessation", *Journal of the American Medical Association*, 278:1759-66.

Evans, W.N. and M.C. Farrelly (1998), "The compensating behavior of smokers: taxes, tar and nicotine", *RAND Journal of Economics* (in press).

Galbraith, J.W. and M. Kaiserman (1997), "Taxation, smuggling and demand for cigarettes in Canada: evidence from time-series data", *Journal of Health Economics*, 16:287-301.

Gold, M.R., J.E. Siegel, L.B. Russell and M.C. Weinstein (1996), *Cost-effectiveness in Health and Medicine*, New York, NY: Oxford University Press.

Gori, G.B., B.J. Richter and W.K. Yu (1984), "Economics and extended longevity: a case study", *Preventive Medicine*, 13:396-410.

Hamilton, J.L. (1972), "The demand for cigarettes: advertising, the health scare, and the cigarette advertising ban", *Review of Economics and Statistics*, 54:401-11.

Harris, J.E. (1987), "The 1983 increase in the federal cigarette excise tax", in Summers, L.H. (ed.), *Tax Policy and the Economy*, vol. 1, Cambridge, Mass: MIT Press.

Hodgson, T.A. (1992), "Cigarette smoking and lifetime medical expenditures", *Milbank Memorial Fund Quarterly*, 70:81-125.

Hodgson, T.A. and M.R. Meiners (1982), "Cost-of-illness methodology: a guide to current practices and procedures", *Milbank Memorial Fund Quarterly*, 60:429-62.

Hu, T.W., T.E. Keeler, H.Y. Sung and P.G. Barnett (1995), "Impact of California anti-smoking legislation on cigarette sales, consumption, and prices", *Tobacco Control*, 4(suppl):S34-8.

Keeler, T.E., Hu, T.W., P.G. Barnett *et al.* (1996), "Do cigarette producers price-discriminate by state? An empirical analysis of local cigarette pricing and taxation", *Journal of Health Economics*, 15:499-512.

Leu, R.E. and T. Schaub (1983), "Does smoking increase medical care expenditure?", *Social Science and Medicine*, 17:1907-14.

Lewit, E.M. and D. Coate (1982), "The potential for using excise taxes to reduce smoking", *Journal of Health Economics*, 1:121-45.

Lewit, E.M., D. Coate and M. Grossman (1981), "The effects of government regulation on teenage smoking", *Journal of Law and Economics*, 24:545-69.

Manning, W.G., E.B. Keeler, J.P. Newhouse, E.M. Sloss and J. Wasserman (1989), "The taxes of sin: do smokers and drinkers pay their way?", *Journal of the American Medical Association*, 261:1604-9.

Miller, L.S., X. Zhang, T. Novotny *et al.* (1998), "State estimates of Medicaid expenditures attributable to cigarette smoking, fiscal year 1993", *Public Health Reports*, 113 (in press).

Moore, M.J. (1996), "Death and tobacco taxes", *RAND Journal of Economics*, 27:415-28.

Peto, R., A.D. Lopez and B. Liu (1998), "Global tobacco mortality: monitoring the growing epidemic", in Lu, R., J. Mackay, S. Niu and R. Peto (eds.), *The Growing Epidemic*, proceedings of the *Tenth World Conference on Tobacco or Health*, Beijing, 24-28 August 1997, Singapore: Springer-Verlag (in press).

Rice, D.P. (1966), *Estimating the Cost of Illness*, Division of Medical Care Administration, Health Economics Branch, Public Health Service, Washington, DC: Dept. of Health, Education, and Welfare.

Rice, D.P., T.A. Hodgson, P. Sinsheimer *et al.* (1986), "The economic costs of the health effects of smoking", *Milbank Memorial Fund Quarterly*, 64:489-547.

Roemer, R. (1993), *Legislative Action to Combat the World Tobacco Epidemic*, 2nd ed., Geneva: World Health Organisation.

Shoven, J.B., J.O. Sundberg and J.P. Bunker (1989), "The Social Security cost of smoking", in Wise, D.A. (ed.), *The Economics of Ageing*, Chicago: University of Chicago Press.

Tobacco Institute (1996), *The Tax Burden on Tobacco: Historical Compilation, Volume 30, 1995*, Washington, DC: Tobacco Institute.

Tollison, R.D. and R.E. Wagner (1992), *The Economics of Smoking*, Boston, Mass: Kluwer Academic Publishers.

Townsend, J. (1993), "Policies to halve smoking deaths", *Addiction*, 88:37-46.

Townsend, J., P. Roderick and J. Cooper (1994), "Cigarette smoking by socioeconomic group, sex, and age: effects of price, income, and health publicity", *British Medical Journal*, 309:923-7.

Treyz, G.I. (1993), *Regional Economic Modeling: a Systematic Approach to Economic Forecasting and Policy Analysis*, Boston, Mass: Kluwer Academic Publishers.

US Department of Health and Human Services (1989), *Reducing the Health Consequences of Smoking: 25 Years of Progress: a Report of the Surgeon General*, DHHS Publication No. (CDC) 89-8411, Office on Smoking and Health, Center for Chronic Disease Prevention and Health Promotion, Centers for Disease Control, Public Health Service, Washington, DC: US Department of Health and Human Services.

Van der Merwe, R. and I. Abedian (1997), "An empirical analysis of the output effects of cigarette taxes in South Africa and the regional impact", presented at the *Tenth World Conference on Tobacco or Health*, Beijing, 24-28 August.

Viscusi, W.K. (1992), *Smoking: Making the Risky Decision*. New York: Oxford University Press.

Viscusi, W.K. (1995), "Cigarette taxation and the social consequences of smoking", in Poterba, J.M. (ed.), *Tax Policy and the Economy*, Cambridge, Mass: MIT Press.

Warner, K.E. (1977), "The effects of the anti-smoking campaign on cigarette consumption", *American Journal of Public Health*, 67:645-50.

Warner, K.E. (1981), "Cigarette smoking in the 1970s: the impact of the antismoking campaign on consumption", *Science*, 211:729-31.

Warner, K.E. (1986), "Smoking and health implications of a change in the federal cigarette excise tax", *Journal of the American Medical Association*, 255:1028-32.

Warner, K.E. (1989), "Effects of the antismoking campaign: an update", *American Journal of Public Health*, 79:144-51.

Warner, K.E. (1990), "Tobacco taxation as health policy in the Third World", *American Journal of Public Health*, 80:529-31.

Warner, K.E. (1997a), "Cost-effectiveness of smoking cessation therapies: interpretation of the evidence and implications for coverage", *PharmacoEconomics*, 11:538-49.

Warner, K.E. (1997b), "Dealing with tobacco", *American Journal of Public Health*, 87:906-9.

Warner, K.E. (1998), "Economics of consumption", in Lu, R., J. Mackay, S. Niu and R. Peto (eds.), *The Growing Epidemic*, proceedings of the *Tenth World Conference on Tobacco or Health*, Beijing, 24-28 August 1997, Singapore: Springer-Verlag (in press).

Warner, K.E., F.J. Chaloupka, P.J. Cook *et al.* (1995), "Criteria for determining an optimal cigarette tax: the economist's perspective", *Tobacco Control*, 4:380-6.

Warner, K.E., T. Citrin, G. Pickett *et al.* (1990), "Licit and illicit drug policies: a typology", *British Journal of Addiction*, 85:255-62.

Warner, K.E., V.L. Ernster, J.H. Holbrook *et al.* (1986), "Promotion of tobacco products: issues and policy options", *Journal of Health Politics, Policy and Law*, 11:367-92.

Warner, K.E. and G.A. Fulton (1994), "The economic implications of tobacco product sales in a nontobacco state", *Journal of the American Medical Association*, 271:771-6.

Warner, K.E., G.A. Fulton, P. Nicolas and D.R. Grimes (1996), "Employment implications of declining tobacco product sales for the regional economies of the United States", *Journal of the American Medical Association*, 275:1241-6.

Warner, K.E., T.A. Hodgson and C.E. Carroll (1998), "The medical costs of smoking in the United States: quality and implications of the literature", working paper, Dept. of Health Management and Policy, Ann Arbor, MI: School of Public Health, University of Michigan.

Wasserman, J., W.G. Manning, J.P. Newhouse and J.D. Winkler (1991), "The effects of excise taxes and regulations on cigarette smoking", *Journal of Health Economics*, 10:43-64.

Chapter 7

Some Neglected Aspects of the Economics of Tobacco

Kamal Kabra

The economics of tobacco has so far been studied in a fairly restrictive manner, supposedly in the tradition of positive economics. It can be said to have followed two main lines of enquiry: micro, i.e. the costs and benefits of tobacco use to the consumer, and macro, i.e. the economy-wide or regional aggregate effects including linkages and externalities associated with tobacco production, processing, trade, consumption, etc. The benefits of tobacco have typically been enumerated and quantified in terms of employment, contribution to GDP, export earnings, public revenue, inter-industry linkages, etc. These are macro variables and bypass the micro level.

For example, a recent publication has maintained that " . . . tobacco contributes to both the negative and positive aspects of the country's economy — but the losses far outweigh the gains. Unfortunately, this fact is still not well-known and should be proven with sound data. While the gains occur in the form of employment generated by tobacco-related activities and revenue and foreign exchange earnings, the losses occur in the form of costs incurred in providing health care for people with tobacco-related diseases due to loss of productivity caused by decreased efficiency, disability and premature death. The use of wood in tobacco curing and soil erosion also have serious economic implications" (Luthra *et al.*, 1992, p.245). It is clear that some critical effects, both desirable and non-desirable, of tobacco on the economy have been captured in the above formulation. However, the benefits referred to accrue at the macro level to the government and the economy as a whole, while the costs referred to are incurred by the buyers — the micro entities.

One may refer to many other studies which follow a similar approach. For example, Wharton Econometric Forecasting Associates, Pennsylvania (USA) and Bala Cynwyd (1993), in their methodology for the study of tobacco's contribution to the economy, make mention of economy-wide gains in terms of employment, output, public revenue, export earnings, and inter-industry effects; but the direct gains (if any) to the buyer of tobacco products find no mention. Phillips, Kawachi and Tilyard (1993) mention costs only while dealing with smoking, but bring in benefits while moving over to a discussion of smoking cessation. However, they do emphasise both individual and social costs of smoking. It seems that economic studies of tobacco use have neglected the micro-level economic analysis of tobacco use, and ignored the resulting non-commensurability of benefits and costs.

On the benefits side, at the micro consumer level, these approaches skirt the basic issues. The consumption of any commodity is supposed to give some benefit, some satisfaction — real or perceived — to the person who pays for it and consumes it. After all, a payment, a sacrifice, is made by the consumer in terms of parting with a portion of one's money income (which is capable of buying her/him an alternative commodity or commodity bundle) in return for an expected gain/utility or benefit, real or perceived, from the article purchased, obtained and consumed. The failure to take note of and identify the benefits of smoking from a consumer's perspective in the literature on the subject has lately been highlighted by Reekie and Wang (1992), who contend that economic theory is ill-equipped to handle the benefits of smoking.

In order to clarify this issue, one may refer to some other advances in the theory of consumer demand and behaviour. For instance, Johnson (1958, p.25) defines a good as "an object or service of which the consumer would choose to have more". By analysing the implications of this definition, he is able to obtain both income and substitution effects which, taken together, can enable one to arrive at the law of demand. Building upon Johnson's approach, Lancaster (1966, p.54) maintains that "one demands not just physical objects, but the qualities with which they are endowed; it is to their characteristics that the potential purchaser first turns his attention". It is clear that the benefits from consumption of a good flow directly from the "qualities" or "characteristics" of the good in question. As Lancaster maintains, "to proceed as does the literature, to assign a value of zero for smoking benefits is extraordinary".

The fact that economic theory recognises and handles the benefits from most consumer goods, but fails to deal with the benefits from tobacco use, amounts to recognition (albeit implicit) of the special character of tobacco products and the putative benefits derived from them. Hence, not to give explicit and clear attention to the characteristics of tobacco is a serious omission in the study of consumer demand for tobacco products. As a result, as far as an individual consumer is concerned, often only the costs or likely injuries to health from the use of tobacco (to the exclusion of any direct gains) are taken into account. If tobacco is a good in the sense that the consumer would choose to have more of it, especially owing to some characteristics or qualities of tobacco, what is the point of referring only to the negative effects by way of costs, as is done in many analyses of the economics of tobacco? Does this procedure imply that the negative direct effects are the only ones likely to flow from consuming tobacco products, while the benefits are a matter of unrestrained, unspecified and unspecifiable 'sovereignty of the consumer' only, as stressed for example by Reekie and Wang (1992)?

An economic analysis of tobacco use cannot leave matters either to axiomatic rationality or to supposed 'free' choice of the consumer. It cannot reasonably be allowed to refuse to disclose or identify positive substantiable attributes which may be held responsible for any positive value attached to the consumption of tobacco products.

If conventional demand theory were to be applied to study the demand for tobacco products, it would follow that "given preferences, if *individuals* choose to spend their resources of income and wealth on tobacco — this indicates that at the margin they are already allocating their resources to their highest valued use, if so, then the next best alternative consumption opportunities, the opportunity costs, are valued less highly by *society*" (Reekie and Wang, 1992). There are well-known limitations of this kind of analysis: non-measurability of utility, cardinality, assumption of constant utility of money, subjectivity, neglect of externalities, special effects and impulses like keeping up with the Joneses, complementary goods, demonstration effects, impact of information constraints, advertising, etc. As the italicised parts in the above quotation show, often individualistic perspective is automatically transformed into a social one: what is assumed to be the case with the individual, is taken to be true for society as well; individual choice for tobacco products is quietly equated with social choice.

Another limitation of conventional demand theory is its absolutisation of the postulate of consumers' sovereignty. It has been suggested that this way of justifying tobacco consumption is not value-free, but rests rather on a particular tenet of economic liberalism. However, such axiomatically-assumed rational individual economic behaviour, in practice, is always compromised to make way for moral, social and long-term considerations, and corrected by means of public intervention for externalities and informational imperfections and distortions. Thus, such demand becomes to an extent state-mediated demand (a proxy for social mediation), rather than autonomous, unrestrained individual demand. Moreover, it is doubtful whether consumers buy tobacco products with the knowledge of the hazards involved, or that the demand for tobacco products is not to a certain extent supplier-created. This compromises the assumption of axiomatic consumer rationality, making it problematic whether the decision is a submission to demonstration effects based on misinformation or lack of information, and shows elements of herd mentality and the consumer's degree of risk-aversion.

On account of the risk and uncertainty factors involved in decisions to consume tobacco products, and given that lagged effects on health, work efficiency and mortality are involved, such analyses proceed in terms of the concept of expected utility. Following the von Neumann-Morgenstern cardinal utility framework, the analysis of consumer behaviour may proceed in terms of the assumption that the consumer seeks to maximise the mathematical expectation of her/his utility. But in no case can she/he ignore the specific physical, real qualities or characteristics of the good in question and their effects, insofar as these are known or are knowable without excessively high cost and the information is not manipulated.

The analysis of consumer behaviour with respect to tobacco products has some specific, unique characteristics. While people are becoming increasingly aware of tobacco's ill-effects on health, these hazards are rarely known with clarity and unambiguity. Moreover, the health effects are not instantaneous; they are normally slow, spread over a long period and become manifest after a time-lag of varying lengths (see Chapter 3 for a discussion of this phenomenon). During the intervening period, many other factors may intervene for good or bad and obscure the relationship between tobacco and health, and manifestation of any disease or disability can be attributed to a variety of long-term as well as proximate factors. This makes the association between health-related problems and tobacco consumption opaque and, to a certain extent, a matter of perception on the part of actual or prospective consumers of tobacco products, depending on their health consciousness, propensity to bear risk, and exposure to powerful marketing techniques employed by tobacco companies.

A related issue often raised to counter the freedom of the consumer argument is the addiction-causing attribute of tobacco products; a choice initially exercised compromises or restricts freedom subsequently. Only if it could be shown that the consumer is fully aware of the addictive and other disutility-causing nature of tobacco products might it be possible to maintain that their habit-forming and compulsive use is a free, conscious, rational choice, and that addictive properties cannot undermine this feature.

Another argument at a definitional level has been advanced. Reekie and Wang (1992) maintain that "repeat purchasing behaviour is commonplace in almost all consumer non-durable purchases". Hence "when repeat purchasing becomes addiction is basically (an) empirical" question. It can be seen that for all recurring wants for single-use or non-durable goods, repeat purchases (at varying intervals) are made. Hence this feature can hardly be considered relevant for deciding the addiction-causing nature of a product. Ordinarily, for most such repeat-purchase products, substitutes have a fairly high degree of acceptability, which is hardly ever the case for addiction-causing goods. It means that the repeat purchase is not equivalent to addiction, but rather is a response to a recurring want. Addiction refers to a certain degree of lack of choice or compulsion or a non-volitional act; frequency of purchase depends on the nature of the product and of the want to which the product responds, and may not indicate addiction but sheer necessity of frequent repetitive use. Many physiological necessities and cultural needs are repetitive and are satisfied in several ways again and again, but can hardly attract the attribute of addiction. It is well-known that some specific physical-chemical properties of tobacco cause addiction. This, together with deficiencies in and distortions of information regarding tobacco products held by consumers, weakens the arguments of the inherent rationality of consumer's choice and consumer's sovereignty.

It has been maintained that the individual consumer pays, either directly or indirectly, for exercising her/his freedom of choice when "consumers bear the entire burden of their choice", i.e. when lifetime *per capita* health care costs are borne by the consumers themselves personally, and/or when the taxes and duties on tobacco products and insurance premia meet the entire cost of publicly provided health care and social insurance payments. This line of reasoning is rather simplistic. Can one say that one's life is entirely one's own affair in terms of the arguments given, for instance, for the right to commit suicide or for euthanasia?

Moreover, tobacco has been shown by natural scientists and medical experts to cause several adverse effects on those who do not make use of tobacco but are involuntarily made to inhale the smoke emanating from tobacco, the passive smokers. The issue of individual freedom to go in for tobacco products comes in for serious questioning with the entry of passive smokers. In the light of mounting new evidence regarding enhanced risk exposure of passive smokers to asthma, heart diseases and cancer, the employment rights specialists argue that it is not correct to say that the rights of smokers are equal to the rights of non-smokers. As a result, demands for ban on smoking in work-places, public places and in the company of others have acquired a lot of weight. In the United States passive smoking has been recognised as a health hazard since 1988, and "environmental" tobacco smoke is classified as a carcinogen in the same class as asbestos and radon gas. Dealing with the predictable opposition from the tobacco industry to such reports by the British Medical Association and other bodies highlights its contradictory nature. Tobacco interests admit that passive smoking is irritating and harmful for the victim's health, but maintain that "no one can say exactly which of the dozens of chemical substances contained in the product is responsible for causing the damage".

None of these doubts can reduce the validity of the concern over preventable ill-health, disease and premature death caused by passive smoking, i.e. people who are involuntarily made to pay the price of the "rationality" and "freedom" of the others. Since one person's smoke or pleasure is quite literally the poison of another, it is clear that the sovereignty of the consumers of tobacco products has to be given a low value in order to assert the right of others to a healthy and clean environment. It is clear that consumption of products which are not only frivolous but hazardous, and which endanger life, environment and social resources, cannot be supported on the basis of the supposed economic freedom of the individual.

Every society places what it considers to be reasonable restrictions on the exercise of such freedom. Many theoretical writings recognise the concepts of state-dependent and state-independent choice, and qualify the choices made under the framework of public choice theory by considerations of public interests. In matters such as tobacco consumption involving disutility to both the consumer and the rest of society, the political marketplace (involving redistribution of resources, transfer payments, and economic and non-economic rent and externalities) is involved as well. In such cases the conventional theory of consumer demand has to be caveated and qualified by many considerations — some of which may arise from the physical features of the product in question, its form of consumption, and its externalities, while others may follow from broader normative, social considerations.

It follows that the decision to consume tobacco cannot be treated as rational by means of an extension of the argument for consumer sovereignty and axiomatic rationality of consumer's free choice. The discussion above has acknowledged how these decisions may be based on lack of information, disinformation and the hidden persuasion by means of powerful advertising campaigns. It is not unlikely that some people, particularly those at a highly impressionable age, may take to tobacco as a matter of fashion, especially in view of the non-identification or recognition of any positive, objectively-established benefits to the consumer.

Hence, it is some kind of consumer irrationality (which may be based on either lack of information or disinformation or fashion) which impels one to consume tobacco, whose positive, objectively-established benefits remain unspecified. One wonders if it is a commodity which is to be grouped together with various frivolities on which a consumer's disposable income can be spent. Except for the 'sovereign' consumer's right to dispose of her/his money income in ways and on things which are a matter of 'free' choice (a totally subjective personal choice ignoring family or social considerations, supported by a set of values and morality which is highly individualistic), can one support such unrestrained freedom of choice of the consumer on any more objective, palpable, and concrete grounds and thus be able to identify and value the benefits from tobacco consumption?

It is plausible to suggest that consumption of tobacco meets a psychic/ subjective/highly personal need, which need not have any objective basis, either specific to each user or a common one to all users. For instance, Barnum (1994a, p.359) maintains that "consumers derive immediate value, pleasure, from their consumption of tobacco. Producers also derive benefit, their profits, from the market for tobacco." The axiom of consumer rationality justifying every revealed preference would certainly support the freedom-pleasure hypothesis. Even if tobacco products are a frivolity, they are of a kind which in certain forms and certain quantities even the poor can afford. Here one may enter an empirical caveat in the context of the severity of poverty which is endemic to the majority of Indians. For many, the cost of a few *bidis*, or chewable or snuff tobacco or an occasional cigarette tends to involve quite a significant opportunity cost in terms of the alternative consumption foregone. Thus the argument based on consumer's freedom has a very strong, palpable trade-off in terms of essential consumption, not only that of the person who is the consumer of tobacco but of her or his dependants as well.

The gain which is taken by much of accepted economic wisdom to offset the sacrifice involved in parting with some of a consumer's purchasing power, has not been specified in positive terms based on the properties or characteristics with which tobacco is endowed. Here is a commodity which is widely consumed (and in a country like India accounts for an identifiable part of the consumers' money income, including those who are identified as below the poverty line), which cannot be shown to confer any direct benefit on the consumer, whose micro-level justification is based on a certain interpretation of the philosophical premise of consumer's sovereignty, and which causes harm at home, in work places and in public places to the passive smokers.

An illustration of the absence of association of tobacco use with any positive gain or a positive quality or characteristic of tobacco can be seen in the work of an Indian economist whose writings display a fairly sympathetic approach towards the cigarette industry. In making a case "to reduce the taxation on cigarettes", he argues that "lower taxes will not lead to a rise in smoking material consumption; they will shift it from *bidis* to cigarettes which yield more revenue and are less offensive" (Desai, 1993). One can see that all that the author could say in defence of cigarettes is that they are "less offensive" than *bidis* (but, of course, offensive all the same); clearly no positive attribute, suggesting that instead of being a 'good', cigarettes are a 'bad'.

Actually, it can be readily agreed that the economics of commodities/goods of different types may not be capable of being properly handled by means of a common analytical method, concepts and framework. Economic theory classifies commodities/goods in a number of ways. On the basis of a number of different criteria, including their characteristics, goods have been classified either as necessities, comforts and luxuries; or as consumer goods, capital goods and intermediate goods; or as public goods, private goods and mixed goods — to cite a few examples. Tobacco products are generally treated as consumer goods and do not form part of necessities. Insofar as one finds evidence of a high degree of inelasticity of demand for tobacco products, it seems to be an indication of addiction, rather than of being a necessity with invariant demand. Whether to treat them as comforts or luxuries may be quite problematic. For example, can goods be treated as habit-forming/addiction-causing or non-addiction-causing/choice-granting ones?

However, it is clear that the most relevant concept applicable to tobacco products is that of a merit or demerit good. Before working out the implications of this kind of categorisation, it may be useful to spell out some characteristics relevant to an understanding of merit or demerit goods. Our analysis here is based largely on the application to tobacco of the analysis of merit goods as found in the work of Musgrave (1991).

As seen above, the use of tobacco involves certain risks like health hazards, danger of addiction, contribution to third party risks and environmental pollution (negative externalities). Hence it is difficult to put its consumption on par with other commodities whose consumption a society either accepts as an individual and unrestrained right, or at a normative level may like to encourage. On the basis of these factors, one may well classify tobacco products as demerit goods. It is maintained that "rational choice requires correct information" and "the quality of choice is impeded where information is imperfect or misleading" (Musgrave, 1991, p.452). On this reasoning, rational individual choice about tobacco becomes highly unlikely. This factor too may lend support to the treatment of tobacco products as demerit goods.

As Musgrave clarified the issues: "Society may come to reject or penalise certain activities or products which are regarded as demerit goods. Restriction of drug use or of prostitution as offences to human dignity (quite apart from potentially costly externalities) may be seen to fit this pattern. Community values are thus taken to give rise to merit or demerit goods . . .." Without resorting to the notion of an "organic community", community values may be taken to reflect the outcome of a historical process of interaction among individuals, leading to the formation of common values or preferences which are transmitted thereafter. It is evident that as far as merit or demerit goods are concerned, "consumer sovereignty is replaced by an alternative norm".

As has been discussed above, an individual's consumption of tobacco seems to be unrelated to any specifiable positive characteristic of the good. It is likely to be associated with imitation, inertia, irrationality and addiction. Further, it has a number of socially adverse short- and long-term consequences, and the negative effects of tobacco use are increasingly engaging public attention. In view of the above, the community or social or analysts' judgement to treat it as a demerit good seems defensible. In fact, the policies of many governments, such as the recent US attempt to collect a huge indemnity from tobacco companies, as well as legislative and administrative steps to curb tobacco consumption in scores of countries, give this kind of classification the character of normative revealed community preference. It is true that here is a case of "community values as a restraint on individual choice" which means it is a case "where consumer sovereignty is replaced by an alternative norm" (Musgrave, 1991, p.453).

It has been maintained that redistribution through the political process, for example by means of programmes rendering services to the poor, can be classified as merit goods. Musgrave cites an OECD study to stress this logic and argues that non-market distribution, particularly of primary goods, might be viewed as a merit good and involves "ethically superior" choices. Curbing tobacco consumption certainly has redistributive implications, generally favouring consumers, including a large number of poor consumers and imposing costs on tobacco growers, processors, traders, etc. The redistributive implications may acquire sharp regional overtones if there are regions in which there is concentration of production of tobacco products in comparison to their consumption and *vice versa*. Even region or groups of persons who do not benefit from tobacco production, processing, etc. (except probably sharing public spending financed out of imposts on tobacco or making a draft on the foreign exchange earned by means of tobacco exports) have to share the costs imposed by the use of tobacco products, the actual size being a function of the rate of tobacco prevalence. This can hardly be considered a just redistribution. Since some of these implications flow from placing curbs on tobacco consumption (in addition to being serious in themselves) this product would fall in the demerit goods category and would reflect "ethically superior" choices. With the explicit and widely hailed re-entry of ethics into economics, these various considerations are of no mean value.

The major conclusion of the preceding discussion is that tobacco products are a special class of commodities to which conventional theory of demand and consumer behaviour has limited applicability. This is because the axiomatic rationality of revealed preferences and consumers' sovereignty are heavily discounted in the case of tobacco, and the adverse effects of passive smoking, environmental pollution and diversion of scarce resources from socially and individually preferred uses justify the treatment of tobacco as a demerit good. Hence any cost-benefit analysis of tobacco products can take note of direct costs only, as there are no direct objectively identifiable benefits owing to the demerit good character of tobacco. This means that the benefit side of such a cost-benefit analysis would be practically missing, except for indirect macro-level benefits, which remain non-commensurate with the costs incurred both at the micro- and macro-levels.

References

Ault, R.W., R.B. Ekelund *et al.* (1991), "Smoking and absenteeism", *Applied Economics*, 23.

Barnum, H. (1994), "The economic burden of the global trade in tobacco", *Tobacco Control*, 3:358-61.

Desai, A.V. (1993), *My Economic Affair*, New Delhi: Wiley Eastern.

Graaf, J. De Villiers (1957), *Theoretical Welfare Economics*, Cambridge, UK: Cambridge University Press.

Johnson, H. (1958), "Demand theory further revisited or goods are goods", *Economics*, 25.

Koutsoyannis, A.P. (1963), "Demand function for tobacco", *The Manchester School*, Vol. 31.

Lancaster, K. (1966), "Change and innovation in the technology of consumption", *American Economic Review*, May.

Lee, D.R. (1991), "Environmental economics and the social cost of smoking", in *Contemporary Policy Issues*, Vol. 9.

Loksabha Secretariat (1995), *Committee on Subordinate Legislation (10th Loksabha) Rules/Regulations Framed Under the Cigarettes (Regulation and Production, Supply and Distribution) Act, 1975*, mimeo.

Luthra, U.K., V. Sreeniwas *et al.* (1992), "Tobacco control in India: problems and solutions", in Gupta, P., J.E. Hamner and P.R. Murti (eds.), *Control of Tobacco-Related Cancers and Other Diseases*, Bombay: Oxford University Press.

Milgate, M. (1991), "Goods and commodities", in *New Palgrave Dictionary of Economics*, Vol. 2, London: Macmillan.

Musgrave, R.A. (1991), "Merit goods", in *New Palgrave Dictionary of Economics*, Vol. 3, London: Macmillan.

Phillips, D., I. Kawachi and M. Tilyard (1993), "The economics of smoking: an overview of the international and New Zealand Literature", *Pharmaco-Economics*, 3(6).

Reekie, W.D. and L.F.S.Wang (1992), "The benefits and costs of cigarette smoking: a state dependent approach", *Journal of Studies in Economics and Econometrics*, 16:1-12.

Warner, K.E. and G.A. Fulton (1994), "The economic implications of tobacco product sales in a nontobacco state", *Journal of the American Medical Association*, 271:771-6.

Wharton Econometric Forecasting Associates (WEFA) and Bala Cynwyd (1993), "Tobacco's contribution to the Economy: Methodology", mimeo, Philadelphia, PA: WEFA.

Chapter 8

The Role of Taxation Policy in Tobacco Control

Joy Townsend

Tobacco smoking is heavily influenced by economics. The massive profits of the industry motivate its promotion. Economic concerns determine and qualify its use by individual smokers. Tobacco products are cheap to produce; the base cost is low and tobacco is addictive. The combination of these factors result in the high prevalence of its use in each country and its pervasiveness across the globe. Even in countries where the price is relatively high, a cigarette will cost considerably less than a snack item or a drink, so smokers can afford not the odd one or two, but usually twenty or so a day. This is the major health problem of cigarettes.

One of the clearest and most immediate influences on tobacco use is its price, and tobacco control policy influences this price through the medium of tobacco taxation. As an illustration of smokers' response to price changes, Figure 1 shows how cigarette consumption has varied inversely with the real price of cigarettes in the UK over the last quarter of a century (Central Statistical Office (UK), 1965-93). It is apparent that smoking increased during periods when the price of cigarettes fell in real terms, during the early 1970s and late 1980s, and fell when real cigarette prices rose in the mid-1970s and during the early 1980s and 1990s. Similar counter-movements of smoking with relative cigarette price are shown for several countries including Canada (Figure 2), South Africa (Figure 3) and France (Sweanor, 1985-91; Saloojee, 1995; INSEE, 1990). Increasing cigarette taxation is clearly an effective tobacco control policy.

There are many issues to consider around price and taxation, but the basic message is clear — increase price and tobacco use will decline. Let the price fall and tobacco use will increase. Because the price of tobacco can have such a major effect on smoking and health, it is important for tobacco control interests to know *how* it is moving and *what* are its effects. Data for this are available for many countries in the form of routine national economic statistics, but are mostly neither monitored together nor analysed. The World Bank is now preparing a valuable asset by collating this material for as many countries as possible.

Tobacco tax largely determines the price of tobacco products and has two major effects:
- to reduce smoking and so smoking illness and deaths;
- to provide government tax revenue.

There can be a synergy between taxation and health campaigns. Health campaigns and taxation policy can be interdependent in that health publicity

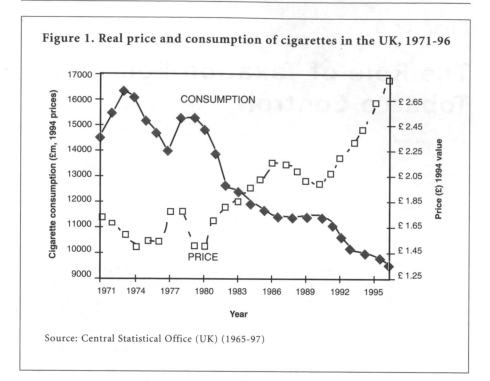

Figure 1. Real price and consumption of cigarettes in the UK, 1971-96

Source: Central Statistical Office (UK) (1965-97)

Figure 2. Daily consumption of cigarettes per capita among people 15 and over, and real price of tobacco, Canada 1950-91

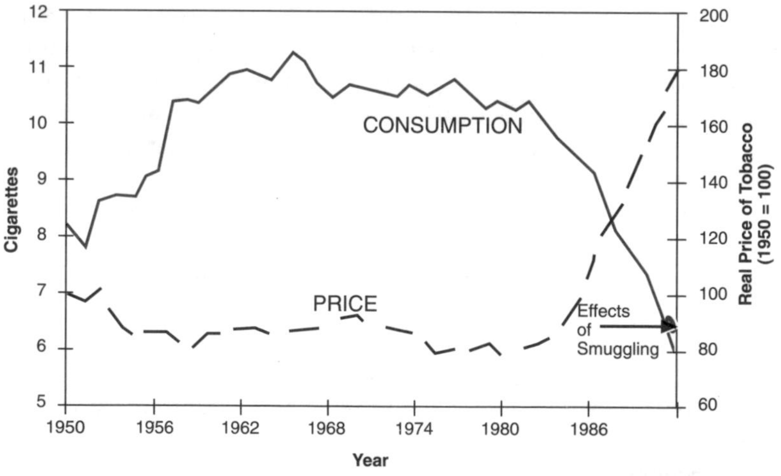

Source: Sweanor (1985-91)

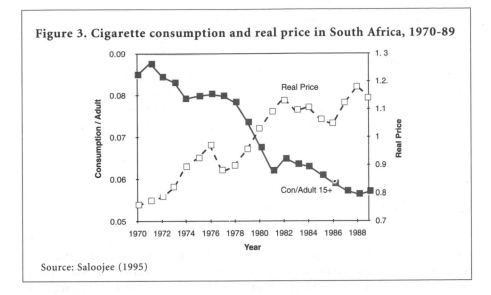

Figure 3. Cigarette consumption and real price in South Africa, 1970-89

Source: Saloojee (1995)

can lay the ground for acceptable tax rises and tax rises can create revenue to pay for health campaigns or compensation. Price changes have been shown to have different effects on different age, socio-economic, gender or ethnic groups. These differential responses are important for both tobacco control and for social policy. They also have financial implications. Each country is unique in its situation and will want to understand these specific responses within its own setting.

Price and tax issues have often been overlooked in tobacco control policy, sometimes with very serious consequences. At times of inflation, particularly of high inflation, tobacco taxes and prices may fall in real terms and give a strong boost to tobacco use. Incomes may be rising, advertising may be rising, each giving strong counter-influences to the health education message. There are many examples, as in the UK where between 1965 and 1980 the real price of cigarettes fell by as much as 40 per cent (Central Statistical Office (UK), 1965-97), encouraging smoking and countering effects of health education. In France between 1963 and 1975 cigarette prices fell by nearly 50 per cent relative to other prices, encouraging a major increase in cigarette smoking. In South Africa, although prices have risen since 1991, they still have not reached the real price level of cigarettes in 1970. Information on smoking, tax and price is available for certain countries, but there are large gaps, particularly of course for much of the developing world.

Which tobacco price?

Expenditure on cigarettes or tobacco is one of many expenditures for the smoker; he or she will be interested in the price relative to that of other goods. The *current* or *nominal* price may not tell one very much. It needs to be adjusted for inflation.

$$\text{Real price} = \frac{\text{Current price}}{\text{Price of all goods and services}}$$

Similarly cigarette consumption needs to be adjusted for changes in the adult *population* and expressed as consumption per adult to allow for population change. Analyses cannot be taken seriously and will be discredited without these adjustments. Tobacco price and tax changes are firm predictors of future smoking patterns and so to be aware of, to monitor, and to measure the impact of them gives an advantage to understanding future "health" trends. Many countries including Finland, Denmark, Egypt, Canada, Nepal, Iceland, Peru, Australia, New Zealand, the UK and France have raised cigarette taxes specifically to reduce smoking for health reasons.

Estimates of price elasticity of demand for cigarettes

Price and income elasticities of demand for cigarettes or tobacco, have been assessed for many countries over several time periods using a variety of econometric models. Estimates of price elasticity have varied between about −0.2 and −0.9 and have clustered about −0.5 (Table 1). Few studies, apart from some for specific subsets of smokers, report significantly different values. Estimates have been surprisingly robust over time, place and price level, being higher mostly for periods of rapid price increase, and lower for countries with relatively low tobacco prices and high incomes such as the USA. There seems to be some indication from USA, Ireland and the UK that price elasticities have fallen slightly over time, possibly due to rising income levels. Higher price responses have been reported for lower income and socio-economic groups and possibly for teenagers, as will be discussed later.

Table 1. Estimates of price and income elasticities of demand for cigarettes

Study	Data	Price elasticity	Income elasticity
Andrews and Franke (1991)	Meta-analysis		
UK		-0.5	0.4
US		-0.7	0.5
Other		-0.7	0.4
Post-1970		-0.4	0.3
Townsend (1988)	Europe 1986-88	-0.4	0.5
Chapman and Richardson*	Papua New Guinea 1973-86	-0.7	0.9
Worgotter and Kunze (1986)*	Austria 1955-83	-0.5	
Walsh (1980)*	Ireland post-1961	-0.4	

Note: * Cited in Andrews and Franke (1991)
Source: Andrews and Franke (1991); Townsend (1988)

The effects of price on tobacco use at different ages

The price response of young tobacco users and young potential tobacco users is of special interest, as this is the age of recruitment to tobacco, and there has been an apparent lack of success of health education, for example in reducing teenage smoking. Lewit and Coate (1982) studied teenage smoking in the USA and concluded that teenagers are highly responsive to cigarette prices (elasticity -1.4). There has been differing evidence from the USA suggesting a much lower price elasticity among teenagers (Wasserman et al., 1991), not significantly different from the estimate of -0.23 for American adults; however, recent work by Chaloupka and Wechsler (1997) confirms the earlier reports of high elasticities when other confounding factors, especially income, are taken into account. A UK study of smoking during 1972-90 reported that the most price-sensitive smokers were women and men aged 25-60 years (Townsend, Roderick and Cooper, 1994). Young men, on the other hand, were more influenced by income than price, showing a high response to income changes and a non-significant response to price. Young people generally have relatively low incomes with a high proportion available for discretionary expenditure, so changes in income are likely to have relatively greater effect on their smoking patterns. These results do not confirm the findings of Lewit and Coate (1982). They do, however, suggest that cigarette consumption in teenage women may be significantly affected by price rises, although for them the effects of price and income appear to be interrelated. There will be an indirect longer-term price influence also via effects on parents, as it is well established that the probability of a young person becoming a regular smoker is positively related to parental smoking.

Price effects by socio-economic and income group

The issue of the polarisation of smoking towards poorer people and the concomitant consideration of the regressivity of tobacco tax have been mentioned in Chapters 2, 5 and 6. Addressed here are some related issues of economic welfare and optimum taxation theory. There is evidence that tobacco price and taxation have different effects on different income and socio-economic groups. In some countries low-income groups tend to smoke more, but also reduce their smoking more in response to tax increases (Townsend, Roderick and Cooper, 1994; Atkinson, Gomulka and Stern, 1984). They are also more likely to be encouraged to smoke by a reduction in real price. The UK analysis of cigarette consumption (Townsend, Roderick and Cooper, 1994) reported that professional workers, managers and their wives did not respond to changes in cigarette price, whereas clerical workers, skilled and semi-skilled manual workers responded with a price elasticity of about -0.5 to -0.7. Unskilled manual workers and their wives showed the highest response, with elasticities of -1.0 for men and -0.9 for women. These are the groups which are often the most affected by tobacco diseases.

There has been much debate about whether cigarette price affects the prevalence of smoking as well as the average adult consumption. The UK analysis (Townsend, Roderick and Cooper, 1994) reported significant elasticities of prevalence of -0.6 for men in socio-economic group 5 (unskilled manual workers), -0.23 for all women and -0.5 for women in socio-economic group 5. These are important results, as socio-economic group 5 is the group with the highest prevalence of smoking, and in which health education has been least effective.

Econometric studies of demand for cigarettes and welfare effects of tobacco price changes

Early work by economists indicated that the price elasticity of demand for tobacco was low: the estimate of Stone (1945) for 1920-38 was about -0.5, while that of Prest (1949) for 1870-1938 was -0.22. Atkinson and Skegg (1973) reported about -0.25 for 1951-1970. Hamilton (1972) estimated -0.5 for the USA during 1925-70. These studies also reported low income elasticity of demand, varying from 0.1 for Stone (1945) and Koutsoyannis (1963) to 0.7 for Hamilton (1972). Since the early 1960s, health publicity against smoking had become a further influence on cigarette smoking.

In order to test if these factors differentially influenced smoking by different socio-economic groups, smoking data by socio-economic group were analysed for the UK (Townsend, 1987) using a single equation model for each group, with a log-linear demand function:

$$q_{ti} = ay_t{}^{\alpha i}(P_{tc}/\pi_t)^{\beta_i}e^{\gamma_i D_1 + \delta_i D_2 + \varepsilon_i D_3 + \Theta_i T + u_i}$$

where:

q_{ti} = average cigarette consumption per week per adult in socio-economic group i for year t;

y_t = annual disposable income per head;

P_{tc} = price index for cigarettes;

π_t = price index for consumers expenditure;

D_1, D_2 and D_3 = dummy variables relating to health publicity in 1962, 1965 and 1971 respectively;

T = a time trend to pick up underlying changes in taste; and

u = random error with expected value zero.

An example is given here of the implications of tobacco price changes on welfare of different socio-economic groups.

Willig (1976) showed that under given conditions, consumer's surplus is a good approximation to an appropriate measure of welfare. He showed that for a single price change, if:

$$\left|\bar{\eta}A / 2m^0\right| \le 0.05, \left|\underline{\eta}A / 2m^0\right| \le 0.05$$

and if $\left| A / 2m^0 \right| \le 0.9$ then:

(1) $\dfrac{\eta|A|}{2m^0} \le \dfrac{C-A}{|A|} \le \dfrac{\overline{\eta}|A|}{2m^0}$

and:

(2) $\dfrac{\eta|A|}{2m^0} \le \dfrac{A-E}{|A|} \le \dfrac{\overline{\eta}|A|}{2m^0}$

where:

A = consumer's surplus area under the demand curve and between the two prices (positive for a price increase and negative for a price decrease);

C = compensating variation corresponding to the price change;

E = equivalent variation corresponding to the price change;

m^0 = consumer's base income; and

$\overline{\eta}$ and $\underline{\eta}$ = respectively the largest and smallest values of the income elasticity of demand in the region under consideration.

This gives bounds on the percentage errors of approximating the conceptual measures (compensating or equivalent variation corresponding to the price change) to the observable consumer surplus. These measures have been used to estimate effects of cigarette tax changes on welfare by each socio-economic group. The welfare change incurred by a tax change $\dot{x}$ is given by:

$$\dot{x}/2q_i\left[1 + ((p+\dot{x})/p)^{\beta_i}\right]$$

The mean tax paid and change in tax paid for each socio-economic group have also been assessed, and similarly the change in consumer expenditure on cigarettes. The change in tax paid is given by:

$$q_i((p+\dot{x})/p)^{\beta_i}(X+\dot{x}) - q_i\cdot X$$

where X is the tax component of price.

The change in consumer expenditure on cigarettes is given by:

$$q_i p\left[((p+\dot{x})/p)^{\beta_i+1} - 1\right]$$

Implication of tax increases for consumption of cigarettes

It has been shown by Pike and Doll (1965) for individuals and Townsend (1978) for cohorts, that lung cancer mortality risk is proportional to the daily consumption of cigarettes. It is therefore the effect of tax on the *number* of cigarettes consumed, rather than on expenditure or tax revenue, which will determine changes in mortality and morbidity risks, is most relevant to policy, and is estimated in this paper.

Loss of consumer surplus was measured and seen to be similar across socio-economic groups and was not regressive, except for the case of men in socio-economic group 1 who smoked at a very low rate and whose welfare loss was on average only half that of the other groups (Figure 4). The effects of cigarette tax rises on cigarette tax paid on average by each group were shown to be progressive rather than regressive (again with the exception of socio-economic group 1 whose tax changes were similar to socio-economic group 4) as the lower the socio-economic group, the more smokers responded to tax increases by reducing their consumption (Figure 5).

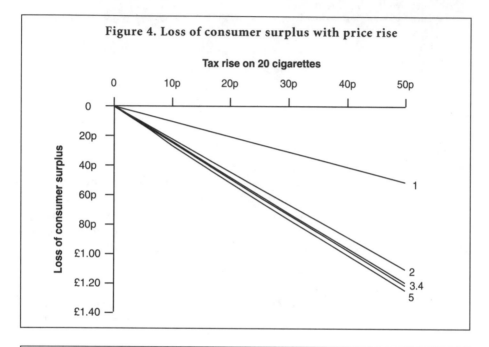

Figure 4. Loss of consumer surplus with price rise

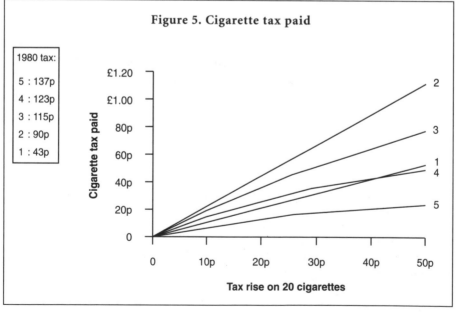

Figure 5. Cigarette tax paid

During the period there had been a reduction in the real price of cigarettes by as much as 25 per cent between 1965 and 1980 and by a third since 1950.

It was therefore concluded that, contrary to common belief that receiving and acting on health information alone had accounted for the widening divergence in social class smoking, the downward drift in prices in the UK during this time may have effectively increased the smoking levels of men in socio-economic groups 3, 4 and 5 relative to socio-economic groups 1 and 2, while smoking levels in all socio-economic groups, but especially in socio-economic groups 1 and 2, may have fallen due to the effects of anti-smoking education. Increases in cigarette tax therefore may fall less heavily on lower social groups despite their higher initial consumption, because they respond more by reducing consumption.

Smoking, taxation and poverty

Before the widespread publicity in the UK about the health effects of smoking in the early 1960s, there was little difference between the smoking habits of different socio-economic groups, but in the UK and in some other countries, smoking prevalence is now highest among people in poor socio-economic circumstances. The decline in UK smoking rates over the last few decades has been relatively low among such people (Townsend, Roderick and Cooper, 1994). Survey results suggest that smoking rates are particularly high among the unemployed and young adults with families (Thomas *et al.*, 1994), especially lone parents (Marsh and McKay, 1994). Families with low incomes tend to have high smoking rates, and to spend a disproportionately large share of their income on cigarettes. Smoking, therefore, decreases the resources available to them more generally, as well as directly harming their health. The differential health effects are quite clear, particularly for mortality from smoking-induced disease. A man in an unskilled manual occupation in the UK is more than four times as likely to die of lung cancer as a professional, and twice as likely to die from coronary heart disease. For women there is a three-fold difference for lung cancer and a four-fold difference for heart disease. For lung cancer, heart disease and chronic bronchitis, the inequalities between manual and non-manual groups widened between 1971 and 1981 (Townsend, Roderick and Cooper, 1994).

As has been discussed, price-responsiveness tends to be particularly high among people in disadvantaged circumstances, and on average they are likely to reduce not only levels of consumption but also total expenditure on cigarettes when there is a price rise. Raising relative prices would be expected to narrow the differentials in smoking prevalence and consumption between socio-economic groups. Unfortunately, a direct consequence of such policies would be to further reduce the effective spending ability of people in poverty if they continued to smoke at the same rate.

This presents a dilemma. Should the price of cigarettes be held down to avoid hardship to families in poor economic circumstances? The difficulty with this is that price does have most effect on smoking by lower-income groups, where health education has had the least. Erosion of cigarette prices could be seriously detrimental to public health, particularly to the health of lower-income groups. The dynamic relationship between smoking, health and inequalities stretches over a lifetime, and price is a potential force to break this link at any stage, reducing the harmful effects in terms of smokers' health and that of their children. A rational solution may be to increase benefits to poor families such as lone mothers, as well as raising cigarette prices. This would provide a disincentive to smoke without a detrimental effect on living standards, while expenditure on cigarettes would mostly be clawed back to the government through the tobacco tax. More work is necessary to find ways of ameliorating these problems.

Health implications

If the price elasticity of demand for cigarettes by the adult population in a country is, say, -0.5 (a mid-estimate, for example, between Turkey and Spain or the USA and Papua New Guinea), it means that a tax rise which increases price by 10 per cent will reduce smoking by 5 per cent, and if sustained, will reduce smoking illness and deaths in the long-run by 5 per cent.

Price and consumption in Europe

Cigarette prices and consumption vary within the European Union both absolutely and relative to incomes. There is a five-fold price range between 0.71 ECUs for the most popular brand of cigarettes sold in Spain and 3.6 ECUs a pack in Denmark (1 ECU is approximately £0.82 or US$1.32). If prices are standardised for cost of living, the range narrows to four-fold (Townsend, 1988). Average smoking varies from about five cigarettes per day per adult in the Netherlands to about twice that level in Greece (Figure 6). A cross-sectional study of smoking and price in 27 European countries (including all EC countries) reported a price elasticity of demand for cigarettes in Europe of -0.4 and an income elasticity of demand of 0.5 (Townsend, 1996). This means that cigarette consumption will rise with incomes unless there are counter policies.

Taxing alternative tobacco products

The type of tobacco used varies between countries, with hand-rolling being particularly important in the Netherlands (49 per cent of all consumption), Denmark (27 per cent) and Belgium (21 per cent), and less important in Germany (10 per cent), France (5 per cent) and UK (4 per cent). This is relevant to pricing policy, as in many countries (although not the UK) hand-rolling materials are taxed at a significantly lower rate than are manufactured cigarettes, although, when made into hand-rolled cigarettes, they often lead to higher tar yields.

In some countries, significant amounts of tobacco are smoked as cigars or in pipes, or used as oral or nasal snuff. The relative price of these alternatives, and

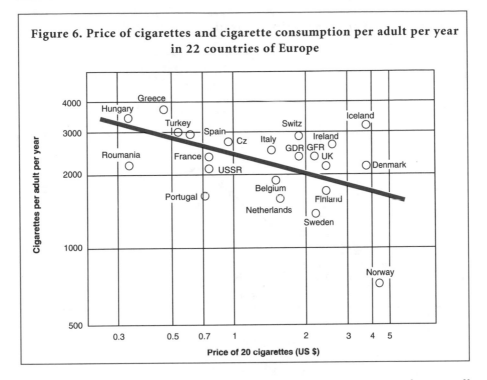

Figure 6. Price of cigarettes and cigarette consumption per adult per year in 22 countries of Europe

the relative associated health risks, have important implications for overall tobacco consumption and disease. If tax is raised on one tobacco product, but not on a substitute, there may be product switching rather than an overall reduction in consumption. In Norway and other European countries where use of hand-rolled cigarettes has become much cheaper than manufactured cigarettes, smokers have switched to hand-rolling rather than cutting down or giving up; in Egypt, where cigarette but not *shisha* tobacco tax was increased, use of the *shisha* has grown. It is therefore important to try to raise taxes simultaneously on all modes of tobacco consumption. It is important to have equivalent taxation of alternative tobacco products, if taxation is to be effective in reducing health risks.

The theory of optimum tobacco revenue

Governments have three reasons to raise taxes: to raise revenue; to correct for externalities, such as health costs; and to deter consumption (sumptuary tax). Tobacco tax fulfils all these criteria. It is in the unique position also of being a popular tax in several countries, as surveys have reported a significant part of the population in favour — even a significant minority of smokers. Tobacco tax is a relatively efficient vehicle for raising revenue as it has a high elasticity (yield) of total revenue with respect to tax rate of 0.6-0.9 in the UK, compared with 0.2 for spirits and 0.6 for wine. This means that a 1 per cent increase in tobacco tax yields about 0.6-0.9 per cent increase in tax revenue (Townsend,

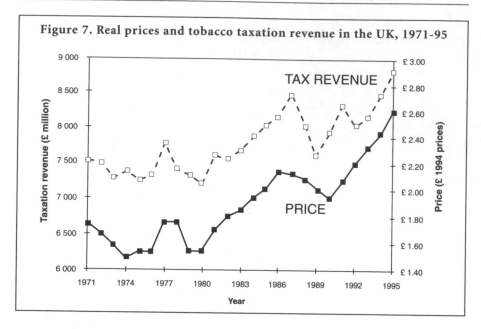

Figure 7. Real prices and tobacco taxation revenue in the UK, 1971-95

1995a). This is demonstrated in Figure 7, which shows how the real value of tobacco tax revenue has risen and fallen with changes in real cigarette price (determined mostly by tax) in the UK 1971-95, and which demonstrates that tax revenue not only rises with tax increases, but falls dramatically if tax does not keep up with inflation. This is logical, and has been demonstrated for other countries as well.

Given that a government needs revenue, the criteria for economic efficiency in taxation are, after Ramsey and Baumol and Bradford, that they should have the effect of reducing demand for all commodities in the same proportion, should distort consumer choice as little as possible, and direct tax payers as little as possible to less preferred patterns of consumption. These efficiency criteria have sometimes been interpreted to mean that all commodities should be taxed at the same rate, but this is false for two reasons. Firstly, a uniform tax will distort the choice both between leisure and work, and between goods with different price elasticities. If higher taxes are levied on goods with inelastic demand, which will be bought in some measure in any case, a lower rate can be levied on other goods, disincentive to work is decreased, and there is little distortion in consumption of goods. Similarly, the argument goes, higher taxes should be imposed on goods which are substitutes for work or complements to leisure, and lighter taxes on activities which are complementary to work.

Secondly, the related argument for higher tax on goods with relatively low price elasticity of demand is that the dead-weight welfare loss or excess burden is thus minimised. (The excess burden of a tax increase is the consumers' loss of utility — roughly, satisfaction — from buying less of the product at the higher price, minus the gain to the government in tax revenue. It can be expressed as a percentage of the tax revenue from the tax increase. For tobacco, the percentage excess burden is relatively low at 17 per cent, compared, for example, with 500 per cent for spirits. This means that £100 extra tax revenue would cost supposedly £117 in 'lost satisfaction' to the smoker or £600 to the spirit drinker (Townsend, 1995a).) It is also argued that the optimal tax rate may well depend, for similar reasons, inversely on the income elasticity of demand. Economic efficiency would, therefore, tend to indicate the taxing of commodities in inverse relation to their price and income elasticities of demand (the average for all goods and services being 1.0) and so, on grounds of economic efficiency alone, there is a strong case for shifting taxes from other commodities to tobacco. This does not include considerations of equity (which may indicate the opposite), nor of health (which would favour the shift).

Tax policies may or should also consider external costs or factors not taken into account by individuals in their consumption decisions, but borne by others in society. One criterion may be to set a tax such that consumers would choose the level of consumption they would have chosen, had they to pay the relevant (external) costs. These externalities include real resource costs, such as extra costs of health services (estimated at £610 million *per annum* in the UK), costs of fires caused by tobacco smoking (£20 million *per annum* for the UK), and loss of real output not borne by the smoker (50 million working days *per annum* in the UK). They may also be considered to include externalities of transfer payments such as retirement pensions, pensions to dependants and sickness and invalidity welfare payments (net £190 million *per annum* in the UK). They would not include tobacco tax as this is included in the price the smoker actually pays and is willing to pay for tobacco. These approximate estimates of externality costs of about £800 million *per annum* would motivate an extra tax for social costs or externalities in the region of £0.20 per packet in the UK (Townsend, 1995a).

The importance of the contribution of tobacco tax to government revenue has fallen in the UK and many other countries, due to the increase in revenue from other sources and the fall in tobacco consumption for reasons other than tax rises. As a result, whereas in 1950 tobacco tax provided 16 per cent of all UK Government revenue, this fell to 8 per cent by the late 1960s, is currently 3.6 per cent, and may be even less significant by the end of the century. If the tobacco

Table 2. Tobacco taxation in different countries, 1993/7

Country	Price (US$)	Tax as % of price
Spain	0.63	67
US	1.80	-
UK	3.70	78
Portugal	-	81
Argentina	-	70
South Korea	-	60
China	0.22	38

tax increases, revenue therefrom will not necessarily continue to rise in the long-run. If tobacco consumption is falling anyway due to other factors and other tobacco control measures, this will tend to reduce tobacco tax revenue. Tobacco tax rises will provide a counter-balance, which may result in a net fall or rise in the long-run, depending on the relative effects.

Use of tobacco revenue

Tobacco tax is a major source of government revenue in some countries; in many countries it could provide far more revenue (Table 3).

Table 3. Tobacco tax as a percentage of total government revenue	
Country	*% of total government revenue*
Congo/Zaire	26.0
Malawi	17.0
Tanzania	16.0
China	9.0
Kenya	9.0
Nigeria	8.0
Tunisia	6.0
Egypt	6.0
Zimbabwe	5.0
Ethiopia	4.0
South Africa	2.0
Algeria	0.2

In some countries, a percentage of revenue from tobacco tax increases has been ring-fenced for tobacco control purposes or for specific health care. In the US state of Massachusetts, voters passed a state-wide initiative five years ago adding an extra 25 cents to the price of a pack of cigarettes, despite a massive campaign against this by the industry. The rise generated millions of dollars for tobacco education and control programmes which led to a major fall in smoking.

Where tobacco tax is raised to reduce smoking, many countries use part of the revenue to support health education, medical research on tobacco diseases, and anti-tobacco media campaigns. For example, in Victoria, Australia, a 5 per cent tax was levied on the sale of tobacco products specifically to finance health promotion. Egypt and Nepal have also used additional tax revenue for health-related programmes, for example for health care for those on low incomes. Few developing countries have yet earmarked taxes for these purposes.

Tobacco tax structure

The structure of the tobacco tax is important for tobacco control because it is likely to affect the level of the tax. Tax may basically be levied as a percentage of the base or selling price, or as a specific tax (per cigarette or by the weight of tobacco) added to the base price. There may also be different tax levels, for example for high-tar tobaccos or hand-rolling tobacco.

(i) *Ad valorem* (tax as percentage of price)

An *ad valorem* tax is an element of tax structure in almost all countries and is the basic structure in many countries. It has the advantages of being simple to operate, and fits in with other indirect taxes such as value-added tax (VAT), sales tax and expenditure tax.

However, it is a structure of tax usually favoured by the tobacco industry because it can attempt to control the tax by keeping the base price as low as possible and thus, even with a high rate of tax, keeping both actual tax and the cigarette price low, such as in Greece, Spain and many countries in South America such as Brazil.

(ii) Specific tax

This is the basis of tax in China, the UK, New Zealand, Ireland, Denmark, Sweden, the USA, Canada, Japan and Egypt, among other countries. As it is a fixed tax added to the price, it allows wide flexibility, and although it can still lead to a low tax, it is in fact the only way of guaranteeing the option to substantially raise cigarette taxes and prices, as there is no way the tobacco industry can avoid its effect. The industry, however, will still seek to minimise its effect. For example, when this became a component of the UK tax structure (after a switch from tax per unit weight) the tobacco industry sought to exploit it: to give "good value", they switched their previous policy of reducing tobacco per cigarette (to minimise tax per cigarette) and instead increased the size of cigarettes, marketing King Size and Super King Size cigarettes: the total tax paid per amount of tobacco smoked was thus lowered, although fixed per cigarette. Clearly, this change leads to increased exposure of consumers to tobacco smoke. Whatever the tax structure in operation, the tobacco industry will try to minimise the impact thereof (Simpson, 1995).

Table 4. Effects of tax structure

Tobacco tax	Effect	Public health implications
Specific:	Manufacturers' influence limited	Beneficial if high
By weight of tobacco	Manufacturers reduce size of cigarette	Beneficial
By cigarette	Manufacturers increase size of cigarette	Mostly beneficial
Ad valorem:	Manufacturers keep base level low	Limited benefit
Low for non-cigarette products	Smokers switch to non-cigarette products	Limits benefit of tax
High tax for high tar	Smokers switch to lower tar	Slightly beneficial

Tobacco industry message to consumers

Bearing in mind that governments need to feel that taxes are politically acceptable, it is worth noting the ways in which the tobacco industry may try to influence public opinion against increased tax, frequently relying on misleading messages. For example, in the UK in the 1980s, industry propaganda advertisements consistently tried to convey the message that a further rise in tax would reduce overall tax takings, while economists, including those in the government, could accurately predict a continued rise in revenue.

In order for taxation to be most useful in controlling consumption, tax structure should have a large specific element of tax either per cigarette or per unit weight of tobacco, and ideally as a combination of both. Also, there should not be a significant difference in tax rates between different types of tobacco, otherwise tax rises may simply shift consumption from one type of tobacco use to another.

Lastly, it is important that there should be awareness of the tobacco industry's strategy on tax, and publicity and action to counteract deliberate tobacco industry misinformation about tax (Townsend, 1995b).

Smuggling

Issues related to smuggling are covered in Chapter 12. Suffice to say here that differential prices of tobacco in neighbouring countries may lead to cross-border smuggling. This would tend to negate the effects of price increase both by modifying the reduction in tobacco use and tobacco revenue. This problem was evident in Canada a few years ago, after tobacco tax increases resulted in smuggling from the US, where prices were relatively low. Smuggling is also widespread in many countries in the Eastern Mediterranean region including Jordan, Lebanon, Pakistan, Afghanistan and Iran. It is also a problem between Mainland China and Hong Kong, and between some European countries. Joossens and Raw (1995) have shown, however, that the problem of smuggling of cheap imports is greatest, not between countries which have the greatest price difference, but where smuggling or cheap importing is easiest — where regulations are lax or the law is not rigorously enforced. In Kuwait, which dropped immigration controls after the war with Iraq, imported cigarettes with no health warnings or taxes flooded the country and tobacco consumption increased dramatically: from 34 per cent to 52 per cent for men, and from 6 per cent to 19 per cent for women during 1989-92 — an increase of over 50 per cent in three years. The ideal economic answer to cross-border smuggling is to persuade neighbouring countries to raise their tobacco taxes to equalise prices.

Conclusion

There is little doubt that tobacco tax has a major effect on cigarette consumption and smoking-induced disease, especially in low-income groups. To use this as a tool of preventive medicine, therefore, seems a highly desirable public health policy. Fiscal policy is not an alternative to other methods of reducing the harm of tobacco, but it is one of the most powerful elements of a comprehensive policy as recommended by the World Health Organisation and other authoritative bodies. Raising tobacco tax also has the advantage of increasing government revenue. Public information and health promotion campaigns reduce smoking in their own right; they may also pave the way to make tobacco tax increases for health reasons politically acceptable. Special measures may be necessary to ameliorate effects of increased cigarette taxes on the cost of living of poor families. Ironically, tobacco tax is frequently missing in discussions of tobacco control, particularly in developing countries, and this is a serious omission. Perhaps the collection and monitoring of trends in real price and tobacco consumption, as well tobacco taxation rates and tobacco tax revenue, will convince policy-makers of the central place it could have in the fight to reduce deaths from tobacco.

References

Andrews, R.L. and G.R. Franke (1991), "The determinants of cigarette consumption: a meta-analysis", *Journal of Policy and Marketing*, 81-100.
Atkinson, A.B., J. Gomulka and N. Stern (1984), *Household Expenditure on Tobacco 1970-1980: Evidence from the Family Expenditure Survey*, London: London School of Economics.
Atkinson, A.B. and J.L. Skegg (Townsend) (1973), "Anti-smoking publicity and the demand for tobacco in the UK", *Manchester School*, 41:265-82.
Central Statistical Office (UK) (1965-97), *National Income and Expenditure Accounts*, London: HMSO.
Chaloupka, F.J. and H. Wechsler (1997), "Price, tobacco control policies and smoking among yo ing adults", *Journal of Health Economics*, 16: 359-73.
Hamilton, J.L. (1972), "The demand for cigarettes: advertising, the health scare and the cigarette advertising ban", *Review of Economics and Statistics*, 54:401-10.
INSEE (1990), Comptes Nationaux Dominique Darman, Première No. 100, August, Paris: INSEE.
Joossens, L. and M. Raw (1995), "Smuggling and cross borders shopping of tobacco in Europe", *British Medical Journal*; 310:1393-7.
Koutsoyannis, A.P. (1963), "Demand function for tobacco", *The Manchester School*, 31.
Lewit, E.M. and D. Coate (1982), "The potential for using excise taxes to reduce smoking", *Journal of Health Economics*, 1: 121-45.
Marsh, A. and S. McKay (1994), *Poor Smokers*, London: Institute of Policy Studies.
Pike, M.C. and R. Doll (1965), "Age at onset of lung cancer: its significance in relation the effect of smoking", *Lancet*, 1:665-8.
Prest, A.R. (1949), "Some experiences in demand analysis", *The Review of Economics and Statistics*, 31.
Saloojee, Y. (1995), "Price and income elasticity of demand for cigarettes in South Africa", in Slama, K. (ed.), *Tobacco and Health*, New York: Plenum.
Simpson, D. (1995), "The structure of tobacco tax", in Slama, K. (ed.), *Tobacco and Health*, New York: Plenum.
Stone, R. (1945), "The analysis of market demand", *Journal of the Royal Statistical Society*, 198:286-382.
Sweanor, D. (1985-91), *Canadian Tobacco Tax Project*, Ottawa: Non-Smokers Rights Association.
Thomas, M., E. Goddard, M. Hickman and P. Hunter (1994), *General Household Survey 1992*, OPCS Series GHS No. 23, London: HMSO.
Townsend, J. (1978), "Smoking and lung cancer: a cohort data study of men and women in England and Wales 1935-1970", *Journal of the Royal Statistical Society*, 1:95-107.
Townsend, J. (1987), "Economic Welfare and Social Class patterns of Smoking", *Applied Economics*, 19:355-65.
Townsend, J. (1988), *Price, Tax and Smoking in Europe*, Copenhagen: World Health Organisation.
Townsend, J. (1995a), "Social cost, externalities and tobacco taxation in UK", CDC Economist meeting on Optimal Taxation, Boston.
Townsend, J. (1995b), "Monitoring and analysing changes in tobacco prices", in Slama, K. (ed.), *Tobacco and Health*, New York: Plenum.
Townsend, J. (1996), "Price and consumption of tobacco", *British Medical Bulletin*, 1:132-42.
Townsend, J., P. Roderick and J. Cooper (1994), "Cigarette smoking by socio-economic group, sex and age: effects of price, income and health publicity", *British Medical Journal*, 309:923-27.
Wasserman, J., W.G. Manning, J.P. Newhouse and J.D. Winkler (1991), "The effects of excise taxes and regulation on cigarette smoking", *Journal of Health Economics*, 1:43-64.
Willig, R.D. (1976), "Consumers' surplus without apology", *American Economic Review*, 66:589-97.

Chapter 9

Earmarked Tobacco Taxes: Lessons Learned

Teh-wei Hu, Xiao-peng Xu and Theodore Keeler[1]

An earmarked tax designates its revenue for spending on specific government or public services (Buchanan, 1963). In other words, earmarking calls for a simultaneous choice both on the level of taxation and expenditures on an item-by-item basis. Although the literature on earmarked taxation is sparse, the actual practice of earmarking revenue for a variety of government services is quite common. In fact, in the United States, at least one-third of all federal, state and local government expenditures are earmarked taxes (McMahon and Sprenkle, 1970). Justification is often based on the benefit principle. Under this logic, for example, gasoline or automobile tax proceeds are used for highway financing, and property tax is used by local governments for residential services, including local public school education. Social security taxes, used for employee retirement income, are another example of earmarked taxation. Clearly, earmarked taxes are not new in government tax financing.

Taxation of tobacco products is similarly not a new phenomenon. The tobacco tax has been almost universal internationally for many decades, and has always been an important part of central or local government revenue. However, earmarking part of tobacco tax revenue for particular expenditures is relatively recent. The usual rationales used to justify a tax on cigarettes are (1) to consider the cigarette tax an efficient instrument with low administrative costs for collecting revenue for government spending; e.g. tobacco tax was used for increasing state revenue in the United States during the Korean War in 1951, and in Finland during 1975-6, and (2) to impose the cigarette tax as "user's fees" or "sin tax". It is argued that the tax covers external costs of smoking and discourages smokers from using cigarettes, thus leading to a reduction in tobacco-related health care costs by reducing the morbidity and mortality associated with cigarette smoking. This second rationale, with its anti-smoking objective for raising cigarette taxes, was initiated after the release of the US Surgeon General's report in 1964 on smoking and health. Since 1980, countries such as Australia, Canada, and New Zealand have all raised cigarette taxes as a means of reducing cigarette consumption. Raising the cigarette tax to control

---

1. This work was supported by the US Department of Human Development, the World Bank's Research Support Board (Grant No. 681-95), and the Robert Wood Johnson Foundation's Addictive Substances Program. The opinions expressed are those of the authors, and not the US Department of Human Development, the World Bank or its member countries, or the Robert Wood Johnson Foundation.

tobacco use and using part of revenue from such taxes to support anti-smoking-related activities and for health-related expenditures, such as health promotion or health insurance, was widely utilised in the late 1980s and early 1990s. In a sense, tobacco tax has become a form of earmarked tax in many instances.

One justification for using an earmarked tax is to ease the pressure on general revenue finance for particular public goods or services when users or beneficiaries of these sources can be easily identified. Therefore, earmarked tax can be considered a replacement for direct charges for services.

However, public finance experts have argued that earmarking may not be a good tax budgeting procedure, since it introduces rigidities and does not permit proper allocation of general revenue among competing uses. On the other hand, one may argue that the use of a tobacco tax for health promotion and disease prevention may be appropriate, in line with the benefit taxation principle, which asserts that inducing better health behaviour and health status contribute to better expenditure decisions. In essence, depending on how the tobacco tax revenue is used, earmarking may thus be an arbitrary fiscal policy leading to budgetary rigidity, or it may be a useful device for a form of benefit taxation (Musgrave and Musgrave, 1980).

During the past decade, earmarking tobacco tax for health causes has been a popular fiscal instrument as well as a public health policy in several developed countries, particularly in the US. The policy formulation, and the impact of earmarked tobacco tax on consumption, government revenue, the tobacco industry, and the economy in general, are valuable for other countries to examine. This information is especially useful because some less-developed countries (LDCs) are also tobacco-producing countries, which have economic stakes in maintaining the well-being of tobacco farmers and the tobacco industry (Warner, 1990; Warner and Fulton, 1994). It is important to examine the economic implications and the total social welfare loss or gain of earmarked tobacco taxes, so that more informed tobacco control policy-making can be considered for the future.

The purpose of this chapter is to review international experiences with earmarked tobacco taxes, to analyse the economic implications of earmarked tobacco taxes, to draw lessons learned from these tax experiences, and to provide options and further recommendations for the international community. The following section will provide policy content, and the direct and indirect impact of earmarked tobacco taxes in the US, Canada, Finland, and Australia. Thereafter the chapter will present theoretical and some tentative quantitative estimates of total social welfare loss or gain from different sectors of the economy (using the US and China as examples). Finally, options and recommendations are presented.

International experiences of earmarked tobacco taxes

(i) US experiences

Tobacco taxes in the US are collected at the federal and state levels of government. The amount of tobacco tax on each pack varies considerably among the 50 states, ranging from a low of 2.5 cents in Virginia to 81.5 cents in the state of Washington as of December 1995 (Fishman *et al.*, 1996). Several states have used tobacco tax for government expenditures. Although California is not the state with the highest tobacco tax (it ranked only 18th in 1995), in 1988 it became the first state in the United States to legislate additional tobacco tax to deter cigarette consumption and to further earmark the revenue to be used for anti-smoking health education programmes, indigent health care, research, environmental programmes, and tobacco health-related research, among other uses (Bal, 1990). The California Tobacco Tax and Health Promotion Act, Proposition 99, was passed in 1988 by a popular vote of 58 per cent to 42 per cent, designed to increase tax from 10 cents a pack to 35 cents per pack. The goal of the Act was to achieve a 75 per cent reduction in smoking among adults in California by the year 2000 (to 6.5 per cent of the population, from 26 per cent in the pre-initiative period). The Act created the Tobacco Product Surtax Fund, composed of six accounts, which allocates 20 per cent of funds to health education and media campaigns, 35 per cent for indigent hospital services, 10 per cent for indigent physician services, 5 per cent for research, and 5 per cent for environment, with the remaining 25 per cent to be placed in an unallocated account. The justifications for the additional taxation on tobacco and for the earmarking of its revenue are:

- smoking is harmful to health, and has increased costs of health care among smokers, thereby placing a burden on non-smokers (who are tax-payers and pay insurance premiums);
- smoking will also expose non-smokers to its pollutants; and
- resources are required to initiate tobacco control programmes, other than taxes, to discourage youth and adult smoking.

The basic philosophy of the earmarked tobacco tax is that population-based tobacco control programmes through the media, schools, worksites and public areas will both reduce smoking prevalence and protect non-smokers. Needless to say, the legislation and implementation of Proposition 99 required numerous and complex negotiations between public health organisations, politicians, and the tobacco industry (Novotny and Siegel, 1996). Between 1989 and 1995, about US$1.5 billion in revenue has been appropriated for these earmarked accounts.

The direct impact of California tobacco tax increases on cigarette consumption was studied by a number of econometric analyses (Flewelling *et al.*, 1992; Glantz *et al.*, 1993; Hu *et al.*, 1994). They have all shown a significant reduction in *per capita* cigarette consumption in California, directly associated with the implementation of Proposition 99. For instance, it was reported that six months after the tax increase, cigarette sales had declined by about one pack per adult per month, or 11 per cent (Hu *et al.*, 1994). One year after the tax increase, the decline *per capita* had remained at a rate of 3/4 pack per adult per month, or about a 10 per cent reduction throughout the next three years. From January 1989 through December 1992, Proposition 99 reduced cigarette consumption by 1.3 billion packs of cigarettes, attributable to tax increase alone (Hu, Sung and Keeler, 1995). Other studies confirmed these findings (Pierce *et al.*, 1994; Glantz *et al.*, 1993).

Although there was a significant reduction in cigarette sales due to the tax increase, the state of California experienced an impressive increase in revenue. This was because the percentage increase in tax, reflected by the increase in retail price, is higher than the percentage decrease in quantity. The estimated price elasticity of demand for cigarettes in California during this period was about -0.40 (Keeler *et al.*, 1993; Sung *et al.*, 1994). It was shown that a 10 per cent increase in price reduced the quantity demanded by 4 per cent. Thus, the percentage increase in price is higher than the percentage decrease in quantity by 6 per cent. In other words, the value of lost sales is more than offset by the value of gain due to the increased price. Therefore, tax revenue will increase. The actual California state cigarette tax revenue increased 200 per cent in 1989, (US$764 million in 1989 *versus* US$254 million in 1988), despite a 14 per cent reduction in total cigarette sales (2538 million packs in 1988 *versus* 2184 million packs in 1989). Cigarette sales continued to decline each year, while revenues continued to be much higher than the pre-tax (1988) period. The state cigarette tax revenue in 1993 was still 170 per cent (US$690 million) higher than that in 1988, as shown in Table 1.

Table 1. California cigarette sales, tax revenue, and tax rates: 1989-93

Year	Sales (millions of packs)	Tax revenue (US$ million)	Tax rate (US$)
1987	2 563	258.25	0.10
1988	2 538	253.85	0.10
1989	2 184	764.42	0.35
1990	2 205	771.70	0.35
1991	2 054	719.09	0.35
1992	2 019	706.70	0.35
1993	1 970	689.64	0.35

Source: California Tax Equalisation Board

This is a very important finding for policy-makers in tobacco control and tax revenue departments. As long as the price elasticity of the demand for cigarettes is less elastic than a value of -1, the increase in taxes will result in a net gain in total tax revenues. The less elastic the demand, the less effective the tax will be in reducing cigarette consumption, but the more the gain in tax revenues. To plan for the desired level of reduction in cigarette consumption and the desired amount of increase of tax revenues, it is important to know the magnitude of the price elasticity of demand for cigarettes.

On the other hand, the direct effect of additional cigarette tax on the tobacco industry was obviously negative. It was estimated (Glantz *et al.*, 1993) that from 1989 to June 1993, Proposition 99 reduced cigarette consumption by 802 million packs, resulting in a loss of US$1.1 billion in pre-tax sales and approximately US$286 million in profit for the tobacco industry.

As noted, one unique feature of California's Proposition 99 is its earmarking of revenue from cigarette taxes on tobacco control activities, tobacco-related disease research, and expenditures for indigent health care services. For instance, US$125 million a year has been allocated for health education. Because of the extra tax revenues, the California Department of Health Services spent US$26 million on a state-wide media campaign designed to change tobacco-related attitudes and behaviours of certain target groups, including adult smokers, pregnant women, children and ethnic minorities.

Time-series regression analysis, based on cigarette sales data in California during 1989-92, indicates that both the 25 cent per pack state tax and the anti-smoking media campaign were statistically significant in reducing cigarette consumption (Hu, Sung and Keeler, 1995). The estimated results show that cigarette sales decreased by 819 million packs from the third quarter of 1990 through the fourth quarter of 1992 as a result of an additional 25 cents state tax increase, while the anti-smoking media campaign reduced the cigarette sales by 232 million packs during the same period. In other words, both taxation and anti-smoking media campaigns are effective ways of reducing cigarette consumption. The strength of these effects, however, is influenced by the magnitude of the taxes and the amount of media campaign expenditure. It is perhaps easy to overstate the magnitude of the effects of taxes *versus* media campaigns, given that they represent two different ways of reducing cigarette consumption. Taxation provides an economic disincentive, whereas the media campaign educates the public, by directing its focus on the psychological basis underlying the demand for cigarette consumption.

The implementation of Proposition 99 in California indicates that raising taxes and using part of the tax revenue for an anti-smoking campaign is an effective approach to reducing cigarette consumption. The tax is an economically effective and revenue-producing method of reducing cigarette consumption. At the same time, a tax increase may not deter some segments of the population from smoking. A media campaign, financed by the earmarked tobacco tax revenue, may reach those segments of the population. Thus, additional tobacco tax and earmarking part of its revenue for media and other anti-smoking educational campaigns provide appealing policy instruments for tobacco control policy-makers.

There are other impacts of Proposition 99, such as the reduction of and decreased exposure to environmental tobacco smoke for non-smokers. The California Department of Health Services reported in 1994 that children's protection from exposure to environmental tobacco smoke increased 6.2 per cent (from 75.2 per cent to 80.4 per cent protected at home in 1993), because the number of children living in smoke-free homes increased. In addition, 22.8 per cent fewer adults were exposed to environmental tobacco smoke at workplaces in California (Pierce *et al.*, 1994).

Other earmarked tax revenue has been spent on classroom teaching, which reached over two thirds of Californian schoolchildren. Over one-half of all students in California (more than 2.9 million) have also participated in anti-tobacco assemblies and community programmes involving teens teaching teens through sports, theatre, and music activities. Public school health education, teachers' training, and new methods of delivering tobacco use prevention programmes have been utilised. The actual quantitative impact of these on cigarette consumption has been difficult to document. However, public opinion indicated that 95 per cent of Californians approved the tobacco education that Proposition 99 initiated (Tobacco Education Oversight Committee, 1993).

Some argue that the cigarette tax is a "sin tax" (Manning *et al.*, 1989) because smoking causes economic burdens to society, through the increased use of medical services. Between 1989 and 1994, the California Department of Health Services received US$660 million for hospital services and physician services to cover medically indigent patient costs.

California's anti-smoking legislation, Proposition 99, is a major success for voters of California. Several other states in the US, including Massachusetts, Oregon, and Arizona, have implemented similar legislation by earmarking revenue for specific health education and medical uses. Michigan earmarked its tobacco tax for local public education. This paper will briefly summarise the experiences of Massachusetts, Arizona, and Oregon.

Voters in Massachusetts approved a ballot petition in November 1992 to increase cigarette tax on each pack from 26 cents to 51 cents (i.e. a 25 cents increase), beginning January 1, 1993. The petition requested that the legislature spend the proceeds on tobacco control and health education. After one year, in early 1994, the state began funding local boards of health, and youth programmes to promote policies to reduce public expenses to environmental tobacco smoke and to restrict youth access to cigarettes. Efforts were also made to support health education programmes, primary care providers, and other services to help smokers quit. Through June 1996, the Massachusetts Tobacco Control Program (MTCP) expenditures totalled US$116 million, including US$43 million for the mass-media campaign.

The impact of the increase of tobacco tax, its earmarked expenditures, and the anti-smoking media campaign in Massachusetts indicates that in the three years after the implementation of the petition in 1993, the smoking prevalence rate declined to 21.3 per cent, down from 23.5 per cent during 1990-92 (Centers for Disease Control, 1996). The number of packs of cigarettes sold per adult was also reduced from 117 packs in 1992 to 94 packs in 1996, a decline of 19.7 per cent. These are gross estimates; possible cross-border purchases due to lower taxes in neighbouring states (New Hampshire) and the overall declining national trend are not accounted for in these reduced figures.

By comparing the number of packs of cigarettes purchased per adult in Massachusetts, California and the 48 remaining states (and the District of Columbia), the Centers for Disease Control (CDC) (1996) reported that from 1992 through 1996 *per capita* consumption declined 19.7 per cent in Massachusetts and 15.8 per cent in California, but only 6.1 per cent for the rest of the nation. The CDC concluded that the significant declines in cigarette consumption in Massachusetts and California suggest that a tax increase combined with earmarked expenditures for an anti-smoking campaign can be more effective in reducing *per capita* consumption than a tax increase alone, as shown in Table 2.

Table 2. Number of packs of cigarettes purchased per adult* by year, selected US sites, 1990-96⁺

Year	Massachusetts	California	Other states and District of Columbia
1990	125	100	139
1991	120	92	134
1992	117	89	131
1993	102	88	125
1994	101	73	127
1995	98	76	125
1996**	94	75	123

Notes: * 18 years of age or older
+ Based on reports of tax receipts for wholesale cigarette deliveries
** Estimated as twice the cumulative values for January-June
Source: Centers for Disease Control (1996)

A national study (Chaloupka and Grossman, 1996), based on 1992, 1993 and 1994 youth survey data, further confirmed that those states that have earmarked a portion of their tobacco tax revenue for anti-smoking education, in the media or in schools, have experienced a negative and statistically significant impact on both the probability that a youth will smoke and on the average daily cigarette consumption among young smokers.

Voters in the state of Arizona approved the Tobacco Tax and Health Care Act in the 1994 general election. The Act increased cigarette tax from 18 cents per pack to 58 cents per pack. Additional revenues were earmarked for establishing a Health Education Account, 23 per cent of the increased tax revenue. In addition, the Act allocated 70 per cent of the revenue for health care for the medically needy, medically indigent, and low-income children, and 5 per cent for research on prevention and treatment of tobacco-related disease and addiction. The remaining 2 per cent was used for an adjustment account for appropriate uses in the case of future decline in tobacco tax revenue.

The Health Care Act formally became law in July 1995. The administration of funding was carried out by the Arizona Department of Health Services, and the media campaign was implemented in January 1996. Survey evaluation was initiated in April 1996. No published findings have yet been available.

Following California, Massachusetts, and Arizona, in late 1995 a state-wide coalition of health care and tobacco use prevention interests in Oregon began a citizen petition to increase the tax on each pack of cigarettes from 38 cents to 68 cents, and to increase the tax on non-cigarette tobacco products from 35 per cent to 65 per cent of wholesale prices, beginning February 1, 1997. The initiative authorised 10 per cent of the new tobacco tax revenue for use in developing and implementing state-wide tobacco use prevention and education programmes, and the remaining 90 per cent for use in expanding insurance coverage under the Oregon Health Plan for medically underserved persons. Both Arizona and Oregon have only recently initiated additional tobacco tax and used its earmarked revenue for tobacco control. They are in an early stage of impact evaluation.

Besides these four states, Michigan passed an initiative in 1994 to raise taxes an additional 25 cents per pack, to add to property tax funding of schools. Two states, Montana in 1990 and Colorado in 1992, have tried to use citizen initiatives to raise cigarette tax and earmark the revenue for tobacco control activities, but failed to gain voter approval.

In summary, there are four major states in the US that have used voter initiatives to support additional tobacco taxes and earmark portions of the new tax revenue for health education, tobacco prevention, and health care services, as shown in Table 3. Although there are variations of percentages of allocation, the largest portion has been allocated for health care, at least 50 per cent or more. Health education and media campaigns have been identified as a common earmarked item. The issue of economic efficiency and welfare loss or gain to the society of this type of earmarked tobacco will be analysed in the following section.

Table 3. Earmarked tobacco tax in four US states

	California[a]	*Massachusetts*[b]	*Arizona*[c]	*Oregon*[d]
Year enacted	1988	1992	1994	1995
Amount of tax increase (US$)	0.25 (to 0.35)	0.25 (to 0.51)	0.40 (to 0.58)	0.30 (to 0.68)
Earmarked allocation:				
Health education/media campaign	20%	65%	23%	10%
Indigent health care	50%	33%	70%	90%
Research	5%	2%	5%	-
Environment	5%	-	-	-
Unallocated	20%	-	2%	-

Sources: a - Bal (1990)
b - Centers for Disease Control (1996)
c - Centers for Disease Control (1997)
d - Arizona Department of Health Services, Center for Prevention and Health Promotion

Economic effects of earmarked tobacco tax: theory and implications

The basic criteria used to evaluate taxation are (1) efficiency and (2) equity. Efficiency in taxation means that tax revenue should be maximised with minimum alteration of consumers' choices among various goods or services. The less responsive the consumer is to changes in price of a given commodity (i.e. the demand is inelastic), the more effective taxes are in collecting revenue. Less response to changes in price means less negative change to consumers' satisfaction, if the tax has been shifted to an increase in price. Since demand for cigarettes is regarded as relatively inelastic, with estimates of price elasticity of demand of -0.4 to -0.5 in many industrialised economies, taxes on cigarettes should be efficient. A study in the United Kingdom (Jones and Posnett, 1988) indicates that a 1 per cent increase in the tax rate generates about a 0.9 per cent increase in revenue. The example of California also illustrates that cigarette tax is a powerful tool in generating revenue.

Equity in taxation means that there should be an equal tax burden among tax payers. There are two main principles to evaluate equity: (1) taxes should be based on individual benefit received from services provided by the government, and (2) taxes should be based on an individual's ability to pay. These two principles are not necessarily always consistent or contradictory to each other, depending on the type of taxation. For instance, some excise taxes are collected on the basis of the benefit principle, while income taxes are assessed on the ability-to-pay principle. Proponents of tobacco control groups have cited the benefit principle, indicating that smokers should pay for the burdens (negative benefits) that smoking brings about, such as pollution, social costs (e.g. fire hazard), and additional medical costs, which are imposed on others through insurance premiums or added government expenditures. The concept of users' fees or "sin tax" is based on the benefit principle. In other words, one of the goals of cigarette taxation is to raise the retail price of cigarettes to a level that fully reflects the social costs generated by their consumption (Manning *et al.*, 1989; Elleman-Jensen, 1991). In terms of this objective, an economically efficient price for cigarettes is one where the net benefit of cigarette smoking is at least larger than the price of the cigarettes, where part of the cigarette's price reflects social costs of consumption. Thus, the amount of tax on cigarettes should be set such that total tax revenue extracted from smokers would be equal to total social cost generated by smokers.

While additional cigarette taxation based on both efficiency and equity (the benefit principle) seems quite convincing, the use of the tobacco tax instrument alone may not be able to bring about tobacco control. The inelastic demand for cigarettes may result in revenue maximisation, but it is inconsistent with the goal of public health, which is minimising cigarette consumption. For instance, a 10 per cent increase in price can result in 4 per cent of tobacco consumption reduction. The anticipated health gain in reducing smoking will be limited with tax increases through price increases. That is, consumers may not respond to price change alone. Also, youth may have less understanding of the negative impact of smoking on their health. Therefore, the earmarking of a collected cigarette tax for spending on media or other educational anti-smoking campaigns is fully justified, because education makes up for the shortfalls of price effects under the efficiency arguments. In addition, earmarked revenues for research on tobacco-related disease and medical care costs, especially for those incurred by indigent people, are justified under the benefit principle.

The justification for earmarking tobacco tax revenues for health promotion, disease prevention, and medical care services on the grounds of efficiency and equity do not convince all fiscal specialists (Wagner, 1991), smokers, and the tobacco industry. On efficiency grounds, there is always a loss of consumer surplus (a reduction of utility or satisfaction) due to price (tax) increase and lesser consumption, a loss of producers' surplus (a reduction of revenue), and dead-weight loss (excess burden) to the society. On equity and efficiency grounds, although there is a high correlation between smoking and increased medical costs (Bartlett *et al.*, 1994), it is also necessary to consider inter-generational transfer between current young or adult smokers, and patient costs incurred by those who smoked years ago, as well as the possible medical costs and social security cost savings due to tobacco-related early death. There is much debate about these issues, but there is not yet conclusive agreement (Warner *et al.*, 1995).

To evaluate economic implications of an earmarked tobacco tax, it is necessary first to estimate the welfare effect of the increase of tobacco tax for consumers and producers, and the net loss (excess burden) to society, and then to consider the magnitude and type of tax revenue transfer affected. One should examine the distributional impact of tobacco tax, and the possible options of using earmarked tax to compensate losers as result of increased tobacco tax.

The economic and welfare effects of a tobacco tax increase depend on both the response of market price to a change in the tax rate, the response of demand to the change in market price, and the response of supply to the change in market price. The simplest assumption of tax incidence on retail price is that price changes by the full amount of the tax. In fact, most of US studies show that after each tax increase the retail price rose by an amount greater than or equal to the amount of tax. Two studies in the United Kingdom (Townsend, 1987; Jones and Posnett, 1988) have shown the welfare effects of cigarette taxes. To illustrate the estimation and magnitude of the economic and welfare effects of a tobacco tax increase, the cases of the US and China will be presented in this section.

(i) United States

From 1993 the US Federal government taxed cigarettes at a rate of 24 cents per pack. In addition to that, as of mid-1996, state governments in the US taxed cigarettes at an average rate of 31.7 cents per pack, so that the average total tax per pack in the US at that time was 55.7 cents; this yielded revenues of US$7.3 billion to various US governments (Tobacco Institute, 1997). Obviously, the effects of US cigarette taxation, at various government levels, are quite substantial, but it is clear that consumption of cigarettes could be further reduced by an increase in the tax. To provide insight into the potential effects of an increase in cigarette taxation on consumption and economic welfare, this chapter presents calculations simulating the effects of a further one cent increase in the US Federal cigarette tax.

These calculations are based on the earlier work of Barnett, Keeler, and Hu (1995), but they extend that work in some important ways. Before describing those extensions, the discussion will summarise the methods on which the work by Barnett, Keeler, and Hu (1995) is based. That earlier research takes account of several important facts crucial to the US cigarette industry. Firstly, it is an oligopoly, so the model is based on Cournot-type behaviour with conjectural variations. The relevant model assumes that the firms are profit-maximising oligopolists, who, at the same time, take account of their interdependence in setting prices. Secondly, it takes account of the fact that cigarette manufacturers are able to set wholesale prices to maximise profits, and that they can, as a result, respond to the Federal tax, and to an average state tax, but they cannot set retail prices. The cigarette distribution and retail sales businesses are likely to be much more competitive in nature. Thirdly, the model is based on separate estimates of marginal costs for manufacturing, distribution and retailing of cigarettes. Knowledge of each of these costs, as well as the knowledge of taxes at the Federal and State levels, is necessary to get a full picture of how taxes are passed on as prices.

The details of the model, cost function estimates, and other underlying assumptions of this analysis are set forth in Barnett, Keeler and Hu (1995). Further modifications of this model are set forth below; results are shown in Table 4.

Table 4. Simulation of a one cent increase in US Federal cigarette tax

λ (Consumer surplus weight)	1	0	-0.25	-0.5	-1
Mean change in qty (million packs/year)	-226	-226	-226	-226	-226
Mean change in price (real 1990 cents/pack):					
Retail price paid by consumers	1.106	1.106	1.106	1.106	1.106
Price received by retailers	0.016	0.016	0.016	0.016	0.016
Wholesale price	-0.134	-0.134	-0.134	-0.134	-0.134
Change in consumer surplus (λCS)	-394	0	99	197	394
Change in producer surplus	-101	-101	-101	-101	-101
Total change in welfare	-495	-101	-2	96	293
Consumer's share	0.8	0	-49.5	2.1	1.3
Producer's share	0.2	1	50.5	-1.1	-0.3
Dead-weight loss	222	-171	-270	-368	-565
Government revenue	272	272	272	272	272
Total change in gain	495	101	2	-96	-293
Dead-weight loss as % of lost welfare	0.45	-1.7	-1.08	3.84	1.93

Source: The table is based on Barnett, Keeler and Hu (1995) with two modifications: (1) price elasticity is adjusted down from -0.709 in the above study to -0.5; (2) a more general form of social welfare function is used, namely, PS + λCS, where PS and CS are the producer and consumer surplus, respectively, and λ is the relative weight that the government assigns to the consumer welfare. In Barnett, Keeler and Hu (1995), λ = 1.

The first change that has been made is that the price elasticity has been adjusted downward from -0.709, as it was estimated in Barnett, Keeler and Hu (1995), to -0.5. This is because the recent consensus of estimates of the price-elasticity of demand for cigarettes in the United States is much closer to -0.5 than to -0.7, as has been established above.

The second change made from Barnett, Keeler and Hu (1995) is that allowance has been made for different weightings of consumer and producer surplus in the social welfare function. In doing welfare analysis of taxation, one often calculates the "dead-weight" or welfare loss from a tax under the assumption that everyone's welfare (i.e. a dollar that either the consumer or producer is willing to pay) is weighted the same, regardless of the person or whether he or she is a consumer or producer. However, in the case of goods that are thought by most in society to be "vices", such as tobacco or alcohol, the society may choose to attach a welfare weight to such consumption less than that for consumption of other goods. Indeed, the welfare weight attached to such "vices" could be zero or even negative.

Therefore, the calculations shown in Barnett, Keeler and Hu (1995) have been further revised to allow for welfare weights on consumer surplus in cigarette consumption. Specifically, weights have been allowed that are either less than one (allowing positive consumer surplus from the consumption, albeit less than from other goods) or less than zero (allowing for negative weights in the social welfare function from consumption of cigarettes). The alternative levels of consumer welfare weight attached to cigarette consumption are shown in Table 4. Barnett, Keeler and Hu (1995) assume that the welfare weight for consumers is 1 ($\lambda = 1$). A lower weight has been shown ($\lambda = 0$), and negative weights, from -0.25 to -1.

It can be seen from Table 4 that the welfare change from a one cent tax increase (based on 1990 prices and consumption figures) for the US ranges from an additional dead-weight loss of US$222.5 million (with consumer surplus weighted at 1), to a dead-weight welfare gain of over US$500 million (with a welfare weight of -1 for consumer surplus from cigarettes). Such a tax increase would, at the same time, increase government revenues by over US$270 million, again in 1990 prices.

Further, based on these calculations it can be shown that a one cent Federal tax increase in 1990 would reduce cigarette consumption in the US by 226 million packs per year, with corresponding improvements in health. This assumes that none of the tax increase would be earmarked for anti-smoking media and school advertising. The analysis included in preceding parts of this paper indicates clearly that earmarking a significant part of such a tax increase to anti-smoking activities could further reduce cigarette consumption.

(ii) China

The 1996 National Survey of Smoking in China indicates that 66.9 per cent of adult males and 4.2 per cent of adult females in China were current smokers. The overall prevalence rate was 37.6 per cent (State Statistical Bureau (China), 1993). This implies that more than 300 million individuals in China are smokers, and approximately 30 per cent of the world's smokers live in China (*Tobacco International*, 1993). China produced 82 billion packs of cigarettes and used 1.85 million hectares for tobacco production in 1992, which represents a 93 per cent increase in production and a 25 per cent increase in tobacco growing since 1981.

A recent study indicated that 12 per cent of male deaths and 3 per cent of female deaths in 1987 were due to tobacco-attributable diseases (Liu, Peto, Chen *et al.*, 1998).

The economic loss in medical care expenditures due to smoking was estimated at 6.9 billion yuan in 1989, while the value of lost productivity or premature death was about 20.13 billion yuan in 1989. The value of these resources could be used for many other productive services in the society (Jin, 1995).

China has made major progress in reducing cigarette consumption by banning all advertising, increasing import duties on cigarettes, and banning cigarette smoking in some public places. However, China has not used cigarette tax as a tobacco control instrument. Cigarette tax revenue in China was 31.0 billion yuan in 1992, representing 9.4 per cent of total government revenue, and clearly a major source of revenue (Hu, 1997). Although the Ministry of Health is interested in seeing an increase in tobacco tax, the Ministry of Agriculture and the state-controlled tobacco industry have opposed the tax increase due to the potential negative impact on tobacco farmers' employment. Several major tobacco-producing provinces, such as Yunan, Guizhou, and part of Sichuan, are relatively poor. The government and the population in these provinces have relied upon tobacco as their main source of income for some time. Furthermore, the Ministry of Finance is not quite sure about the long-run tax revenue impact of a tax increase on cigarettes. It is only in recent months that, in response to public health opinions, the government has tentatively agreed to raise a minimal amount of additional tobacco tax in a few metropolitan areas, such as Shanghai, Tianjin, etc., as experiment sites for tobacco control.

To illustrate the possible impact on revenue of an increased excise tax on cigarette sales in China, 1992 data on price and sales figures are used. China has sold 32.65 million cases of cigarettes (one case contains 2 500 packs), with an average retail price of 3 320 yuan per case (State Statistical Bureau, (China) 1993). A recent study (Mao, 1996) estimated that the price elasticity of demand for cigarettes in Sichuan province in China ranges from -0.65 to -0.80, which is somewhat higher than many other developed countries. It is assumed that -0.65 is the price elasticity of demand for the Chinese population. Given this information, and assuming the Chinese state cigarette industry imposes a 10 per cent increase in price from 3 320 yuan to 3 652 yuan, additional tax will result in a 6.5 per cent reduction in sales, from 32.65 million cases to 30.53 million cases. However, the total revenue will increase from 108.41 billion yuan to 111.5 billion yuan, an increase of 2.9 per cent. Thus, given the inelastic demand for cigarettes, the total revenue will increase when the price is increased. Assuming the effective tax rate in 1992 was 37.9 per cent (Hu, 1997), to achieve a 10 per cent increase in price, the effective tax rate would have to rise to 43.43 per cent, an increase of 15 per cent of the effective tax rate, and an increase of 26.5 per cent in the amount of tax. Given these assumptions, the total tax revenue would rise by 18.2 per cent, while total sales revenues would rise by 2.9 per cent.

Following the same approach used in estimating consumer and producer surplus, and the "dead-weight" or welfare loss from a tax in the US, a simplified version is applied to the Chinese example. It is assumed that the price elasticity of the supply of cigarettes in China ranges from 1.0 to 1.5. The estimated demand elasticity is -0.65 (Mao, 1996), with the 1992 cigarette consumption being 81 625 million packs. A linear demand and supply function are used to estimate the impact of a one cent increase on consumer surplus, producer surplus, government revenue, and net welfare loss. Table 5 is a summary of these calculated results, allowing for different weightings of consumer surplus in the social welfare function, from traditional weighting ($\lambda = 1$) to the maximum negative weights (sin or vice behaviour, $\lambda = -1$).

Table 5: Impact of a 1 cent increase in cigarette excise tax in China					
$\varepsilon^D = -0.65, \varepsilon^s = 1\lambda$	1	0	-0.25	-0.5	-1
Reduction in consumer surplus (λCS) (millions of 1992 Yuan)	494.0	0	-123.5	-247.0	-494.0
Reduction in producer surplus	321.1	321.1	321.1	321.1	321.1
Reduction in Welfare	815.1	321.1	197.6	74.1	-172.9
Increase in government revenue	813.8	813.8	813.8	813.8	813.8
Net dead-weight loss	1.2	-492.7	-616.2	-739.7	-986.7
$\varepsilon^D = -0.65, \varepsilon^s = 1.5\lambda$	1	0	-0.25	-0.5	-1
Reduction in consumer surplus (λCS)	568.5	0	-142.1	-284.2	-568.5
Reduction in producer surplus	246.4	246.4	246.4	246.4	246.4
Reduction in Welfare	814.9	246.4	104.3	-37.9	-322.1
Increase in government revenue	813.5	813.5	813.5	813.5	813.5
Net dead-weight loss	1.4	-567.1	-709.2	-851.4	-1135.6

It can be seen from Table 5 that the welfare change from a one cent tax increase (based on 1992 prices and consumption figures) for China ranges from an additional dead-weight loss of 1.2 million yuan, with consumer surplus weight at one, to a dead-weight welfare gain of almost 1 billion yuan, with welfare weight of -1 for consumer surplus from cigarettes. Such a tax increase would, at the same time, increase government revenues by over 800 million yuan. Therefore, these results indicate that even if smoking is not considered a negative behaviour ($\lambda = 1$), the dead-weight loss due to tax increase is very small (1.2 to 1.4 million yuan) as compared to the gain in government revenue (813.5 million yuan). Furthermore, when a reduction in smoking is considered a societal gain, then the dead-weight loss becomes society gain with a magnitude ranging from 0.5 billion yuan to over 1 billion yuan.

If the tax is not earmarked, the increase in revenue could be appropriated as general government revenue. For example, one informal recommendation from the State Economic Council regarding the pending increase in cigarette tax among experimental sites is to subsidise deficit-ridden state enterprises. However, from the viewpoint of public health and the benefit principle of earmarked taxation, although there is no change of total dead-weight loss or gain, some of the additional tax revenue could be allocated to:
- health promotion and disease prevention activities, such as anti-smoking media campaigns and community education;
- health care insurance premiums for rural and low-income households; and
- subsidies for tobacco farmers and tobacco industry for their loss of revenue for possible transition and technology transfers from tobacco production to

other productions such as tea, coffee, horticulture, and other agricultural products.

The first two allocations will help to reduce consumer surplus and the third type of allocation will reduce producer surplus and further enhance the cause of tobacco control.

Conclusion: lessons learned

Cigarette smoking is harmful both to the health of the smoker and the health of those who are exposed to secondary smoke, causing premature death through tobacco-related illness. Smoking has also increased health care costs and resulted in a loss of productivity due to early death and illness. Because, as has been shown, consumers are less sensitive to changes in the price of cigarettes compared to other goods, taxes could be a powerful tool to raise revenue. In other words, both from an efficiency and equity point of view, it is important to use cigarette tax as a fiscal instrument, not only for revenue purposes, but also for tobacco control. Further, it would be useful to designate the earmarked tax revenues for health education and anti-smoking media campaigns to complement the goal of tobacco control.

Questions remain about (1) what amount of tax should be levied on cigarettes, and (2) how that tax revenue should be used. To determine the appropriate amount of tax on cigarettes, one would not only need to examine the price and income elasticities of demand for cigarettes, but also the social consequences of taxation. Any tax increase would effect a loss of consumer surplus (the difference between the value of cigarettes to smokers and the amount that they pay for it), producer surplus (the loss in revenue to producers less the costs of production and distribution), and the net welfare costs (the loss in consumer surplus less the revenue generated from the tax). This chapter has shown examples from the US and China concerning the possible impact of an increase in cigarette tax. Given the magnitude of the negative externalities associated with cigarette smoking, the appropriate magnitude of loss of consumer surplus may not be negative. That is, reducing smoking will improve the health of smokers and non-smokers. Thus, depending on the relative weight assigned to consumer surplus *versus* producer surplus, it seems that raising cigarette tax in the US and China would be especially appropriate, since the relative cigarette tax rate in these two countries is much lower than many other countries in the world. The increase in tax revenue is always smaller than the loss of consumer surplus. When the loss of consumer surplus is considered a positive gain, there is more reason to raise cigarette tax. The net welfare costs of the tax would also be offset by the positive gain of consumer surplus. Conceptually, the amount of tax on cigarettes should be set such that total tax revenue extracted from smokers would be equal to total social costs generated by smokers.

The question as to how cigarette tax revenue should be allocated is the subject of this paper. Although an earmarked tax is not always an ideal tax-expenditure fiscal instrument (since it introduces rigidities and does not permit proper allocation criteria of general revenue among competing uses) evidence and experience have shown that the use of tobacco tax for health promotion and disease prevention may be quite appropriate, in line with the benefit taxation principle, consistent with the principle that inducing better health behaviour and health status contribute to better expenditure decisions.

One area that previous studies have not discussed is the use of earmarked tobacco tax revenue to compensate producers' surplus loss. In other words, if a portion of the tax revenue can be allocated to tobacco farmers and tobacco manufacturing industries to transfer productivity to alternative cash crops and industries, the loss of producer surplus can be reduced. At the same time, the future economy can rely less upon tobacco products. This is especially true for developing countries where tobacco products are a major source of income and tax revenue.

Several lessons may be learned from the review of international experiences with cigarette taxation and the use of earmarked tax:

1. A tobacco tax is an effective and efficient instrument in raising government revenue, because there is a relatively price-inelastic demand for cigarettes.
2. Tobacco tax policy should be linked to tobacco use. Government policy-makers should consider using tobacco tax as an intervention in accomplishing the goals of health promotion and disease prevention.
3. When earmarked tobacco taxes are used for anti-smoking campaigns and other health promotion or health education activities, tobacco control is further enhanced. These additional measures have been more effective than using a tax alone.
4. Although any tax increase will increase the welfare cost to society and reduce consumer and producer surplus, the reduction of external costs of smoking will offset the loss of consumer surplus and welfare costs to society. In addition, if a portion of the earmarked tax can be allocated for producers to transfer production away from the tobacco sector, the loss of producers' surplus will also be minimised. The use of portions of earmarked tax revenue for health care and health insurance premiums will also reduce the magnitude of the loss of consumer surplus.

Tobacco tax is a major instrument of health policy as well as of fiscal policy. Each country varies in terms of its demand, production, and tax treatment of tobacco products. Many countries around the world have taken the initiative to control tobacco use, but may not have earmarked tax, or used tobacco tax specifically as a policy instrument. More information and study are needed to consider the feasibility of imposing additional taxes on tobacco and earmarking these revenues for various purposes. This is a critical time for researchers and policy-makers to contemplate this important issue.

References

Ahmad, Ehtisham and Stern (1985), "The theory reform and Indian indirect taxes," *Journal of Public Economics*, 25:259-98.

Bal, D. (1990), "Reducing tobacco consumption in California — development of a state-wide anti-tobacco use campaign", *Journal of the American Medical Association*, 264:1570-74.

Barnett, P., T. Keeler and T. Hu (1995), "Oligopoly structure and the incidence of cigarette excise taxes" *Journal of Public Economics*, 57:457-70.

Bartlett, J., L. Miller, D. Rice, W. Max and Office on Smoking and Health, Centers for Disease Control (1994), "Medical care expenditures attributable to smoking — United States, 1993," *MMWR*, 43:469-72.

Buchanan, J. (1963), "The economics of earmarked taxes," *Journal of Political Economy*, October.

Centers for Disease Control (1997) "Tobacco tax initiative — Oregon: 1996", *MMWR*, 46:246-248.

Centers for Disease Control (1996), "Cigarette smoking before and after an excise tax increase and an anti-smoking campaign — Massachusetts: 1990-1996", *MMWR*, 45:966-970.

Chaloupka, F. and M. Grossman (1996), *Price, Tobacco Control Policies and Youth Smoking*, Working paper no. 5140, Cambridge, Mass: National Bureau of Economic Research.

Elleman-Jensen, P. (1991), "The social costs of smoking revisited", *British Journal of Addiction*, 86:957-66.

Fishman, J. *et al.* (1996), *State Tobacco Control Highlights 1996*, Centers for Disease Control, Atlanta, GA: US Department of Health and Human Services, 1996.

Flewelling, R. *et al.* (1992), "First year impact of the 1989 California cigarette tax increase on cigarette consumption", *American Journal of Public Health*, 82:867-869.

Glantz, S. *et al.* (1993), "Changes in cigarette consumption, prices and tobacco industry reviews associated with California's Proposition 99", *Tobacco Control*, 2:311-314.

Hu, T. (1997), "Cigarette taxation in China: lessons from international experiences", *Tobacco Control*, 6:136-40.

Hu, T., J. Bai, T. Keeler, P. Barnett and H. Sung (1994), "The impact of 1989 California major anti-smoking legislation on cigarette consumption", *Journal of Public Health Policy*, 15:26-36.

Hu, T, T. Keeler, H. Sung and P. Barnett (1995), "The impact of California anti-smoking legislation on cigarette sales, consumption and prices", *Tobacco Control*, 4:534-8.

Hu, T., H. Sung and T. Keeler (1995), "Tobacco taxes and the anti-smoking media campaign: the California experience", *American Journal of Public Health*.

Jin, S. (1995), "Smoking-induced health-related economic costs in China", *Journal Biomedical and Environmental Sciences*.

Jones, A. and J. Posnett (1988), "The revenue and welfare effects of cigarette taxes", *Applied Economics*, 20:1223-32.

Keeler, T., Hu T., P. Barnett and W. Manning (1993), "Taxation, regulation and addiction: a demand function for cigarettes based on time-series evidence", *Journal of Health Economics*, 12:1-18.

Lee, D. and R. Wagner (1991), "The political economy of tax earmarking", in Wagner, R. (ed.), *Charging for Government*, New York: Routledge, Chapman and Hall.

Liu, B.-Q., R. Peto, Z. Chen *et al.* (1998), "Tobacco hazards in China: proportional mortality study of 1 000 000 deaths", *British Medical Journal* (in press).

Manning, W., E. Keeler, J. Newhouse, E. Sloss and J. Wasserman (1989), "The taxes of sin: do smokers and drinkers pay their way?", *Journal of the American Medical Association*, 261:1604-9.

Mao, Z. (1996), *Demand for Cigarettes and Pricing Policy: a Time-series Analysis* (in Chinese), Working paper, School of Public Health, Sichuan, Chengdu: China West China University of Medical Sciences.

McMahon, W. and C.M. Sprenkle (1970), "A theory of earmarking", *National Tax Journal*, 23:255-61.

Ministry of Health (China) (1997), *Smoking and Health in China — 1996 Natural Prevalence Survey of Smoking Patterns*, Beijing: China Science and Technology Press.

Musgrave, R. and P. Musgrave (1980), *Public Finance in Theory and Practice*, New York: McGraw-Hill.

Novotny, T. and M. Siegel (1996), "California's tobacco control saga", *Health Affairs*, 15:58-72.

Pierce, J. *et al.* (1994), *Tobacco Use in California: An Evaluation of the Tobacco Control Programs, 1989-1993*, La Jolla, CA: University of California at San Diego.

State Statistical Bureau (China) (1993), *1993 Statistical Yearbook of China*, China Publishing Ltd.

Sung, H., T. Hu, and T. Keeler (1994), "Cigarette taxation and demand: an empirical model", *Contemporary Economic Policy*, 7:91-100.

Tobacco Education Oversight Committee (1993), *Toward a Tobacco-Free California: Exploring a New Frontier, 1993-1995*, Sacramento, CA: TEOC.

Tobacco Institute (1997), *The Tax Burden on Tobacco*, Washington, DC: Tobacco Institute.

Tobacco International (1993), "Chinese smokers pass the 300 million mark", *Tobacco International*, 7.

Townsend, J. (1987), "Cigarette tax, economic welfare and social class patterns of smoking", *Applied Economics*, 19:355-65.

Wagner, R. (ed.) (1991), *Charging the Government: User Charges and Earmarked Taxes in Principle and Practice*, London: Routledge.

Warner, K.E. (1990), "Tobacco taxation as health policy in the Third World," *American Journal of Public Health*, 80(5):529-531.

Warner, K.E., F. Chaloupka, P. Cook, W. Manning, J. Newhouse, T. Novotny, T. Schelling and J. Townsend (1995), "Criteria for determining an optimal cigarette tax: the economist's perspective", *Tobacco Control*, 4:380-86.

Warner, K.E. and G.A. Fulton (1994), "The economic implications of tobacco product sales in a non-tobacco state", *Journal of the American Medical Association*, 271:771-6.

Zimring, F. and W. Nelson (1995), "Cigarette taxes as cigarette policy", *Tobacco Control*, 4:525-33.

Chapter 10

A Framework for Cost-Benefit Analysis

Frank Chaloupka, Prabhat Jha and Richard Peck[1]

This chapter presents a framework for assessing the net benefits of global tobacco production and consumption. The framework is consistent with that of Barnum (1993) but permits the assessment of total net benefits of tobacco consumption, that is, benefits minus costs. The framework proposed by Barnum considers only marginal net benefits. The benefits of tobacco consumption flow from two sources. First, there are the profits earned by producers. The second source of benefits is the satisfaction derived by the consumers of tobacco products. The primary social cost of tobacco consumption arises because years of productive activity are lost through disability and premature death as well as through exposure to environmental tobacco smoke. In determining the costs of tobacco consumption, it is important, however, to distinguish between external and internal costs. Rather than attempting this task, it is proposed instead to determine the minimum dollar amount that needs to be placed on the external value of a human life so that the net benefits of tobacco consumption are zero. In other words it is proposed to determine the minimum external cost associated with the loss of human life which would result in zero net benefits from tobacco consumption. It is then up to policy-makers to determine if this threshold value of human life is sufficiently low so that intervention is warranted.

The benefits of tobacco consumption

(i) Consumer Surplus

For any standard economic commodity, there are two distinct, equally legitimate ways to measure the benefits to consumers. The first approach considers willingness to accept payment. One can ask, what is the total amount of compensation required by consumers so that they are just willing to give up tobacco products? Under consideration here is the cash amount which makes a consumer indifferent between consuming the product and not consuming the product. This benefit measure is referred to as compensating variation. In the case of tobacco products, this is equivalent to asking how big a bribe is required to induce smokers to quit.

1. This work was supported by the World Bank's Research Support Board (Grant No. 681-95). The opinions expressed are those of the authors, and not the World Bank or its member countries.

The second approach is based on willingness to pay. In particular, one measures benefits by determining the maximum amount consumers are willing to pay to prevent the loss of tobacco products. In this approach, one is asking how much a consumer would be willing to pay to continue smoking. This measure of consumer benefit is called equivalent variation. Both approaches are equally sound, but give different answers. In particular, willingness to accept payment is always larger than the willingness to pay. For reasonable preferences, these two measures tend to move together: a large compensating variation implies a large equivalent variation. The two measures do assume different entitlement. In measuring compensating variation, one is implicitly assuming that individuals have the right to smoke and that one must pay them not to do so. In contrast, equivalent variation, it has been argued, implicitly assumes that smokers do not possess the right to smoke and therefore must buy the right to smoke.

The framework which has been outlined for determining consumer benefits is very general and can be applied to a variety of consumer goods. Of course, many have argued that the demand for tobacco is distinctive and special because tobacco is an addictive substance. A natural question to ask is what willingness to pay and willingness to accept payment mean for a good that is addictive. For economists, the analytical definition of an addictive good is that it is a good for which current consumption depends on past and future consumption, as well as on current price.[2] Since past and future consumption depend on past and future prices, this implies that for an addictive good current consumption levels are determined by past, current and future prices. This analysis assumes that long-run steady states can be compared so that the long-run use of tobacco remains constant over time. Thus discussion of willingness to pay refers to how much an individual is willing to pay to maintain the long-run price of tobacco at its current level. The compensating variation measure of benefits when the current long-run price of tobacco is p is determined by how much payment is required to ensure that utility level remains constant when the long-run price of tobacco is set arbitrarily high.

This can be stated more formally using the framework provided by Becker, Grossman and Murphy (1994). There is a composite good y and an addictive good c. Utility U at any period t depends on present consumption of the composite good, y_t and past and present consumption levels of the addictive good, c_{t-1} and c_t respectively.[3] It is assumed that the composite good is the numeraire and that the price of the addictive good is constant over time, p. W is the discounted present value of the individual's wealth. The individual chooses consumption path $\{y_t, c_t\}$ to maximise the discounted sum of utility subject to an inter-temporal budget constraint. β is the discount rate; the personal discount rate is assumed to be equal to the market rate of interest. The

2. For so-called myopic addiction, current consumption depends on current price and past consumption. For so-called rational addiction, current consumption depends on current price, past consumption and future consumption. This means that for a so-called rational addict, present consumption will be influenced by the future price of the commodity.
3. There is an initial level of consumption, c_0, which is specified exogenously.

individual's indirect utility function, which depends on W and p is defined as follows:

$$V(p,W) = \max \quad \sum_{t=1}^{\infty} \beta^{t-1} U\left(c_t, c_{t-1}, y_t\right)$$

subject to:

$$\sum_{t=1}^{\infty} \beta^{t-1} \left(y_t + pc_t\right) = W$$

$V(\infty, W)$ is the level of utility that can be obtained when the addictive good is unavailable, that is:

$$V(\infty, W) = \max \quad \sum_{t=1}^{\infty} \beta^{t-1} U\left(0,\ 0,\ y_t\right)$$

$$\sum_{t=1}^{\infty} \beta^{t-1}\left(y_t\right) = W$$

The compensating variation is the amount of additional wealth that is required to compensate the individual for the absence of tobacco.[4] In terms of the notation used here, this amount is defined by the equation:

$$V(p,\ W) = V(\infty,\ W + CV)$$

The equivalent variation is defined as the amount of wealth that an individual is willing to give up to continue to have tobacco products available at price p. Equivalent variation, EV, is defined by the equation:

$$V(p,\ W - EV) = V(\infty,\ W)$$

This provides an overview of the approach used here to measuring consumer benefits. As the above equations indicate, determination of compensating and equivalent variation requires knowledge of the indirect utility function. If there is sufficient data, indirect utility functions can be recovered and the benefits of tobacco consumption determined from the equations above.

When there is insufficient data available to recover either expenditure functions or indirect utility functions, it is standard to approximate benefits by considering consumer surplus. The justification for such an approximation is provided by Willig (1976). The applicability of the Willig results for addictive goods remains an area of active research. The standard interpretation of consumer surplus is that it is total willingness to pay for a given amount of the commodity minus what is actually spent. Geometrically, this is the area under the demand curve up to the level of consumption curve the total amount paid for tobacco; this is shown as area *PBA* in Figure 1.

---

4. If the initial level of consumption c_0 is not at the steady state value associated with price p, then the analysis is more complicated. In particular, defining consumer surplus for each period becomes problematic. Note that the consumer surplus changes over time as the consumption level of the addictive good adjusts to the steady state. The definitions of equivalent and compensating variation are, however, easily modified to deal with this case.

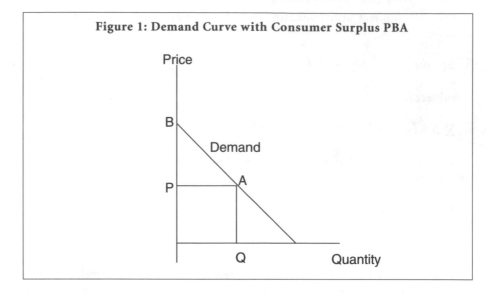

Figure 1: Demand Curve with Consumer Surplus PBA

In applied work it is assumed that the long-run demand curve is linear, that is:

$P = a - bQ.$

With a linear demand curve, if the current price is P, current consumption is Q and the price elasticity of demand at P and Q is e, then annual consumer surplus, CS, is:

$CS = PQ/2e.$

This formula indicates that consumer surplus varies inversely with the price elasticity of demand. When the price elasticity is infinite consumer surplus is zero, and when the price elasticity is less than 0.5 in absolute value, consumer surplus exceeds total expenditures.

In implementing this formula, it is expected that price and quantity varies across region. It is also likely that the price elasticity will vary from region to region, since the income share of tobacco expenditures varies. To compute total world annual consumer benefits, the following formula applies:

$CS_{World} = 1/2 \sum_{all\ regions} p_i q_i/e_i,$ where i = region i.

A natural division, given the type of data one is likely to have, is to divide the world into two regions, established market economies (EME) and rest of the world (Non-EME). To convert this annual stream of consumer surplus into a discounted present value, the amount $0.5pq/e$ is divided by the social discount rate, that is:

Discounted present value of consumer surplus = $CS_{World}/r.$

The traditional range for the social rate of discount is between 3 and 6 per cent.

A shortcoming of the approach as outlined is that it does not account for economic growth or population growth, which will shift out the demand curve and lead to a higher estimate. It is straightforward to amend this framework, however, to account for growth. A final advantage of this methodology is that it can be easily adapted to provide a breakdown of present discounted value of consumption benefits for the eight World Bank Regions or other regional breakdowns of interest.

By comparison, Barnum (1993) considers the incremental change in consumer surplus that arises from a 1 000 ton increase in output. An increase in output pushes down the price of tobacco products and enables consumers to consume more which leads to an increase in consumer surplus. He assumes an iso-elastic demand curve (a linear demand curve is assumed) and uses a price elasticity of 0.6 in absolute value. It should be noted that his modelling does not explicitly take into account the distinction between tobacco leaf and machine-manufactured cigarettes, while the approach used here allows one to make this distinction. Barnum's approach suggests that a 1 000 ton increase in world tobacco output increases consumer surplus by US$1.7 million.

(ii) Producer surplus

Net benefits to tobacco producers and cigarette manufacturers depend on the alternative products that can be grown or manufactured with the assets currently used for tobacco products. Producer surplus is the payment that producers receive in excess of their opportunity cost, and is normally equated with economic rent. Economic rent is the amount that a payment exceeds the minimum amount that is necessary to ensure that the good is supplied at the specified quantity. Thus if a star basketball player receives a salary of US$5 million but would be willing to play for only US$2 million, then US$3 million of his US$5 million dollar salary is said to be economic rent. Producer surplus and economic rent are equivalent. This connection between economic rent and producer surplus is made clear in the following alternative definition of producer surplus: it is the amount that can be taken from producers without diminishing the amount supplied.

As a measure of economic profits, producer surplus is simply revenue minus opportunity costs.[5] Geometrically, producer surplus is the area between price P and the supply curve, that is the area above the supply curve and below the price line. Producer surplus arises from the production of tobacco leaf and from the manufacture of cigarettes. As a first approximation it is assumed that production of tobacco leaf occurs under competitive conditions. For the manufacture of cigarettes, this assumption is less tenable and the approach is modified to take into account the monopoly power of cigarette manufacturers.

With a standard supply curve diagram, the connection between producer surplus and the ease with which assets can be re-deployed in the production of alternative products is easy to see. For example, if it is easy for tobacco growers

---

5. In general, the area underneath the supply curve is total variable cost. If firms are infinitesimal, that is, efficient scale is small relative to total market demand, then one can show that the area under the supply curve is exactly total costs.

to produce a lucrative alternative product, then small changes in price will lead to big changes in output. As the price for the product declines, producers will quickly shift assets into the production of the lucrative alternative product. In this case, the supply of tobacco will be relatively elastic as indicated in Figure 2. Total producer surplus will, all else equal, be relatively small, as shown in Figure 2 as *PAB*. On the other hand, if there are no alternative products, producers will not be able to readily re-deploy assets in the event of price decline. The supply curve, in this case, will be relatively inelastic. Here, producer surplus will be relatively large. This is shown in Figure 3; producer surplus is the area *PEF*.

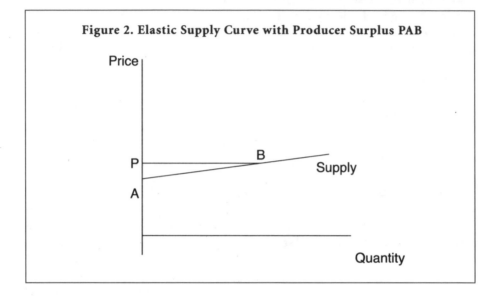

Figure 2. Elastic Supply Curve with Producer Surplus PAB

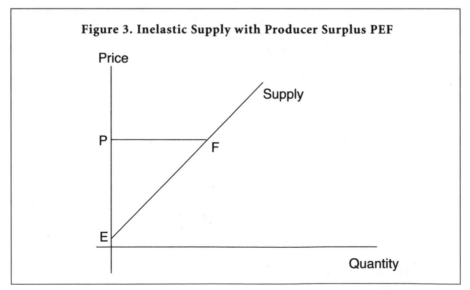

Figure 3. Inelastic Supply with Producer Surplus PEF

In general, producer surplus is given by the area between price and the supply curve; given a supply curve, generating producer surplus is a matter of computing the appropriate integral. It is assumed that supply curves are iso-elastic (this is the same assumption as Barnum (1993)), that is,

$$Q_S = AP^\eta$$

where η is the supply elasticity.[6] For this supply curve, producer surplus, PS, is given by

$$PS = PQ/(1 + \eta)$$

In this particular case, only the supply elasticity, η, output, Q, and the market price P are needed to determine producer surplus. This is the annual producer surplus. To convert this flow into a stock, the present discounted value of the flow of producer surplus is computed as follows:

Discounted Present Value of Producer Surplus = PS/r

where r is, of course, the social discount rate.

As with consumer surplus, Barnum (1993) looks at the incremental producer surplus that arises when there is a gross increase in output of 1 000 metric tons. He uses, as this analysis does, an iso-elastic supply curve. He finds that the incremental producer surplus is -$400 000. The reason the amount is negative is that the incremental increase in output reduces the equilibrium price of tobacco. This decline in the price of tobacco causes the net producer surplus to decline. This means, of course, that Barnum's estimate cannot be used to compute total producer surplus.

Cost of tobacco consumption

(i) Internal and external costs

The central issue in determining the social costs of tobacco consumption is distinguishing internal and external costs. Internal costs are costs which are taken into account (and typically borne) by the smoker. The reason why these costs are not subtracted from measured benefits in determining the net social benefit or loss from smoking is as follows. In the standard neo-classical model of consumer behaviour, an individual will smoke when total benefits of smoking exceed total cost from smoking. These are the benefits and costs as perceived by the consumer. If the consumer decides to smoke, then, according to the neo-classical paradigm, internalised costs are offset by benefits which must be at least as great.[7] External costs are costs which are not taken into account by the

---

6. We estimated agricultural supply functions from World Bank data. Our estimated supply elasticities were on the low side (0.2); the literature gives estimates that range from 0.4 to 0.8. We attribute this low elasticity estimate to two factors: firstly, we are estimating short-run elasticities; secondly, there is probably measurement error in the price data. Measurement error tends to bias estimates downwards. We control for year and country fixed effects.
7. In plotting the consumer demand curves, it assumed that the health risks associated with smoking are fixed. Thus consumer surplus arising from the consumption of tobacco products gives the net benefits from smoking, holding the associated health risks fixed. Thus consumer surplus approximates willingness to accept payment, given the existing level of health risks.

decision maker but are imposed upon others. External costs need to be counted explicitly as part of the social costs.

There are three major cost categories to account for. These are the indirect costs arising from premature death and disability, and the net direct costs arising from morbidity. What are external costs associated with premature death and tobacco-related disability? First, there are burdens on taxpayers and the general population. Additional burdens are imposed on taxpayers to the extent that ᵗobacco-related death and disability increase tax-supported disability benefits and pension payments to survivors (widows and dependent children). The general population may incur additional expenses since the presence of smokers may raise life and medical insurance premiums for non-smokers. Second, premature death imposes burdens on family members, that is, loss of income and status and emotional trauma, which can be regarded, at least in part, as an external cost. Some (Manning *et al.*, 1989) have argued that smokers take into account the impact of premature death on family members (the loss of income and emotional trauma that results from premature death is being considered here) and so such costs should be regarded as internal. On the other hand, there is some evidence that family members systematically under-value the benefits and costs accruing to others in the same family. To the extent that these observations apply to smoking, some of the effects of smoking on other family members can be regarded as external costs.[8] If the total benefits from tobacco consumption are B and the total external costs of tobacco consumption are C, then $B-C$ is the net social benefit from tobacco consumption. Assuming a negative $B-C$, this represents the present value of the amount that society would be better off from the initial point of time measured into the indefinite future, if tobacco products were never present.

To finesse the issue of distinguishing external and internal costs directly, the following alternative procedure is proposed. One can estimate the annual total DALYs (disability-adjusted life years) associated with tobacco use for the next 30 years and on into the indefinite future. To convert this flow into a dollar amount, DALYs are multiplied by an amount L which is the external value of a year's loss of life. The present discounted value of this stream of costs is then determined which is denoted as $C(L)$. Then:

$B - C(L) = 0$

is considered as a function of L. The solution of this equation, L^*, is the external value of a year of life that makes the net benefits from tobacco equal to zero. L^* is the amount that society must value a year of life so that it is indifferent between having tobacco products and not having tobacco products. A small value of L^* suggests that the net benefits of tobacco are likely to be negative. One can interpret L^* as the minimum level of external cost that is required for the net benefits of tobacco to be zero.

---

8. The net, direct costs of morbidity may be relatively small to the extent that if individuals didn't acquire tobacco-related diseases, they would instead contract some other equally expensive disease.

There is another more esoteric consideration which comes from the environmental literature. Existence value is the value placed on an object that is not related to any consumption or changes in consumption associated with the good.[9] Put differently, existence value measures the utility obtained from the presence of an entity which does not arise from any direct or indirect interaction with the entity. For example, one may be willing to pay to prevent the extinction of wild Siberian tigers, even though one has no intention of seeking out tigers in the wild; utility is obtained just from knowing that such tigers exist in the wild. Recent work has suggested that on net, income may be transferred from smokers to non-smokers because premature death from tobacco-related illness reduces claims against pension and medical plans, leaving more funds for non-smokers. By the same logic, this suggests that society is, on net, better off when, say, a healthy, single 60-year-old commits suicide. The fact that many find this assertion repellent suggests that for many there is positive existence value which they assign to human life. In other words, collectively there may be a positive existence value placed on the continued good health of individuals even though such individuals are not personally known and the chance of any encounter is effectively zero. One way to interpret L^* is, in the absence of other external costs, that it is the minimum existence value that can be collectively placed on human life such that the net benefits of tobacco are zero. More modestly, part of the external cost of tobacco smoking may arise because of the value placed on the existence of human life, that is, so called existence value.

In comparison, Barnum (1993) assumes that there is a one-time increase in tobacco production of 1 000 metric tons which results in a one-time net increase in output of 500 metric tons. The incremental producer and consumer surplus are just for the initial year; Barnum does not consider a discounted stream of consumer and producer surplus. Barnum then assumes that this increase in production is consumed in the initial year. As a result of this one-time increase in consumption, there are subsequent rises in the death and morbidity rates. The incremental cost of additional deaths, in the Barnum analysis, is US$3.1 million. The incremental cost due to disability and morbidity is US$3.4 million. Barnum also considers the direct cost of added morbidity, at US$2.3 million. The net change in consumer and producer surplus is 1.7 million. Totalling the Barnum figures gives US$7.2 million costs per 1 000 metric tons. Assuming that this marginal rate is also the average rate, this implies a total cost of US$46.8 billion per year (6 500 times US$7.2 million). If it is assumed that this rate is constant over time, the total discounted costs are US$1.7 trillion. The Barnum estimate is for a one-time increase in tobacco production of 1 000 metric tons. If this were sustained indefinitely, then the marginal increase in present discounted value of net benefits would be 7.2/.05 or US$-144 million.

---

9. Existence value was first discussed by Krutilla (1967). A more up to date discussion can be found in "Symposia: Contingent Valuation", published in the *Journal of Economic Perspectives* (1994).

Conclusion

The approach which has been outlined here provides a framework with which to assess the economic impact of tobacco consumption. The approach used here is different to Barnum's approach and has some novel features. Instead of considering an incremental change in tobacco production and then determining the marginal consumer and producer surplus and the incremental costs, total consumer surplus and total producer surplus are considered. The minimum external value that needs to be placed on human life is then considered so that the net social benefit to tobacco consumption is equal to zero.

References

Barnum, H. (1993), *Initial Analysis of the Economic Costs and Benefits of Investing in Tobacco,* unpublished manuscript, Human Development Department, Washington, DC: The World Bank.

Barnum, H. (1994), "The economic burden of the global trade in tobacco", *Tobacco Control,* 3:358-61.

Becker, G.S. and K.M. Murphy (1988), "A theory of rational addiction", *Journal of Political Economy,* 96:675-700.

Becker, G., M. Grossman and K.M. Murphy (1994), "An empirical analysis of cigarette addiction", *American Economic Review,* 84:396-418.

Journal of Economic Perspectives (1994), "Symposia: Contingent Valuation", 8.

Krutilla, J.V. (1967), "Conservation reconsidered," *American Economic Review,* 57:777-86.

Manning, W., E. Keeler, J.P. Newhouse, E. Sloss and J. Wasserman (1989), "The taxes of sin: do smokers and drinkers pay their way?", *Journal of the American Medical Association,* 261:1604-9.

Willig, R. (1976), "Consumer surplus without apology", *American Economic Review,* 66:589-97.

Chapter 11

Trade Policy and Tobacco: Towards an Optimal Policy Mix

Frank Chaloupka and Michaelyn Corbett

Over the past several decades, cigarette consumption in the United States and other developed countries has either fallen or remained relatively stable (see Figure 1). Much of the declines can be attributed to a variety of tobacco control activities, including increased information about the health consequences of cigarette smoking, higher cigarette excise taxes, limits or bans on cigarette advertising and promotion, restrictions on cigarette smoking in public places and private workplaces, and limits on the availability of tobacco products (Chaloupka and Warner, 1998).

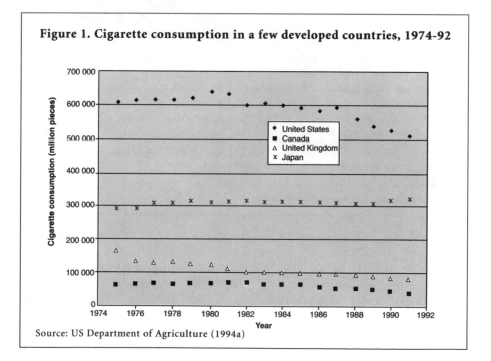

Figure 1. Cigarette consumption in a few developed countries, 1974-92

Source: US Department of Agriculture (1994a)

In contrast, cigarette smoking has risen rapidly in developing and undeveloped countries, particularly in Asia (see Figure 2). In contrast to developed countries, organised tobacco control movements and strong tobacco control policies are rare in these countries. In addition, cigarette smoking appears to be an economically superior behaviour in developing countries, where it is rising with income, in contrast to developed countries where higher income is associated with lower smoking (Chaloupka and Warner, 1998). In response to the rising incomes and cigarette demand in these countries and the opportunities for higher profits, multinational cigarette companies have been aggressively expanding into developing countries in recent years (Holzman, 1997; Mackay and Crofton, 1996).

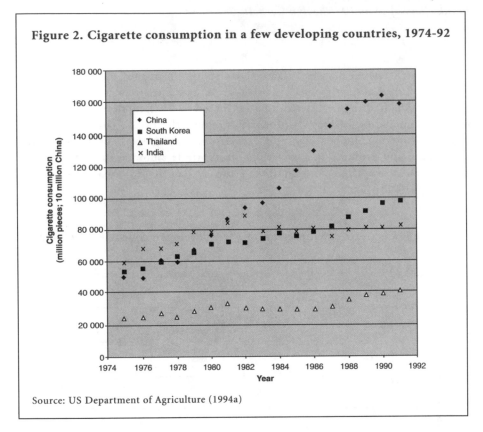

Figure 2. Cigarette consumption in a few developing countries, 1974-92

Source: US Department of Agriculture (1994a)

As a result, global cigarette consumption rose by approximately 50 per cent during 1975-96 (US Department of Agriculture, 1994a; US Department of Agriculture, 1996a). China is by far the world's largest tobacco consumer, accounting for approximately one-third of global consumption, followed by the United States (11 per cent) and India (8 per cent) (see Figure 3).

Recent trends showing declining cigarette consumption but increasing cigarette production in the US are typical of those in many developed countries. In the United States, for example, overall cigarette consumption declined by about 20 per cent during 1975-95, from 607.2 billion cigarettes in 1975 to 487.0 billion in 1995, while total production rose by almost 15 per cent during the same period (US Department of Agriculture, 1994a; 1996b). A 370 per cent surge in cigarette exports accounts for the difference (Figure 4).

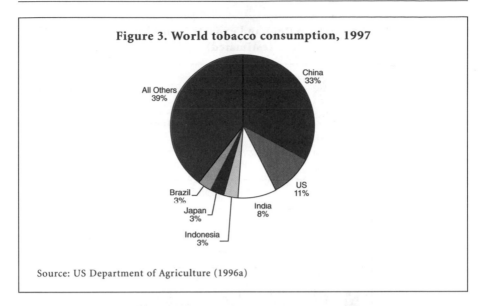

Figure 3. World tobacco consumption, 1997

Source: US Department of Agriculture (1996a)

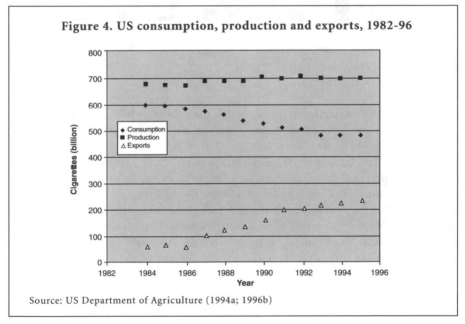

Figure 4. US consumption, production and exports, 1982-96

Source: US Department of Agriculture (1994a; 1996b)

The situation in the United States is similar to that in many of the world's top cigarette producing countries, from which a significant share of total production is exported (see Figure 5). The United States, for example, exported 31 per cent of total production in 1996, while Germany and Brazil exported 38.5 and 34.2 per cent of their cigarette production, respectively (US Department of Agriculture, 1996a). Other major cigarette producing countries, however, produce largely for domestic consumption. China, for example, consumes 96.2

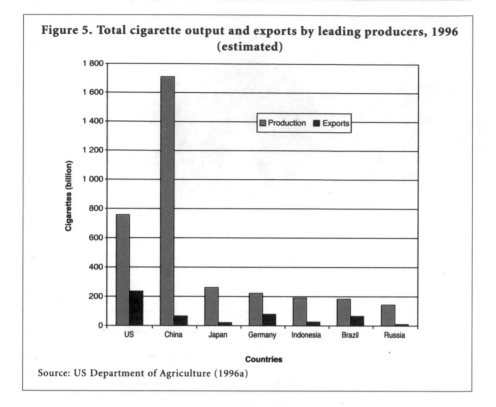

Figure 5. Total cigarette output and exports by leading producers, 1996 (estimated)

Source: US Department of Agriculture (1996a)

per cent of the cigarettes it produces domestically, while Japanese smokers consume 92.4 per cent of domestic cigarette production (US Department of Agriculture, 1996a).

Relatively few countries account for most cigarette exports (see Figure 6). Almost 70 per cent of global cigarette exports come from the seven largest exporting countries. The United States is the world's leading cigarette exporter, accounting for approximately one-quarter of global exports (US Department of Agriculture, 1996a). Some of these countries export much of their production; the Netherlands, for example, exports over 86 per cent of total production, while the United Kingdom exports almost 60 per cent of the cigarettes it produces (US Department of Agriculture, 1996a).

The same is true for cigarette imports, as is seen in Figure 7. Over half of all cigarette imports are received by the seven leading importing countries, with the Russian Federation and Japan each accounting for about 11 per cent of global imports (US Department of Agriculture, 1996a). Asian countries account for nearly one-third of global imports, and are the leading destination of cigarettes exported from the United States, importing nearly 40 per cent of US cigarette exports (US Department of Agriculture, 1996a).

The high levels of trade in cigarettes are a relatively recent phenomenon (see Figure 8). In 1975, for example, just over 5 per cent of total global cigarette production was exported (US Department of Agriculture, 1994a). By 1996,

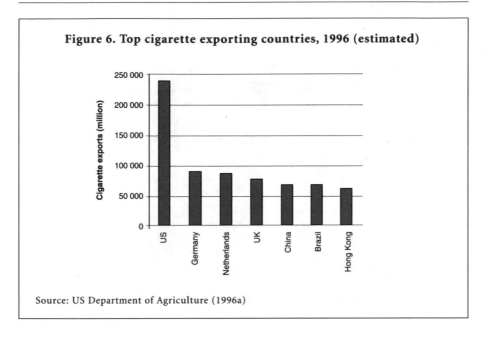

Figure 6. Top cigarette exporting countries, 1996 (estimated)

Source: US Department of Agriculture (1996a)

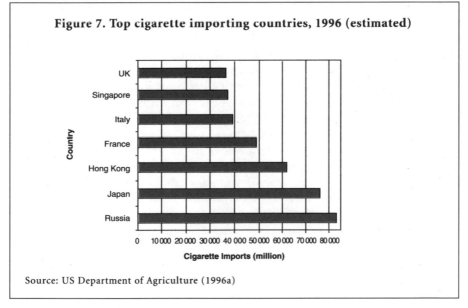

Figure 7. Top cigarette importing countries, 1996 (estimated)

Source: US Department of Agriculture (1996a)

however, 17.5 per cent of total production was exported, with total global cigarette exports nearly six times higher than they were in 1975 (US Department of Agriculture, 1996a). During this time period, there were rapid increases in cigarette exports from all of the leading exporting countries. Much of the increase in cigarette exports went to Asian countries, where imports have risen nearly 15-fold since 1975 (US Department of Agriculture, 1994a; 1996a).

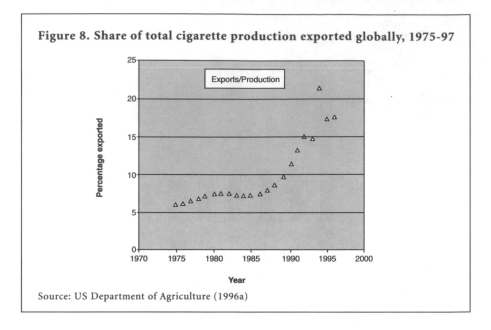

Figure 8. Share of total cigarette production exported globally, 1975-97

Source: US Department of Agriculture (1996a)

A similar pattern emerges for trade in un-manufactured tobacco. Although the land area devoted to tobacco production has declined world-wide, improvements in technology have led to overall increases in tobacco production (Roemer, 1993). In 1997, estimated global production of tobacco was over 7 million tons, with nearly 70 per cent of this accounted for by four countries: China (44.0 per cent), the United States (9.4 per cent), India (7.7 per cent), and Brazil (7.0 per cent) (US Department of Agriculture, 1997a).

In 1997, nearly 27 per cent of all tobacco grown globally was exported (US Department of Agriculture, 1997a). In some tobacco growing countries, nearly all tobacco production is exported, while in others, most is used for the domestic production of cigarettes and other tobacco products. For example, Zimbabwe, the sixth leading tobacco producing country, exported virtually all of its domestically grown tobacco in 1997, while Brazil exported nearly 60 per cent of total production (US Department of Agriculture, 1997a). China, on the other hand, exported less than 3 per cent of the tobacco grown domestically, while the United States, by comparison, exported over one-third of its domestically grown tobacco in 1997 (US Department of Agriculture, 1997a).

Over 50 per cent of global trade in un-manufactured tobacco is imported by six countries (US Department of Agriculture, 1997a). In addition to being a major exporter, the United States is the world's leading importer of raw tobacco, accounting for over 17 per cent of global imports, followed by Germany (12.6 per cent), the Russian Federation (7.5 per cent), the United Kingdom (6.6 per cent), the Netherlands (4.9 per cent) and Japan (4.8 per cent) (US Department of Agriculture, 1997a).

Grise (1990) suggests several reasons for trade in tobacco and tobacco products, including:

- an inability to domestically produce tobacco and tobacco products in sufficient quantity to satisfy domestic demand;
- an inability to domestically produce tobacco and tobacco products of high enough quality to satisfy domestic demand; and
- differences in prices among countries for different types and qualities of tobacco and tobacco products.

In addition, recent trade figures suggest a fourth reason: the importing of un-manufactured tobacco for use in producing tobacco products for export. This appears to have become increasingly important in the United States, the United Kingdom, Germany, the Netherlands, and other major cigarette exporting countries.

The economics of trade barriers

As Grise (1990) notes, world trade in tobacco and tobacco products would be even higher if not for a variety of restrictive trade policies and other policies protecting domestic tobacco growers and producers of tobacco products. These policies include high tariffs on imported tobacco and tobacco products, quotas or complete bans on imports, domestic price support programs, marketing restrictions, licensing requirements, restricted product lists, exchange controls, domestic content requirements, and growing and production subsidies (Grise, 1990). In many cases, these policies have been adopted to protect state-owned monopolies on tobacco production which generate a significant share of total government revenues in these countries.

In general, economic theory predicts that barriers to trade in tobacco and tobacco products will reduce the total supply of tobacco and tobacco products, while raising the quantity supplied by domestic growers and producers. Consequently, the prices for raw tobacco, cigarettes, and other tobacco products will be higher. Given the well-documented effects of price on cigarette smoking and other tobacco consumption (Chaloupka and Warner, 1998), higher prices will lead to less smoking and lower use of other tobacco products, and consequently to reductions in the long-run health consequences of tobacco use. Domestic suppliers will benefit from their higher level of growing and production and from the higher prices they receive. Foreign suppliers, however, will lose as a result of their reduced access to protected markets.

Trade liberalisation

Much of the recent explosion in global trade in tobacco and tobacco products is likely to be the result of a variety of bilateral, regional, and multilateral trade agreements that have significantly reduced trade barriers for a wide variety of goods and services, including un-manufactured tobacco, cigarettes, and other tobacco products. The most far-reaching multilateral trade agreement is the General Agreement on Tariffs and Trade (GATT). The most recently completed round, the Uruguay round completed in 1994, included 117 member countries; in addition, many non-member countries agree to abide by the provisions of the

GATT. The general principles of the GATT include:
* a commitment to achieving free trade and fair competition;
* limits on, and eventual elimination of, tariff and non-tariff barriers to trade;
* the non-discriminatory treatment of all trading partners;
* the non-discriminatory treatment of domestically produced and foreign products;
* predictability, by ensuring that trade barriers are not erected arbitrarily;
* negotiated elimination of trade barriers and settlement of trade disputes; and
* opposition to retaliatory trade sanctions (World Trade Organisation, 1998a).

Since the conclusion of its first round in 1948, the GATT has led to sharp reductions in tariffs and non-tariff barriers to trade in manufactured goods. Consequently, global trade in manufactured goods and world incomes have risen significantly (World Trade Organisation, 1998a). Before the most recently completed round, trade in services and agricultural commodities, including un-manufactured tobacco, was not covered by the GATT. The 1994 Uruguay round, however, significantly expanded the coverage of the GATT to include trade in agricultural commodities, services, and more. Moreover, the new agreement created the World Trade Organisation to help the GATT better resolve trade disputes (World Trade Organisation, 1998a).

The 1994 agreement called for significant reductions in tariff and non-tariff barriers to trade in tobacco products. For example, it called on the European Union to reduce its tariffs on cigars by 50 per cent, on cigarettes and other manufactured tobacco products by 36 per cent, and on un-manufactured tobacco by 20 per cent (US Department of Agriculture, 1997b). Similarly, the United States was supposed to eliminate its tariffs on cigar wrappers and reduce its tariffs on cigar filler and binder tobacco, cigars, and most cigarettes by 55 per cent, on tobacco stems and refuse by 20 per cent, and on other manufactured and smoking tobacco by 15 per cent (US Department of Agriculture, 1997b). Furthermore, it led to the elimination of domestic content legislation that required that all cigarettes produced in the United States contain at least 75 per cent domestically grown tobacco. In addition, the agreement led to the elimination of or reduction in tariff and non-tariff barriers to trade in tobacco and tobacco products in numerous other countries (US Department of Agriculture, 1997b).

In addition to the GATT, there are a number of multilateral trade agreements aimed at liberalising trade among countries in various regions. The World Trade Organisation, for example, reports that nearly all of its members have entered into regional trade agreements, with over 80 of these agreements currently in force (World Trade Organisation, 1998b). Many of these agreements have significantly reduced barriers to trade among member countries in a wide variety of goods and services, including tobacco and tobacco products. Major agreements and/or regional trade associations that have either significantly reduced trade barriers and/or are working for further trade liberalisation include: the North American Free Trade Area (NAFTA), the European Union (EU), the Association of South East Asian Nations (ASEAN), the Common Market of Eastern and Southern Africa (COMESA), the Economic

Community of West African States (ECOWAS), the Organisation of American States (OAS), and many others.

In addition to the international and regional trade agreements, there are numerous bilateral trade agreements. Several of these specifically address trade in un-manufactured tobacco and tobacco products, including the bilateral agreements between the United States and Japan, South Korea, Taiwan, and Thailand resulting from actions taken by the United States Trade Representative under Section 301 of the Trade Act of 1974 (discussed below).

The economics of trade liberalisation

Economic theory implies that trade liberalisation will significantly increase trade in goods and services, including tobacco and tobacco products. The reduction of trade barriers will lead to increased competition in the markets for these products, which should lower prices, particularly in cigarette and other tobacco product markets that had been monopolised and protected in the past. In addition, the entry of new firms into these markets is likely to be accompanied by significant increases in marketing and promotion, as the new entrants attempt to establish a foothold in the markets and compete with the existing domestic firms. Domestic tobacco growers and producers are likely to face reduced demand for their products, while foreign producers will see increased demand for their products. In the case of government-run monopolies, the reductions in price and demand for their products will lead to significant reductions in government revenue from these products.

Since overall market demand responds to changes in price and advertising, cigarette smoking and consumption of other tobacco products are likely to rise as a result of trade liberalisation. The prevalence of tobacco use will likely increase, as well as the consumption of these products by continuing users. As a result, the long-term health consequences of cigarette smoking and other tobacco use are likely to be exacerbated by trade liberalisation.

The agreements reached in the Uruguay round appear to have had a dramatic impact on global trade in tobacco and tobacco products. From 1994 to 1997, for example, there was a 12.5 per cent increase in un-manufactured tobacco exports globally after over a decade of virtually no growth (US Department of Agriculture, 1994a; 1997a). Similarly, the upward trend in cigarette exports appears to have been accelerated by the 1994 agreement, with global cigarette exports rising by 42 per cent during 1993-96. Global cigarette consumption rose by over 5 per cent during the same period (US Department of Agriculture, 1994a; 1996a).

The liberalisation of trade in all goods and services is expected to have a number of positive economic effects, including increased incomes, greater employment, and more stable prices (World Trade Organisation, 1998a), with perhaps the greatest impact in developing countries (Dollar, 1992; Edwards, 1992). Past research and recent data provides strong evidence on the link between income and health, particularly at low income levels (Preston, 1976) (see Figures 9 and 10). In aggregate, the evidence suggests that trade liberalisation leads to improved health outcomes.

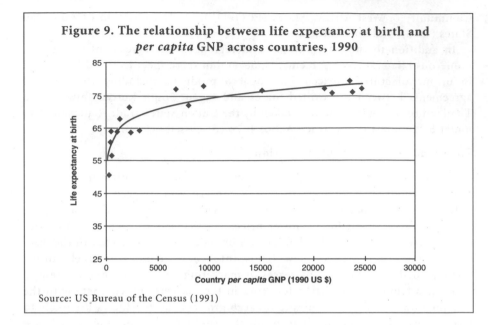

Figure 9. The relationship between life expectancy at birth and *per capita* GNP across countries, 1990

Source: US Bureau of the Census (1991)

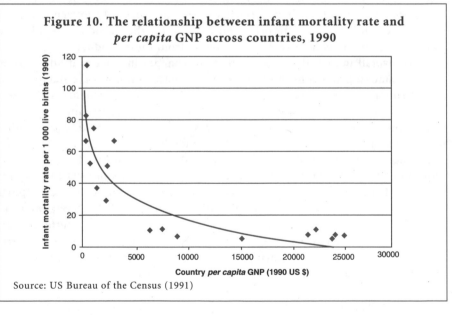

Figure 10. The relationship between infant mortality rate and *per capita* GNP across countries, 1990

Source: US Bureau of the Census (1991)

Case studies of trade liberalisation and cigarette smoking: the Section 301 cases

Section 301 of the 1974 Trade Act gave the President of the United States the authority to investigate unjustifiable, unreasonable or discriminatory trade practices used by other countries to limit access by US companies to their markets. When such practices were identified, the 1974 Act called for negotiations to eliminate them and allowed the President to impose retaliatory trade sanctions if the negotiations proved unsuccessful. Amendments to the 1974 Trade Act in 1984 and 1988 significantly strengthened Section 301, more recently known as "Super 301". These amendments made the process more formal by requiring the US Trade Representative to annually identify countries and their trading practices that limit the access of US firms to their markets. Once these practices have been identified, the US Trade Representative is supposed to negotiate for their elimination. Mandatory retaliatory trade sanctions are to be imposed if the negotiations to eliminate these practices fail.

Two minor cases involving Japanese barriers to trade in cigars and pipe tobacco were brought under Section 301 in 1979 at the prompting of the Cigar Association of America and the Associated Tobacco Manufacturers. The two cases were eventually combined and led to an agreement enabling US cigar and pipe tobacco producers to gain some access to Japanese markets.

The more significant Section 301 cases dealt with cigarettes and were usually prompted by the United States Cigarette Export Association (USCEA). This association is a cartel created by Philip Morris, R.J. Reynolds and Brown and Williamson to increase their cigarette exports to foreign markets. While US antitrust laws prohibit this type of cartel activity in US markets, they allow it in foreign markets. Asian countries were the first targets of the cartel. For many years, US cigarette producers had tried to develop a significant presence in many Asian markets, but were generally unsuccessful. This failure was largely due to a variety of trade barriers, including high tariffs, quotas, bans on imports, limits on advertising and distribution, and other non-tariff barriers to trade. In most cases, the trade barriers protected a domestic, state-run monopoly on production and distribution that generated a significant share of total government revenue.

In the mid- to late-1980s, four Asian countries were targeted by the USCEA for actions under Section 301. The first of the Section 301 cases was brought against Japan. Historically, the Japanese tobacco industry was monopolised by the Japan Tobacco Company which was protected by high tariffs on imported cigarettes, Japanese distribution practices which discriminated against imported cigarettes, and other non-tariff barriers to trade. The Reagan Administration initiated an investigation of the Japanese trade practices in late 1985, threatening retaliatory trade sanctions if they were not eliminated. A bilateral agreement was reached between Japan and the United States in October 1986. This agreement eliminated the trade barriers and opened the Japanese cigarette markets to US producers. Existing Japanese policies with respect to cigarette advertising and promotion were not affected by the agreement.

After the Japanese markets were opened, there was a significant increase in cigarette advertising in Japan resulting not only from aggressive marketing by US cigarette producers, but also from a significant increase in advertising by the Japan Tobacco Company. At the same time, Japanese cigarette consumption began increasing, reversing the downward trend prior to the agreement, with the most noticeable increases in smoking among women and youth (Connolly and Chen, 1993).

Shortly after the agreement with Japan, a similar pact was negotiated with Taiwan (see Chapter 24). Historically, the tobacco industry in Taiwan was monopolised by the government's Taiwan Tobacco and Wine Monopoly Bureau. The domestic monopoly was protected by high tariffs on imported cigarettes that made them three times more expensive than domestic brands, and a number of non-tariff barriers to trade. These restrictions limited the market share of foreign cigarette brands in Taiwan to less than 1 per cent. In late 1986, the Reagan Administration initiated a Section 301 investigation of the Taiwanese cigarette markets. Less than two months later, a bilateral agreement was signed opening Taiwan's cigarette markets to US producers. The agreement contained several tobacco control-related provisions, including a required health warning label on all cigarette packaging, and restrictions on advertising and promotional activities. After the agreement, there was a rapid rise in US cigarette exports to Taiwan accompanied by a sharp increase in cigarette advertising and promotion. In addition, the Taiwan Tobacco and Wine Monopoly Bureau significantly increased its imports of higher quality US-grown tobacco for use in domestic cigarette production. *Per capita* cigarette consumption rose sharply in 1987, but fell somewhat since in response to Taiwanese tobacco control activities. Nevertheless, *per capita* consumption remains higher than it was prior to the opening of Taiwan's cigarette markets (Hsieh and Hu, 1997).

After the successes in opening the Japanese and Taiwanese cigarette markets, the USCEA petitioned the US Trade Representative to begin a Section 301 investigation of the South Korean cigarette markets in early 1988. Historically, the Tobacco and Ginseng Corporation controlled all aspects of tobacco growing and production in South Korea, and was protected by high tariffs on foreign cigarettes. In addition, in 1982, the South Korean government enacted and aggressively enforced legislation making it a criminal offence to sell, buy or possess foreign cigarettes (Eddy and Walden, 1993). Moreover, in 1987, nearly all cigarette advertising and promotion was banned by the Tobacco Monopoly Act. A bilateral agreement was reached between South Korea and the United States in May, 1988. The agreement opened South Korean cigarette markets to US producers by eliminating the ban on foreign cigarettes, reducing the tariff on imported cigarettes, allowing the distribution of free samples, and allowing some cigarette advertising and promotion. Under the agreement, cigarette packages are required to contain a health warning label and advertising targeting women and children is prohibited.

After the opening of cigarette markets in South Korea, the rate of growth in smoking nearly tripled (Roemer, 1993). Much of the increase in smoking was the result of increased consumption of imported cigarettes, and part of the increase may be attributable to an increase in advertising by US cigarette companies. In late 1988, South Korea passed the Tobacco Business Act limiting advertising and promotional activities to point-of-purchase advertising, magazine advertising and sponsorship of public events (US General Accounting Office, 1992). In 1991, the South Korean tobacco monopoly and the USCEA developed a voluntary marketing agreement to comply with the Tobacco

Business Act and the bilateral trade agreement. However, the South Korean government alleged that some promotional activities of US cigarette companies violated the spirit of the agreement. As a result, the agreement opening the tobacco markets was modified in 1995 to allow the South Korean government greater flexibility in imposing non-discriminatory, health-focused measures for reducing tobacco use, including stronger limits on advertising and promotion.

The final and most contentious tobacco-related Section 301 case was brought by the US Trade Representative against Thailand in 1989 at the request of the USCEA. Historically, the Thai cigarette market was controlled by a government-run monopoly protected by a virtual ban on the import of cigarettes. The domestic monopoly voluntarily stopped its cigarette advertising and promotion in April, 1988. Foreign companies, however, continued their activities, prompting the government to enact a complete ban on cigarette advertising in Thailand in 1989. Unlike Japan, Taiwan, and South Korea, the Thai government did not quickly agree to open its cigarette markets to US producers. Instead, the US and Thailand agreed to take their argument before the GATT dispute resolution process.

In October, 1990, the GATT Council ruled that the Thai ban on cigarette imports was a violation of the international trade treaty and that the Thai cigarette markets should be opened to foreign producers (General Agreement on Tariffs and Trade, 1990). However, the GATT has long recognised that countries can adopt policies to protect human life or health, as long as they are applied in a non-discriminatory way to domestic and foreign firms. Given this, the GATT Council upheld the Thai government's right to impose the same cigarette excise tax on US-produced cigarettes as on domestically produced cigarettes (General Agreement on Tariffs and Trade, 1990). More importantly, the Council upheld the government's right to ban all cigarette advertising by domestic and foreign producers, even if the ban made it more difficult for foreign entrants to compete with the established domestic monopoly (General Agreement on Tariffs and Trade, 1990). The decision by the GATT Council clearly indicates that strong tobacco control policies aimed at reducing the death and disease associated with tobacco use can be adopted and implemented without hindering free trade.

The GATT ruling led to a bilateral trade agreement between Thailand and the United States in November 1990 that opened the Thai cigarette markets to US producers, and subjected US cigarettes to the same laws and regulations applied to domestically produced cigarettes. After its success in upholding its ban on advertising and promotion, the Thai government enacted two additional strong tobacco control policies in 1992. The Non-Smokers Health Protection Act restricted smoking in a variety of public places, while the Tobacco Products Control Act required that the ingredients of all tobacco products be disclosed (a provision yet to be fully implemented), allowed the Ministry of Public Health to determine all aspects of labelling, including health warnings, and banned the following: smoking by those under 18 years of age; vending machine sales; distribution of free samples, exchanges, and gifts of cigarettes; tobacco advertising (including the use of cigarette logos and other symbols on non-tobacco products), except in international magazines and on live telecasts originating outside Thailand; advertising products with the same name as tobacco products; producing, importing, advertising, and selling products imitating tobacco products; and selling cigarettes not complying with the labelling provisions (Roemer, 1993).

The combination of these policies has limited the impact of US entry into the Thai cigarette markets on smoking in Thailand. Thai imports of US cigarettes rose from less than 1 per cent of the market prior to the agreement to about 4 per cent in 1993. There have been some increases in smoking prevalence among women and young people (US Department of Agriculture, 1994a), but *per capita* consumption has changed little in the early 1990s (World Health Organisation, 1997).

Chaloupka and Laixuthai (1996) empirically examined the impact on cigarette smoking of the United States' use of Section 301 to force open the domestic cigarette markets of other countries. The cigarette industry argued that their presence in these markets does not impact on overall cigarette smoking, but affects only brand choice. To quote a Philip Morris spokeswoman, "The same number of cigarettes is consumed whether American cigarettes are present or not. Whatever one may feel about the smoking and health controversy, the presence or absence of American cigarettes is not a consumption factor" (Shenon, 1994). Critics of the industry, however, contend that cigarette smoking increases as a result of the US presence, particularly among women and children who, they argue, are targeted by multimillion dollar advertising and promotional campaigns (Holzman, 1997; Mackay and Crofton, 1996; Shenon, 1994; Sesser, 1993; Eddy and Walden, 1993).

Chaloupka and Laixuathai (1996) addressed this question by constructing a database containing annual information for 10 Asian countries — the four countries affected by the Section 301 cases and six control countries — for the period 1970-91. The outcome variables they analysed were *per capita* cigarette consumption and the market share of US cigarettes. Key independent variables included an indicator for the years in which the Section 301 agreements applied and a measure of income. Given the lack of consistent data across countries and over time on other key determinants of cigarette smoking, they estimated fixed effects models to control for other unmeasured country-specific and time-specific influences on demand.

Chaloupka and Laixuthai (1996) conclude that there was a substantial rise in the market share of US cigarettes in the countries affected by the bilateral trade agreements. Their estimates imply that US market shares were 600 per cent higher in 1991 than they would have been in the absence of these agreements. These estimates are consistent with the industry arguments that brand switching will occur in response to the presence of US companies in formerly closed, monopolised markets.

More importantly, they conclude that overall cigarette smoking rose as a result of the Section 301 agreements. Chaloupka and Laixuthai (1996) estimate that *per capita* cigarette consumption in 1991 was 10 per cent higher, on average, in the four countries than it would have been had the markets remained closed to US cigarettes. Moreover, their estimates imply that *per capita* consumption would rise by as much as 7.5 per cent in China and other Asian countries with closed markets if they were to open their markets to US producers. These findings are clearly inconsistent with the industry arguments that overall cigarette smoking is not affected by the presence of US firms.

As described above, economic theory and previous research on cigarette demand suggest two reasons for increases in smoking in response to trade liberalisation. Economic theory predicts that prices will be highest in monopolised markets. Prior to trade liberalisation, the tobacco product markets in Japan, Taiwan, South Korea, and Thailand were all effectively monopolised with a single firm controlling well over 90 per cent of the market. These monopolies were protected by high tariff and non-tariff barriers to trade and, consequently, were likely to be setting high prices for cigarettes and other tobacco products. The elimination of the trade barriers and the subsequent entry of US firms is likely to have made the markets much more competitive, which in turn is expected to have reduced prices. Given the available evidence on the price-sensitivity of cigarette demand, the lower prices would result in higher cigarette consumption. Recent evidence from Taiwan supports this argument: Hsieh and Hu (1997) show that inflation-adjusted prices for both imported cigarettes and domestic cigarettes fell sharply after the Taiwanese cigarette market was opened to US cigarette producers. In addition, Hsieh and Hu conclude that cigarette demand in Taiwan is relatively more price-sensitive than demand in more developed countries. The combination of the two, therefore, led to a significant increase in smoking in Taiwan. The same is likely to have happened in the other affected countries.

A second factor which more than likely contributed to the increase in smoking following conclusion of the Section 301 agreements is the increased cigarette advertising and promotion that occurred after the opening of the markets. As noted above, after markets were opened, cigarette advertising and promotion increased sharply in most of the countries affected by the Section 301 agreements. In Japan, for example, total cigarette advertising and promotion by US cigarette companies nearly doubled between 1987 and 1990, and the Japan Tobacco Company responded by increasing its advertising as well. As a result, cigarettes went from being the 40th most advertised product on Japanese television to being the second most advertised (Sesser, 1993). Hagihara and Takeshita (1995) conclude that US cigarette advertising significantly increased the market share of US cigarettes in Osaka, and suggest that this advertising may explain the increase in smoking prevalence among young Japanese women in the late 1980s. Again, given the evidence on the effects of advertising and promotion on cigarette demand, part of the increased smoking found in the other countries with Section 301 agreements is likely to be the result of increased cigarette advertising after their cigarette markets were opened.

The Clinton Administration, unlike its predecessors, has not used Section 301 to pry open tobacco markets for US cigarette producers. Former US Trade Representative Mickey Kantor, for example, stated that his office "would no longer oppose countries that want to restrict cigarette advertising or enact other health measures even if those measures violate provisions of trade agreements with the United States", and went on to say that the Clinton "Administration believes that health-based regulations (in other countries) are legitimate and that we ought to adhere to them" (Sesser, 1993). In addition, the Clinton Administration has included a representative from the US Department of Health and Human Services in trade negotiations related to tobacco.

More recently, this philosophy was formalised by the Doggett amendment to the 1998 appropriations act for the US Department of Commerce which states that: "None of the funds provided by this Act shall be available to promote the sale or export of tobacco or tobacco products, or to seek the reduction or removal by any foreign country of restrictions on the marketing of tobacco or tobacco products, except for restrictions which are not applied equally to all tobacco or tobacco products of the same type" (Public Law 105-119). In addition to notifying them of this provision, all US diplomatic posts were informed of new guidelines on trade and tobacco control activities in February, 1998. These guidelines encourage posts to assist in tobacco control efforts in host countries and discourage them from promoting the sale or export of tobacco and tobacco products or from assisting US firms or individuals in doing this (National Economic Council and National Security Council of the White House, 1998).

Conclusion

Global trade in tobacco and tobacco products has exploded over the past 25 years, at least partly in response to the numerous international, regional, and bilateral trade agreements that have significantly reduced high tariff and non-tariff barriers to trade in these products. Economic theory and the empirical evidence clearly suggests that the liberalisation of trade in tobacco and tobacco products has led to increases in tobacco use and, consequently, will lead to increases in the death and disease burden attributable to tobacco. This does not, however, imply that erecting high barriers to trade in tobacco and tobacco products should be a part of a country's optimal mix of tobacco control policies.

The decision by the GATT Council in the US *versus* Thailand case, and the shift in US tobacco-related trade policy under the Clinton Administration, make it clear that strong tobacco control policies aimed at reducing the health consequences of tobacco use are consistent with international trade agreements, *as long as these policies are applied evenly to domestic and foreign cigarettes and other tobacco products.* Discriminatory tobacco control policies or barriers to trade in tobacco and tobacco products, however, can not be defended under multinational trade agreements, and are likely to invite sanctions under these agreements and/or retaliatory measures affecting trade in other goods and services.

Given the economic benefits of free trade and the clear link between income and health, the health benefits of trade liberalisation almost certainly exceed the health consequences resulting from the liberalisation of trade in tobacco and tobacco products. Given this, both strong tobacco control policies and trade liberalisation are likely to be key ingredients in the optimal policy mix aimed at improving a country's overall health and welfare.

References

Chaloupka, F.J. and A. Laixuthai (1996), *US Trade Policy and Cigarette Smoking in Asia*, Working Paper No. 5543, Cambridge, Mass: National Bureau of Economic Research.

Chaloupka, F.J. and K.E. Warner (1998), "Smoking", in Newhouse, J.P. and A. Cuyler (eds.), *Handbook of Health Economics*, Amsterdam: North-Holland (in press).

Connolly, G. and T. Chen (1993), "International Health and Tobacco Use", in Houston, T.P. (ed.), *Tobacco Use: an American Crisis. Final Conference Report and Recommendations from America's Health Community: January 9-12*, 1993, Chicago: American Medical Association.

Dollar, D. (1992), "Outward-oriented developing economies really do grow more rapidly: evidence from 95 LDCs, 1976-85", *Economic Development and Cultural Change*, 40:523-44.

Eddy, P. and S. Walden (1993), "Invasion", *Telegraph Magazine*, May 22:18-32.

Edwards, S. (1992), "Trade orientation, distortions and growth in developing countries", *Journal of Development Economics*, 39:31-58.

General Agreement on Tariffs and Trade (GATT) (1990), *Thailand — Restrictions on Importation of and Internal Taxes on Cigarettes. Report of the Panel*, Geneva: GATT.

Grise, V.N. (1990), *The World Tobacco Markets — Government Intervention and Multilateral Policy Reform*, Staff Report No. AGES 9014, Commodity Economics Division, Economic Research Service, Washington, DC: US Department of Agriculture.

Hagihara, A. and Y.J. Takeshita (1995), "Impact of American cigarette advertising on imported cigarette consumption in Osaka, Japan", *Tobacco Control*, 4:239-44.

Holzman, D. (1997), "Tobacco abroad: infiltrating foreign markets", *Environmental Health Perspectives*, 105:178-83.

Hsieh, C.R. and T.W. Hu (1997), *The Demand for Cigarettes in Taiwan: Domestic versus Imported Cigarettes*, Discussion Paper Number 9701, The Institute of Economics, Academia Sinica.

Mackay, J. and J. Crofton (1996), "Tobacco and the developing world", *British Medical Bulletin*, 52:206-21.

National Economic Council and the National Security Council of the White House (1998), *FINAL Guidelines on Health, Trade, and Commercial Issues*, Washington, DC: National Economic Council and the National Security Council of the White House.

Preston, S.H. (1976), *Mortality Patterns in National Populations*, New York: Academic Press.

Roemer, R. (1993), *Legislative Action to Combat the World Tobacco Epidemic*, Geneva: World Health Organisation.

Sesser, S. (1993), "Opium war redux", *The New Yorker*, 69:78-89.

Shenon, P., "Asia's having one huge nicotine fit", *The New York Times*, 15 May, S4:1.

US Bureau of the Census (1991), *World Population Profile*, Washington, DC: US Bureau of the Census.

US Department of Agriculture (1994a), *US Tobacco Statistics, 1935-1992*, Economic Research Service, Washington, DC: US Department of Agriculture.

US Department of Agriculture (1994b), *Tobacco Situation and Outlook Report*, Economic Research Service, Washington, DC: US Department of Agriculture.

US Department of Agriculture (1996a), *Tobacco: World Markets and Trade*, Foreign Agricultural Service, Washington, DC: US Department of Agriculture.

US Department of Agriculture (1996b), *Tobacco Situation and Outlook Report*, Economic Research Service, Washington, DC: US Department of Agriculture.

US Department of Agriculture (1997a), *Tobacco: World Markets and Trade*, Foreign Agricultural Service, Washington, DC: US Department of Agriculture.

US Department of Agriculture (1997b), *GATT/WTO and Tobacco*, http://www.fas.usda.gov/itp/policy/gatt/tobacco.html.

US General Accounting Office (1992), *International Trade: Advertising and Promoting U.S. Cigarettes in Selected Asian Countries*, Washington DC: US General Accounting Office.

World Health Organisation (1997), *Tobacco or Health: A Global Status Report*, Geneva: World Health Organisation.

World Trade Organisation (1998a), *About the WTO*, http://www.wto.org/wto/about.

World Trade Organisation (1998b), *Development: Regionalism and Multilateral Trading*, http://www.wto. org/wto/devlop/regional.htm.

Chapter 12

Tobacco Smuggling: an Optimal Policy Approach

Luk Joossens

Incentives for smuggling

The laws of supply and demand dictate that the more expensive a product is, the fewer people will be inclined to buy it. Despite the fact that tobacco is an addictive product, price has, nevertheless, been shown to have an important influence on consumption. Taxation has often been considered as one of the most effective measures for reducing consumption. The tobacco industry opposes tax increases and is using the smuggling argument more and more to contest them.

The threat of smuggling has been used by the tobacco industry in order to persuade Ministers of Finance not to raise taxes on tobacco products. In the past few years, governments in many countries have become concerned about smuggling, because it can lead to loss of tax revenue. According to the tobacco industry the smuggling problem can be explained in the following way:

1. smuggling is increasing and is a real problem in many countries (with a slight tendency to overestimate the number of smuggled cigarettes);
2. smuggling is an organised crime, with cheap cigarettes moving from countries with a lower tax to countries with a higher tax;
3. the only solution to the problem of smuggling is to lower cigarette taxes, as Canada did in 1994;
4. any increase in taxes will lead to an increase in smuggling and a loss of revenue for governments;
5. smuggling is damaging for the image of the industry. It is not the tobacco industry but organised crime that is responsible for smuggling.

While it is true that the incentive for smuggling is the avoidance of taxes, it is not always true that smuggling is linked to the level of taxes. For example, in countries with the highest taxes in Europe, such as the Scandinavian countries, there is little evidence of smuggling, while in Spain, Italy and many Central and Eastern European countries, where taxes and prices are much lower, the illegal sale of international cigarette brands is widespread.

Smuggling in Europe does not involve the movement of cigarettes from the cheaper South to the more expensive North, but the illegal movement of duty-free imported international brands from Northern ports to the South and the East. The truth about smuggling is that the tobacco companies are the chief beneficiaries of this illegal trade. The tobacco industry benefits from smuggling in different ways. First, they gain their normal profit by selling the cigarettes (legally) to distributors. The cigarettes then find their way on to the black market to be sold at greatly reduced prices, stimulating demand. This puts pressure on governments not to increase tax because of the loss of revenue, which may also result in lower prices and higher consumption. Then the industry uses this to urge governments to reduce, or not to increase taxes. Finally, contraband cigarettes that are intercepted by customs have to be replaced — yet more sales (Joossens and Raw, 1995).

Transnational tobacco companies lay the groundwork for smuggling by introducing top brands at reduced prices to encourage low-income consumers in developing countries to buy the much desired Western brands and to penetrate closed markets. According to an analysis in the *New York Times* in 1997, the transnational companies may be involved in smuggling, and have avoided taking significant measures to reduce it (Bonner and Drew, 1997).

Country examples

Argentina: in the early 1960s, the entry of transnational companies (TNCs) into the Latin American market had a strong temporal relationship with contraband trafficking in cigarettes. Contraband was used in order to open the closed domestic markets for TNCs. Contraband rose from 2 per cent to 12 per cent of total consumption. Only when all the nationally-owned firms were acquired by TNCs did contraband finally decline in the early 1970s (US Department of Health and Human Services, 1992).

Italy: this country has the longest history of smuggling in Europe. The production of cigarettes is controlled by state monopoly. Despite a ban on advertising since 1963, brands made by Philip Morris were able to conquer and dominate the cigarette market, having a market share of more than 50 per cent in 1996. Marlboro is by far the most commonly smuggled brand in Italy, and contraband Marlboro is sold at a cheaper price than the price of the leading national brand, MS. The Italian state monopoly lost the battle for market share against cigarettes made by Philip Morris; the main explanation was smuggling.

Bulgaria: is one of the few countries in Eastern Europe which still has a state-controlled tobacco industry. It is also one of the poorest countries in Europe with an average income of US$90 a month in 1996. In 1995 the consumption of domestic cigarettes was estimated to be 13 billion cigarettes. Illegal imports were estimated to be about 5 billion cigarettes or 38 per cent of the legal sales. American cigarettes are popular among young people, but most are unable to buy them at the official price. The official price of a pack of Marlboro in 1997 was US$3, the price of smuggled or counterfeit Marlboro only US$1. At the official price the market for American cigarettes would have been extremely limited.

China: this country is the biggest cigarette market in the world. Smuggling of cigarettes has already started and it has been estimated that some 40 billion cigarettes are smuggled into China every year (*Tobacco Reporter*, 1997).

The advantages of smuggling for transnational companies are even described in tobacco trade documents. The trade journal *World Tobacco* (1996) admitted in a recent report that: "Although sales of contraband cigarettes have affected the level of income that governments world-wide derive from tobacco sales, smuggling has also helped to promote some of the world's leading brands in markets which previously remained closed to foreign imports and where demand for Western cigarettes continued to grow."

Not the local tobacco industry, but the big multinationals benefit from smuggling. "Whose brands sell best in contraband trade? Traditional smuggling has focused on well-known international brands, since instant recognition and confidence in the merchandise are essential to these quick, furtive transactions. Smugglers are impatient of little-known brands. They focus on what the multinationals make." (Barford, 1993)

How big is the problem?

The magnitude of the smuggling problem can be estimated by looking at the difference between global exports and imports; most of the "missing" cigarettes are smuggled. World cigarette production is known fairly accurately, and since cigarettes do not keep indefinitely, world production is very close to world consumption, i.e. there are no large quantities of cigarettes in storage. Global imports should thus be close to exports, after allowing for legitimate trade usually excluded from national statistics. (These are principally imports for duty-free sales to travellers, to the diplomatic community, and military establishments.) But for many years imports have been lower than exports to a degree that cannot be adequately explained by legitimate duty-free sales. Although the volume of duty-free trade is not on public record, it has been estimated with some confidence by the tobacco trade at about 45 billion cigarettes a year. Even the time lag of three to six months between recording export and import statistics cannot explain the export-import differences, which have remained at high levels for years (Joossens and Raw, 1995).

Table 1. World cigarette imports and exports (billions of sticks)

	Imports	Exports	Difference
1975	171	223	42
1980	254	323	69
1985	313	356	43
1990	418	543	125
1991	526	712	186
1992	568	804	236
1993	600	780	179
1994	886	1 156	270
1995	668	987	319
1996	707	1 107	400

Source: US Department of Agriculture (1997a)

Table 1 shows annual global exports and imports during 1975-96. There has been a steady increase in the number of missing cigarettes. In 1996, 1 107 billion cigarettes were exported but only 707 billion imported, a difference of 400 billion. After deducting 45 billion for legitimate duty free sales, there are still almost 355 billion cigarettes missing. The only plausible explanation for these missing cigarettes is smuggling.

(i) Smuggling in Europe

In 1997 a Committee of the European Parliament published a report of over 1 000 pages on the transit trade in the European Union (European Parliament, 1997). Transit is a concession system aimed at facilitating trade, and allows the temporary suspension of custom duties, excise and VAT payable on goods originating from and/or destined for a third country while under transport across the territory of a defined customs area. The following example illustrates. Cigarettes from the United States are entering Antwerp for onward transport to North Africa. In this case, the goods would be placed under a transit regime for transport by road from Antwerp to Spain, from where they would be shipped to North Africa. Provided the re-export of goods is confirmed, no taxes would be due in the European Union. Fraud occurs when these duty-free goods, destined for a country outside the EU, are sold on the black market within the EU. Transit fraud and related criminal activities cover a wide range of products, but tend to be focused on so-called sensitive goods. According to the Committee, the product most consistently targeted by transit fraudsters has been cigarettes. The market for contraband cigarettes in the European Union appears to be in the region of 60 billion cigarettes annually, with a consequent loss of excise revenue of US$6 billion a year (Barford, 1993).

The attractiveness of cigarettes to the fraudster lies in the magnitude of the difference between the duty-free and the duty-paid price of a cigarette, giving scope for substantial profits even at the relatively low street prices needed to attract the consumer. The attractiveness of cigarettes to the fraudster is further enhanced by their relative ease of handling. Other high-tax products, such as petroleum products, or even alcohol, although frequently the subject of fraud, cannot compete with cigarettes on a tax-value per weight basis (see Table 2), nor in terms of the conditions required for their transport. One so-called "masterpack" of 10 000 cigarettes is the size of the sort of cardboard box common in supermarkets. A container load of cigarettes carries a potential fiscal value of about US$1.2 million, almost all of which is potential profit for the smuggler.

Large-scale smuggling also requires a willing market and a good local distribution network to supply it. Such markets and networks have existed for many years, especially in Italy and Spain where tobacco smuggling is a long-standing problem. The recent expansion in cigarette smuggling has therefore, to some degree, exploited these countries as a base for its infiltration of markets in the rest of the EU, this being most spectacularly the case in Germany, where the activities of Vietnamese gangs made headlines in the spring of 1996 (European Parliament, 1997).

Table 2. Fiscal revenue at risk for one lorry load (US$)

Live animals	24 000
Milk powder	36 000
Meat/butter	54 000
Alcohol	480 000
Cigarettes	1 200 000

Source: European Parliament (1997)

According to information on nine countries from the European Confederation of Cigarette Retailers (European Parliament, 1997) and other sources (Her Majesty's Treasury, 1997; Persson and Andersson, 1997), the 15 countries of the European Union can be classified into three categories:

- high smuggling countries with a contraband market share of 10 per cent or more: Spain (15 per cent), Austria (15 per cent), Italy (11.5 per cent) and Germany (10 per cent);
- medium smuggling countries with a contraband market share of between 5 and 10 per cent: Netherlands (5-10 per cent), Belgium (7 per cent), Greece (8 per cent) and probably Luxembourg and Portugal (no studies available);
- low smuggling countries with a contraband market share of less than 5 per cent: France (2 per cent), UK (1.5 per cent), Ireland (4 per cent), Sweden (2 per cent), and probably Denmark and Finland (no studies available).

Table 3. The price of cigarettes and level of smuggling in countries of the European Union

Country	Price of 20 cigs., most popular price category (US$, 1 June 1997)	Level of smuggling
Spain	1.20	High
Portugal	1.75	Probably Medium
Greece	2.06	Medium
Italy	2.07	High
Luxembourg	2.12	Probably Medium
Netherlands	2.43	Medium
Austria	2.69	High
Belgium	2.95	Medium
Germany	3.02	High
France	3.38	Low
Finland	4.26	Probably Low
Ireland	4.27	Low
UK	4.35	Low
Denmark	4.55	Probably Low
Sweden	4.97	Low

Source of prices: World Health Organisation (1996c)

If one compares the level of smuggling with the level of prices in the countries of the European Union, as shown in Table 3, it becomes evident that smuggling is not linked with high prices. Low smuggling countries are all high price countries, while high smuggling countries are mainly low price countries. Price levels do not explain smuggling. It is not prices, but smuggling routes that provide one with a better understanding of the smuggling problem.

(ii) The smuggling routes

One of the more absorbing aspects of the European Parliament Committee's work has been to learn of the complexity of the routes by which contraband cigarettes now enter free circulation in the EU.

The port of Antwerp in Belgium provides cigarette warehousing facilities unparalleled anywhere in Europe. In 1988, 27 billion cigarettes were imported from the US (Table 4), but in 1996, all in all, around 100 billion cigarettes passed through the port: 62 billion cigarettes were imported from the US (mainly from Philip Morris and R.J. Reynolds) and 38 billion from Brazil (from factories of Philip Morris and BAT in Brazil) into Belgium (Table 5).

Aside from the relatively small proportion intended for duty free sale, none of these cigarettes are destined for the EU market, but are meant for export to third countries. As the large American producers supply their legitimate EU markets entirely out of EU production facilities, any person wishing to purchase American duty-free cigarettes for European black markets — including clandestine markets — is likely to purchase products warehoused in Antwerp. This is simply because that is where the cigarettes are.

The arrival of 100 billion tax-free cigarettes in transit in Antwerp represents a huge sum, as its value can be estimated to be US$14 billion on the legal market (taxes included). The key issue of the smuggling problem in Europe is these

Table 4. US cigarette exports to Belgium (billions of sticks)

Year	Exports
1986	17.5
1987	23.0
1988	26.7
1989	33.7
1990	53.5
1991	48.2
1992	53.3
1993	51.2
1994	71.8
1995	71.4
1996	61.8

Source: US Department of Agriculture (1997a)

Table 5. Cigarette exports from Brazil (billions of sticks)

Year	Exports
1990	10
1991	20
1992	25
1993	30
1994	55
1995	55
1996	78 (of which 38 billion went to Belgium)

Source: US Department of Agriculture (1997a)

transit cigarettes, which will end up mostly in the contraband markets of several European countries.

From Antwerp, the first two major trade routes involve the transport of cigarettes into Eastern Europe and the former Soviet Union.

A first transit operation is used to transfer cigarettes by road from Belgium to a free zone in Switzerland. The operation is concluded quite regularly there. Cigarettes then leave Switzerland under a new transit procedure for a destination in Central or Eastern Europe or one of the former Soviet Republics. This operation is also routine. A transit operation is used to transfer cigarettes from port warehouses to regional airports in Belgium or the Netherlands. Cargo aircraft fly the cigarettes (up to five container loads per aircraft) to destinations in the East.

From their destinations in Eastern Europe, cigarettes return to the EU in a number of ways. The two countries most affected are Germany and Italy. In Germany, the problem has been described as "ant smuggling" ("Ameisen-schmuggel"): the clandestine transport of cigarettes across the Eastern border in a vast number of small consignments, carried in private cars and small vans. This supplies not only the Italian market, but also other EU countries.

In Italy, the route is a slightly more conventional one. Cigarettes are transported in vast quantities from the Republics of the former Yugoslavia and Albania across the Adriatic in fast boats and landed at places on Italy's long coastline. From there, they supply not only the Italian market, but also other EU countries beyond.

The third route, to some extent replacing traditional routes through Gibraltar and Andorra, involves sea transport from Northern European ports. Documents are prepared indicating the delivery of cigarettes to destinations in North Africa. The route taken involves passing close to Spanish territorial waters, across which a short trip in a fast boat suffices to land the cigarettes on the Spanish coast (European Parliament, 1997).

The complexity of the routes is remarkable, as is the structure of the transactions. The key point for the fraudster is not to be discovered. One mechanism employed to render investigation as difficult as possible is to arrange for a consignment of cigarettes to pass through a bewildering range of owners in a short space of time. The object is to make the final owner untraceable, and to make the links between successive owners as obscure as possible (European Parliament, 1997).

To summarise, the main characteristics of smuggled cigarettes are:

• international brands;
• duty-free cigarettes;
• transported in transit;
• passed through a wide range of owners;
• distributed in non-official outlets;
• sold at a lower price than the official price;
• mostly without adequate health warnings.

Solutions

(i) Ensure that all tobacco products prominently display an indication of the applicable taxes having been paid

This has been done in various ways in different countries. The key is to clearly distinguish between legal and illegal goods. This makes the contraband products much easier to detect and the laws, therefore, easier to enforce. Many European countries require "tax-paid" stamps to be affixed to each cigarette packet under the cellophane wrapping.

(ii) Revise the penalties for tobacco smuggling

Many of the penalties for tobacco smuggling are long out of date and the applicable reporting requirements for revenue purposes may be full of loopholes. The penalties and reporting requirements can be improved as part of a revision of the applicable law on tobacco taxation. The key to such revisions is to ensure that the penalties for smuggling, when combined with the probability of being caught, render tobacco smuggling unappealing.

(iii) Restrict illegal sales

Clamping down on outlets for smuggled cigarettes, which in some countries are almost part of the local culture, would require not only law enforcement, but a considerable change in smokers' attitudes towards authority. Restricting sales to licensed premises and charging heavy fines to unlicensed premises and unlicensed vendors would clearly help. In the Czech Republic both policies had a measurable impact in 1994.

(iv) Reduce cigarette supply and adopt an international convention on tobacco smuggling

Finally, and probably most important, is the reduction of supply. This will require greater co-operation between customs officials. As with illegal drugs (which from the control point of view, nicotine seems increasingly to resemble), it would seem that an international convention controlling all means of transport of cigarettes would be appropriate. In view of the involvement of organised crime, this convention would need the support of governments throughout the world and of some central organisation (Joossens and Raw, 1995). The World Health Organisation is seeking to address these international issues through an international framework for tobacco control. The adoption of an international convention is needed, which would strictly limit the transit-trade of cigarettes. The actual situation, that about one-third of legal global cigarette exports disappear, in the sense that they not appear in legal import figures, is not acceptable. This convention should stipulate that the transport of cigarettes would only be allowed, if there is an agreement on the final destination, a control that the cigarettes have the adequate health warnings and tax stamps and a sufficient way to control that the cigarettes arrive at their final destination.

References

Barford, M.F. (1993), "New dimensions boost cigarette smuggling", *Tobacco Journal International*, 3:16-18.
Bonner, R. and C. Drew (1997), "Cigarette makers are seen as aiding rise in smuggling", *New York Times*, 25 August 1997.
European Parliament (1997), "Committee of inquiry into the community transit system", 4 volumes, Brussels: European Parliament.
Her Majesty's Treasury (UK) (1997), *Dawn Primarolo Parliamentary Answer*, 1 July 1997, London: HMSO.
Joossens, L. and M. Raw (1995), "Smuggling and cross border shopping of tobacco in Europe", *British Medical Journal*, 310:1393-1397.
Persson, L.G.W. and J. Andersson (1997), *Cigarette Smuggling*, Stockholm: Swedish National Police College.
Tobacco Reporter (1997), "Cigarette production down; contraband & counterfeits flourish", 4:32.
US Department of Agriculture (1997a), *Tobacco: World Markets and Trade*, Foreign Agricultural Service, Washington, DC: US Department of Agriculture.
US Department of Health and Human Services (1992), *Smoking and Health in the Americas*, Atlanta, GA: US Department of Health and Human Services.
World Health Organisation (1996c), *Tobacco Alert: the Tobacco Epidemic: a Global Public Health Emergency*, Geneva: World Health Organisation.
World Tobacco (1996), *World Tobacco File 1996*, London: World Tobacco.

Chapter 13

Estimating and Disaggregating the Social Costs of Tobacco

David Collins and Helen Lapsley[1]

To produce a book on the economics of tobacco control naturally presupposes the position that tobacco consumption needs to be controlled. To the economist, the basis for this position is the belief that tobacco consumption imposes uncompensated externalities upon the community as a whole. Tobacco consumption is, consequently, above optimum levels and policies aimed at reducing tobacco consumption are justified. It then remains to determine optimal consumption levels and the policy mix which will most efficiently achieve these levels. In practice, public health objectives may well prove to be inconsistent with the economist's concept of optimum consumption levels. Public health professionals frequently consider an objective of public health policy to be zero smoking prevalence and often find the economist's approach difficult to accept.

The achievement of optimal tobacco consumption levels is, in practice, extremely complicated and fraught with theoretical, methodological, political and data difficulties. Among these are:

1. the nature of the external costs of smoking;
2. problems involved in evaluating some types of costs, particularly intangibles;
3. the interpretation of estimates of smoking costs;
4. the relevance of the existence of private smoking benefits to public policy analysis;
5. the public benefits of tobacco growing and/or cigarette manufacture; and
6. structural, smoking prevalence and public policy differences between countries, particularly between developed and developing nations.

To aspire to be able to recommend an optimal tobacco policy mix is indeed a high ambition. Such a task is certainly impossible without knowledge of the extent of the external costs of smoking and of the disaggregation of these costs into their constituent parts. This paper explores the problems and issues involved in estimating and interpreting smoking costs and draws some preliminary conclusions on the public policy implications of smoking cost estimates.

---

1. Since this paper discusses many issues which the present authors have addressed in previous papers, it draws heavily on analysis in various of these papers, particularly Collins and Lapsley (1991; 1996; 1997).

Background to Australian tobacco cost estimation

In 1990 the present authors were commissioned by the Australian federal Department of Human Services and Health to estimate the economic costs of drug abuse in Australia, including tobacco, alcohol, prescribed pharmaceuticals and illicit drugs. Extensive work had previously been undertaken in taxation economics and health economics respectively, but this was the first substantial work in the drug area for either author. Previous work of both authors had achieved significant recognition but little dissent. Almost no previous work on drug abuse costs in Australia had been published.

Estimating the economic costs of drug abuse in Australia (Collins and Lapsley, 1991) was publicly launched by the federal Minister of Health early in 1991. It attracted extensive press coverage, an amount of favourable reporting and very significant adverse reaction from tobacco and alcohol industry lobby groups. These groups commissioned three separate consultancies to review the work of Collins and Lapsley. These studies achieved a degree of harmony in purporting to refute the methodology, finding errors of calculation and recalculating consumption benefits which they claimed were substantial underestimates. In some cases in which this methodology tended to _reduce_ the estimated costs of abuse, for example where account was taken of the reduced health care costs resulting from premature drug-related mortality, acceptance was gained for the methodology (even when it was claimed that the evidence for the premature mortality was inadequate).

These consulting reports themselves attracted considerable public attention. At one point the authors were forced to seek redress for what was perceived to be a defamatory statement by a tobacco-industry representative made on a popular Sydney radio station, and were eventually able to secure a public retraction of the statement.

The economic study relied heavily upon a major epidemiological study, _The quantification of drug-caused mortality in Australia_, in which aetiological fractions were calculated from the meta-analysis of studies relating to the morbidity and mortality associated with tobacco, alcohol and other drugs. No such information was available for the abuse of prescribed pharmaceuticals and so, without the backing causal information, the cost estimation proved impossible. The epidemiological study was headed by Professors Darcy Holman and Bruce Armstrong, both distinguished epidemiologists from Western Australia.

With the increasing epidemiological evidence, the Australian Department of Human Services and Health supported a second study, in which Dr. Darryl English and Professor Darcy Holman, together with various colleagues, revised and recalculated the aetiological fractions (English _et al._, 1995). During 1995 the final draft of this study was made available to the authors, enabling the recalculation and extension of our earlier work, resulting in the publication early in 1996 of _The social costs of drug abuse in Australia in 1988 and 1992_ (Collins and Lapsley, 1996). The second study used improved data and some improvements in methodology and was able to demonstrate how the costs of drug abuse were changing. Total costs of tobacco abuse were estimated to be, at a minimum, A$12.7 billion in 1992, and were shown to be rising fast.

This time the industry groups were more muted in their public responses but again commissioned consultancies to review the methodology and results. The industry consultants provided submissions on the authors' work to an Australian Industry Commission report on tobacco (Industry Commission, 1994) and to a Senate Community Affairs Reference Committee (1995) on the Tobacco Industry and the Costs of Tobacco-Related Illness. Again the tobacco industry consultants claimed that the authors had over-estimated the costs of tobacco and failed to take sufficient account of its benefits.

The experience of the last few years has been a new one for academics used to working well away from the public eye. It is, however, a useful if minor illustration of some of the problems which may arise in the formulation of optimal tobacco policies.

The nature of external smoking costs

A fundamental issue of abuse cost estimation is whether estimates should incorporate the private costs and benefits of drug consumption and production. In the classic work which explores this issue, Markandya and Pearce (1989) define the total costs of drug abuse as the private costs plus the social costs. "To the extent that the costs are knowingly and freely borne by the consumer or producer himself, they are referred to as private costs but to the extent that they are not so borne but fall on the rest of society they are referred to as social costs." Thus, according to Markandya and Pearce, total costs equal private costs plus social costs. What Markandya and Pearce call social costs are more usually called external costs.

An important issue, as the two authors point out, is "the extent to which the consumer is *aware* of the costs that he bears. If his actions are determined by a perceived cost that is in fact less than his actual cost, the difference between the two can be viewed as a social cost". This is because "the individual himself has not adjusted his behaviour to reflect these higher costs and they are, therefore, unaccounted for".

In these circumstances individuals are not necessarily behaving irrationally. They are simply adjusting their behaviour according to the best available, relevant, information. As Markandya and Pearce (1989) implicitly accept, costs borne by the individual drug abuser can be social costs *even* if that individual is rational, if those costs have not been knowingly incurred.

It is to be expected that rational consumers will consume a product only if the private benefits received at least equal the costs of purchase, so that there is almost certainly a positive net benefit in the form of consumer surplus. The question of whether the estimation of the private benefits accruing to smokers by way of consumer surplus is relevant to public policy analysis is addressed later in this paper.

So the crucial issues in relation to the estimation of the external costs of smoking are:

1. Are smokers fully informed?
2. Are smokers rational?
3. Are smokers required to bear the *total* costs of their tobacco consumption?

If any one of these conditions is not satisfied the resultant costs are social costs. Only if all three conditions are simultaneously satisfied will the relevant costs be private costs.

Being fully informed about the private costs of smoking requires the smoker to have access to, and the ability to process and evaluate epidemiological information on the effects of smoking. It also requires the smoker to be able to evaluate the probable future health and other costs resulting from the smoking. It is difficult to believe that smokers, by their nature, are fully-, or even well-, informed about the costs of their tobacco consumption (Courtwright, Joseph and Des Jarlias, 1989). Current smokers are much less likely to be well-informed than current non-smokers, since smokers who acquire the relevant information are more likely to abandon their dangerous pursuit.

Even if it could be argued that smokers in developed countries were fully informed, it is unlikely that this claim could be supported in developing economies. In most developing countries tobacco is sold with either no or inadequate health warnings, advertising and sponsorship is unimpeded in terms of both content and location and those tobacco control regulations which do exist are often unenforceable.

The question of rationality also raises interesting issues. Rationality, as defined in the paper by Becker and Murphy (1988) on the theory of rational addiction, implies utility maximisation over time. Stevenson (1994) says that the theory of rational addiction "assumes that drug users are rational, forward looking utility maximisers who base consumption decisions on full knowledge of the consequences of addiction".

It should be noted that rational addiction implies full knowledge. The theory of rational addiction, which has been widely quoted by industry groups as supporting their case, does not merely demand rationality; it demands both rationality and full knowledge. A further problem with the theory, from the point of view of the cost estimation studies, is that it may explain the behaviour of addicts but it does not explain the process by which the addiction is acquired. The theory cannot be interpreted as indicating that acquiring the addiction is a rational act, that is that the lifetime benefits of the drug consumption to the addict exceed the lifetime costs. In any case, the "benefits" of addictive consumption can be seen largely as avoidance of the costs of withdrawal rather than as genuine benefits of consumption.

The notion of rationality as maximisation of utility over time is itself an interesting one. The comparison by an individual of benefits and costs accruing over time can only be undertaken by using some concept of a time preference rate. Are very high time preference rates, which place a very high value on current benefits and a very low value on future costs, rational? Is there *any* time preference rate which is not consistent with the notion of rationality? If not, rationality seems to lose any significance since *any* behaviour pattern can be seen to be consistent with utility maximisation. But society itself is clearly unwilling to accept all behaviour patterns (for example, self-destructive behaviour even when it does not impose social costs).

There is some evidence that smokers, particularly youth smokers, may react perversely to the public provision of anti-smoking information or propaganda campaigns by defiantly increasing their tobacco consumption. Can this be considered to be rational behaviour?

External cost estimates and their interpretation

This chapter examines various types of smoking costs estimates. Overwhelmingly the type most frequently encountered in the literature is what might be called the aggregate cost estimate. Usually these estimates are represented as providing "the external costs of smoking in year X". This representation is inaccurate, however it is interpreted. If the calculated costs are interpreted as "the external costs borne in year X", the interpretation is in almost all cases inaccurate since the conventional human capital approach to the valuation of production losses involves the discounting of a future time stream of costs back to its present value. A very significant proportion of the costs are incurred in periods subsequent to year X. If the phrase is interpreted as "the external costs of the tobacco consumption undertaken in year X" it is also misleading because almost all the external costs of smoking result from smoking in previous years (major exceptions being pollution, environmental degradation, and the property loss resulting from cigarette-related fires and bushfires).

The correct interpretation of conventional human capital-based estimates is: *the current value of the time stream of current and future external costs incurred as a result of past and present smoking.* This is hardly a simple concept to explain to the community at large, or to politicians.[2]

These costs are estimated in relation to some (almost always) implicit counterfactual situation of past and present smoking prevalence rates of zero. Since it is, in practical terms, impossible to achieve zero prevalence rates in the future or (except with the aid of a time machine) in the past, the aggregate cost estimate gives no indication of the potential public benefits to be achieved by policies to reduce smoking prevalence. These potential benefits will be much lower than the estimated aggregate costs.

Another problem relates to the general equilibrium impacts of smoking or of reduced smoking prevalence. It is often argued that, if the tobacco industry ceased to exist, or contracted substantially, as a result of public anti-smoking policies, there would be substantial loss of employment, output and income. Thus this employment, output and income are represented as community benefits of smoking. The difficulty with this analysis is the implicit assumption that the opportunity cost of resources used in the production of tobacco is zero.

---

2. At a conference on estimating the costs of substance abuse at the Canadian Centre on Substance Abuse in 1994, such estimates became known as the "Gee whiz estimates" since they tended to provoke the response "Gee whiz, are the costs that high?"

This is an assumption which it would appear impossible to justify. If such a logic were pursued there would be no benefit from microeconomic reform in general, since all resources released as a result of that process would have no alternative uses. For example, it is difficult to imagine that agricultural resources used in the production of tobacco would have zero opportunity cost and it is impossible to imagine that manufacturing and distributive resources employed in the industry would have no alternative use.

A similar problem arises in valuing production losses resulting from smoking. If there were high levels of unemployment the loss of production might be small or zero (because the sick or prematurely deceased could presumably be replaced by workers who otherwise would be unemployed). The costs of smoking borne by society would apparently be much lower in periods of high unemployment than in periods of low unemployment. Increases in unemployment would apparently reduce external smoking costs.

In practice, smoking involves production costs even when it does not result in sickness severe enough to remove the worker from the workplace, either temporarily or permanently. These costs can be reduced productivity resulting from non-chronic disease (for example, respiratory diseases, coughs, effects of carbon monoxide, eye irritation) plus the costs resulting from smoking rituals, litter clean-up and the cleansing of dirty air (Kristein, 1983).

These types of issue can only be settled by the use of an appropriately specified econometric model which can simulate declines in tobacco consumption. Even if such models existed, and the authors are unaware of their existence (although Richter and Gori (1980) made such an attempt), there would still remain, with the human capital approach, the problem of forecasting future rates of unemployment, growth and productivity over the remaining normal lifetime of the prematurely dead. It is not possible to produce robust estimates of the opportunity cost over extended periods of time of resources used in the production of tobacco and tobacco products.

Avoidable costs of smoking

It has been argued that estimates of the aggregate costs of substance abuse do not indicate the potential returns to anti-smoking policies and programs. The latter figure is represented by avoidable costs.

It is assumed that the hypothetical alternative situation of zero smoking prevalence is not realisable under any circumstances. Total external costs of smoking comprise both avoidable and unavoidable costs. Unavoidable costs comprise the costs which the community currently bears as a result of past smoking, together with the costs which will continue to be borne as a result of the community's inability to reduce future smoking prevalence rates to zero. Avoidable costs, on the other hand, are those costs which are potentially amenable to public policy initiatives and behaviour changes.

An estimate of the avoidable percentages of mortality and morbidity is made in a comparative study by Armstrong (1990). Armstrong proposes an "Arcadian normal", which he describes as the lowest age-standardised mortality rate for the relevant mortality or morbidity category amongst twenty selected, comparable Western countries. He implies that the Arcadian normal is the lowest percentage of preventable morbidity and mortality presently achievable in any of the chosen countries, and therefore suggests that this is the most appropriate target. While this is an extremely conservative assumption, it is a very useful tool for quantification of the percentage of preventable morbidity and mortality and their associated costs which can be reduced, and ultimately avoided. The Armstrong estimates would only be applicable to the countries for which he developed the Arcadian normals and to other developed countries for which comprehensive mortality and morbidity data can be used to indicate a sufficient similarity to the original twenty countries. Production of Arcadian normals for developing countries would almost certainly be severely hampered by the absence of appropriate mortality and morbidity data.

Some of the identified costs of abuse, while avoidable, may be reduced or eliminated only over long periods. There will be policy implementation lead times since policies will not be effective immediately. Even after full and effective implementation of policies, there will be long lead times before the health effects of policy changes are achieved. When previously heavy smokers stop smoking, it takes some years before their health status can even approach that of a comparable non-smoker. Thus, the proportion of aggregate costs which are avoidable depends upon the time period for which the analysis is undertaken.

The incidence of smoking costs

The question of who bears the costs of tobacco use is important from the point of view of public policies towards tobacco. It tends to be an unfortunate reality that governments are often seen to concentrate on those costs which they directly bear — for example, the costs to the public purse of health care costs associated with smoking. They display less interest in the very substantial proportion of the costs of smoking which are borne by the non-government sectors. These other sectors consist of individuals (both smokers and non-smokers) and business.

There is also a tendency in many developed nations for governments to attempt to shift health care costs back to individuals. Aggregate cost estimates will not pick up the effects of such policy changes. In developing countries the relatively low levels of health care expenditures mean that a much higher proportion of external smoking costs are directly borne by private individuals.

Collins and Lapsley (1996) have estimated that, in Australia, only about 7 per cent of the total external costs of smoking are borne by government. The remaining costs are borne by individuals and business. As indicated above, in developing countries an even lower proportion is likely to be borne by government.

The public sectors of developing countries can expect to face an increasing cost in terms of smoking-related outlays in the future. This is partly because the full impact of the smoking epidemic has yet to hit most of these countries. They will also rise because, as public health services improve with rising economic prosperity, a higher proportion of smoking-related costs will be funded by public expenditures. Governments acting to reduce the prevalence of smoking now will be reducing their future budgetary problems.

The 1994 Canadian Centre on Substance Abuse (CCSA) conference recommended that substance abuse cost estimates should incorporate some indication of the incidence of the external costs. Abuse costs can be viewed as a form of tax, so that use may be made here of the principles of tax incidence analysis.

Tax analysis makes the distinction between legal incidence and effective (or economic) incidence. Legal incidence indicates which individual is legally required to pay the tax to the revenue authorities. Effective incidence describes who ultimately bears the tax after all the economic adjustments resulting from the imposition of the tax have been worked through. For example, a wholesaler may be required to pay increased sales tax (legal incidence) but the tax may be passed on to the consumer in the form of higher prices (effective incidence). It is a trivial operation to identify the legal incidence of a tax. Determination of effective incidence, on the other hand, will usually be difficult and often impossible.

External costs of smoking can bear upon one or more of four community groups:
1. ill-informed or addicted (irrational) drug users;
2. other individuals (for example, passive smokers, their families and carers);
3. business;
4. government.

It can be assumed that fully-informed and non-addicted smokers (not a large group) will gain benefits from smoking at least equal to the costs which they impose on themselves.

There are various mechanisms the effects of which would result in abuse costs being shifted to other groups. Some of these mechanisms are as follows:

Smokers:	lower work productivity at existing wage rates.
Other individuals:	lower work productivity at existing wage rates.
Business:	higher output prices;
	lower factor input prices.
Government:	higher taxes;
	lower expenditures;
	higher deficits.

Collins and Lapsley (1996) attempt only to estimate the impact incidence of external smoking costs, considering the effects upon the three major groups — individuals (ill-informed and/or addicted abusers and other individuals), business and government.

One sector which bears a very significant proportion of total smoking costs (around 35 per cent in Australia) is the business sector. At the same time it receives very little recognition of that fact. Business bears smoking costs as a result of smoking-related absenteeism, lower productivity and mortality in the workforce. In economies across the world, increasing attention is being paid to structural reform, implemented with the objective of reducing business costs. Policies to reduce the prevalence of smoking will inevitably contribute to the reduction in business costs, and so should properly be considered to be a component of structural reform policies. Incidence estimates will help to support this message.

The budgetary impact of smoking

The estimation of the budgetary impact of smoking is an exercise subsidiary to that of estimating aggregate and avoidable external costs. Aggregate and avoidable costs represent the impact of smoking on the community as a whole. The budgetary impact is largely an indication of the funding impact of smoking on the government sector. The argument is often presented by tobacco industry interests that tobacco consumption generates substantial tax revenue. This, while true, should not be taken to imply that this revenue generates resources for the community as a whole. It merely redistributes resources from one group to another, that is from smokers to the community as a whole. Tax revenue is a pecuniary benefit to governments but not a real benefit to the community as a whole.

There is, however, one sense in which the real and pecuniary effects are inextricably linked — the concept of negative externalities. Smokers impose costs both upon themselves (internal costs such as deterioration in health and fitness) and upon others (external costs such as the health effects on non-smokers of environmental tobacco smoke). The effect of negative consumption externalities is to produce a situation in which consumption is at above optimum levels. The economist's response to this situation is the imposition of taxes which reflect the level of externalities and which are designed to reduce consumption to optimum levels. It is, therefore, sensible to ask whether smokers are, through tax payments, bearing the full costs which they impose upon the rest of the community.

Estimation of the budgetary impact of smoking indicates whether smokers compensate governments for the revenue and expenditure impacts of smoking (that is, whether smoking reduces budget deficits). It does not indicate whether smokers fully compensate the rest of the community for the total costs of smoking because it takes no account of some types of costs borne, for example, by non-smokers (pain, suffering, death and bereavement) or by the business sector (reduced productivity, higher workplace costs). If smokers are to compensate the rest of the community fully for the negative externalities which they generate, tobacco tax revenues should substantially exceed smoking-related public expenditures.

In examining the budgetary impact of smoking, the obvious comparison is between expenditures undertaken and revenue generated. It should, however, also be recognised that smoking reduces revenue from some types of taxes. Smoking-related mortality and morbidity will reduce income tax revenue as a result of a reduction in the size of the employed workforce. Indirect tax revenues will also be reduced as a result of the effect of mortality in reducing consumption levels. There would be other, relatively minor, effects on the revenue from such taxes as fringe benefits tax, payroll tax and company income tax. However, the revenue from these latter types of taxes should be excluded from the budgetary analysis because they do not discriminate against the alcohol or tobacco industry in any way. All industries must bear these taxes at the same rates and they can, at least partially, be viewed as benefit taxes which finance services provided by government to industry generally. Revenue from indirect taxes declines because premature mortality reduces consumption levels and so reduces tax revenue raised from that consumption expenditure.

There is a fundamental flaw in analyses often presented by the tobacco industry of the revenue and expenditure effects of their industries. To include in the analysis all revenues attributable to tobacco taxation implies that the industry, in the absence of taxes targeted specifically at it, would be required to pay no taxes at all. It is quite wrong to attribute all tax revenue from tobacco to be raised as compensation for the smoking-related externalities, rather than attributing some to the tax burden that is inevitably borne by all industries, whether they impose negative externalities or not. Even if there were no externalities, tobacco would still bear sales or other consumption taxes consistent with the tax burden borne by other commodities.

Disaggregated cost estimates

In the hierarchy of external costs estimates there remains the most disaggregated level in which estimates of the individual components of aggregate cost estimates are presented. The broad categories of smoking costs are presented in Table 1.

Table 1. Broad categories of smoking costs

Tangible costs

(a) Health care:
     medical services;
     prescription drugs;
     hospital services;
     other institutional services;
     allied health services.
(b) Production losses resulting from:
     death;
     sickness;
     reduced productivity.
(c) Welfare provision.
(d) Fires and accidents.
(e) Pollution, litter and environmental
     degradation.
(f) Research and education.

Intangible costs

(g) Loss of life by:
     smokers;
     passive smokers.
(h) Pain and suffering of:
     smokers;
     passive smokers;
     others.

(i) Health care

Medical services

Medical services include those services which are provided for medical conditions resulting directly from tobacco consumption, and services associated with co-morbidities. These are conditions not directly related to smoking but where the consultations or treatments are prolonged, more intensive or more complex because of:
1. concurrent conditions related to smoking;
2. conditions caused (or exacerbated) by past smoking;
3. conditions caused (or exacerbated) by passive smoking.

Prescription drugs

Specific use of prescription drugs results from conditions caused directly by smoking. There may also be more intense use of drugs prescribed for conditions which are not directly tobacco-related but where the smoking either makes the drug less effective or necessitates a more extensive or complex drug regimen.

Hospital services

Demand for hospital bed days may be caused directly by smoking or it may result from co-morbidities. The latter refers to illnesses which are associated with smoking and which cause people to become sicker and to stay in hospital longer when they have been admitted to hospital for other reasons.

Other institutional services

These are services in other institutions (such as nursing homes and hospices) where admissions are caused by smoking or where smoking has resulted in the condition being more severe, requiring more intensive treatment or causing greater dependency.

Allied health services

These relate to the use of allied health professionals such as physiotherapists, podiatrists and dieticians for conditions which have been caused or exacerbated by smoking.

(ii) Production losses

Smoking can cause reduced production by an effective reduction in the size of the workforce as a result of the deaths or sickness (resulting in absenteeism) of workers. These costs will not be as high if the absent workers can be replaced from otherwise unemployed workers. However, in practice, it is rarely the case that workers can be fully replaced. This is partly because the pool of unemployed workers may be of insufficient size but more likely in both developed and developing countries because the skills lost to the workforce through smoking may not be replaceable from the ranks of the unemployed. Another significant production cost which must be taken into consideration is reduced on-the-job productivity resulting from smoking-related illnesses.

It should be recognised that it is not only in the paid workforce that production is lost. There may be substantial production losses among the unpaid workforce, for example non-working mothers, the unemployed, the retired and the young. While the output of these people is not counted in conventional national accounts statistics it should be counted as a component of the external costs of smoking. If these people die or become sick, either their output is lost or they need to be replaced by other people, who themselves may be drawn from the workforce.

(iii) Welfare provision

In communities which provide significant sickness or unemployment welfare benefits there will be some welfare costs resulting from smoking. However, a significant proportion of these costs will be pecuniary rather than real. To count both production losses and welfare costs for someone suffering from a smoking-related disease would, from the community's point of view, involve double-counting of costs. Welfare costs will always have an impact but will usually not involve real costs. However, the resources used in administering the welfare system should always be counted as a component of social costs.

(iv) Fires and accidents

Smoking causes fires at home and in workplaces and in some countries is a significant cause of bush and forest fires, as smokers carelessly dispose of cigarette butts. The property losses resulting from these fires represent a significant social cost. Evidence is also starting to emerge that smoking may be associated with road and other accidents, although the mechanisms underlying this relationship do not appear at the moment to be completely clear.

(v) Pollution, litter and environmental degradation

Smoking creates increased pollution and litter as a result of the discarding of packaging and cigarette butts. The resulting costs may be considered to be tangible or intangible. They are tangible if they result in cleaning-up costs. On the other hand, if the litter is allowed to accumulate, rather than being removed, then the costs in terms of a degradation of the environment will be intangible. In some tobacco-producing developing countries, the use of firewood in the curing of tobacco can cause deforestation, leading in turn to erosion and deteriorating land quality (Marshall, 1991).

(vi) Research and education

In many countries considerable resources are allocated to public health programmes providing education about the harmful effects of smoking, and to health and medical research on smoking. It could be argued that these are discretionary costs resulting from public policy decisions, rather than inevitable costs of smoking. This point is debatable since it is likely that in the absence of these expenditures other types of costs (for example, in the health area) would be higher. Thus there is, at the very least, a strong case for identifying these types of costs, even if they are not considered to be a component of external smoking costs.

(vii) Loss of life

There is a value of loss of life to the community over and above the tangible costs of mortality (for example, production losses) borne by the rest of the community. Community attitudes and public policy clearly view premature mortality as highly undesirable. A high proportion of smoking-induced deaths occur beyond the age of retirement so that paid production costs become irrelevant. Indeed, an unduly cynical approach would indicate that there are community benefits accruing from these premature deaths because there is no longer the need to provide the consumption resources for these people. The fact that such an attitude would be considered to be outrageous by any civilised community indicates that life has an important psychological value over and above any material contribution which a person may make to the community. To ignore the intangible benefits of life (and so, the intangible costs of premature death) could lead to the totally unacceptable conclusion that smoking, by leading to the premature deaths of retirees, benefits the community as a whole. Evidence that this conclusion would be unreasonable is that most societies devote very considerable proportions of their health resources to extending the lives, and reducing the pain and suffering, of people of above working age.

(viii) Pain and suffering

Similar considerations apply to the smoking-related pain and suffering borne by smokers, passive smokers and others. Cost utility analysis provides measures such as QALYs (quality-adjusted life years) and DALYs (disability-adjusted life years). Although these costs may be difficult to value they cannot be ignored.

In practice, some of these individual categories of costs will be difficult to estimate accurately, or in some cases at all. Intangible costs present particularly severe valuation problems. Aggregate cost estimates will inevitably be partial. In many developing countries the quality of available data will mean that quite heroic assumptions may need to be made in the estimation exercise, which will still be a worthwhile process if it provides even an approximate indication of the size of the smoking problem. Such estimates will inevitably be open to attack from tobacco industry interests demanding impossibly high standards of research accuracy from independent or government researchers.

The external benefits of smoking

The tobacco industry has tended to counter evidence on the external costs of smoking by contending that these studies unjustifiably ignore both the private and the external benefits of smoking. The private benefits comprise the consumer surplus of smokers. The external benefits comprise any beneficial health effects of smoking (there appear to be minor beneficial effects in relation to Parkinson's disease, ulcerative colitis and hypertension in pregnancy[3]) and national economic benefits (in the form of income, employment, balance of payments, tax revenues) arising from the existence of the tobacco growing and processing industries.

In evaluating smoking externalities for the purposes of determining optimum levels of tobacco consumption, both private costs and private benefits are irrelevant (unless smoking was to be used as a tool of income and/or wealth redistribution). The size of the private benefits in comparison to the uncompensated externalities is irrelevant to policy decisions on optimal consumption levels.

Estimates of external costs should incorporate any external benefits and Collins and Lapsley (1996) net out such benefits as the health effects referred to above and any reduction in health care demand resulting from the premature deaths of smokers. The claimed national benefits resulting from the existence of the tobacco industry have a much more dubious basis.

The tobacco industry frequently asserts that it generates substantial employment, income and output (value added). These are represented as very significant benefits to society in the sense that, if the industry ceased to exist, these social benefits would be lost. This assertion relies on two fundamental assumptions, neither of which is usually stated and both of which should be closely scrutinised.

The first assumption is that, if smokers ceased to smoke, they would not spend the resulting savings on other forms of expenditure. If that happened, the result, it is implied, would be the total loss of the employment, output and income which the industry generates. The analysis is simplistic and this outcome is highly unlikely. It is much more plausible that ex-smokers would spend that money in other ways which would generate similar levels of employment and output. The alternative expenditure avenues would also generate consumer surplus.

Secondly, it is assumed that the resources used in tobacco growing and cigarette production would have no alternative uses. Above all in terms of alternative uses for capital, this assumption is quite unrealistic for both

---

3. See the English *et al.* (1995) aetiological fraction estimates for Australia. The hypertension in pregnancy benefits which smoking confers is considerably outweighed by the damaging effects of the pregnant woman's smoking upon her foetus.

developed and developing economies. Developing economies in particular suffer from a shortage of capital, with the result that alternative uses would be readily available.

A substantial literature is now starting to emerge which examines the output- and employment-effects of the tobacco industry on a more realistic basis. For example, a study by Buck *et al.* (1995) estimates the impact of reducing tobacco consumption on employment in the UK, assuming that the money saved on tobacco expenditure was spent elsewhere in the economy. Not only is it unlikely that declining tobacco consumption would reduce employment, it seems perfectly possible that it would in fact increase employment. This is because the alternative expenditures might well be on goods and services whose production involved a higher use of labour than would the forgone tobacco.

A very similar result is produced by Warner and Fulton (1994) for the U.S State of Michigan, a non-tobacco-producing State. They conclude that a reduction in spending on cigarettes would bolster the State's economy. As consumers in Michigan switched their expenditures from cigarettes (which are produced outside Michigan) to other goods and services, many of which are produced within the State, more money would be recycled within the State and employment and incomes would consequently grow.

Warner and Fulton (1994) produce a telling quotation from a consultant firm's report to the US Tobacco Institute referring to the net impact of tobacco on the entire US economy: "It can be argued, of course, that without the tobacco industry, the expenditures on, and resources devoted to, the production of tobacco products would simply be shifted elsewhere in the economy. That is, if consumers were faced with no available tobacco products, they would reallocate their spending to other goods and services. This reallocated spending would generate additional business opportunities in other sectors of the economy along with the associated employment and incomes. Therefore, except for transitional problems and differential industry levels of productivity, the aggregate economic results would be substantially the same . . . [T]he compensatory responses that would occur automatically within the economy and within the Chase Econometrics US Macroeconomic Model in a total impact-type of study were constrained from taking place within this analysis."

It may be that there is more substance to the argument if the economy under review has a tobacco growing industry. The issue then becomes whether the resources used for tobacco growing have any alternative potential use, that is whether substitute cash crops are available. There can be little doubt that, in developing countries, the *capital* resources devoted to tobacco growing and cigarette production have alternative uses, given the often chronic shortage of capital. The problems may well be greater in relation to the alternative employment of land and labour.

It is notable that industry-sponsored studies of the employment effects of tobacco never, to the authors' knowledge, include the employment-generating effects of tobacco in the health care industry. A charitable explanation would be that it is here assumed that these resources have obvious alternative uses.

Even if it were reasonable to assume that the resources used in tobacco and cigarette production had no alternative uses and that expenditure on tobacco would not be replaced by other forms of consumer expenditure, the change would still have macroeconomic effects via interest rate reductions resulting from higher levels of saving. However, in any industry-sponsored studies known to the authors the money saved seems to disappear into a black hole, since any interest rate effects of higher savings are ignored.

Analysis of the balance of payments impact of tobacco production, manufacturing and production on developing countries would indicate that in almost all circumstances (and as a result of the very high levels of foreign ownership in the tobacco industries of these countries) tobacco has a negative impact. Tobacco poses extra balance of payments problems for those developing countries (Collins and Lapsley, 1997).

Cost estimates and their uses

(i) Types of estimates

Table 2 presents a summary of the various types of exercises involved in estimation of external smoking costs together with the interpretation and significance of each type of exercise.

Table 2. Type of estimate, interpretation and examples of policy use of external smoking cost estimation

Type of estimate	Interpretation of results	Example of policy use
Aggregate costs	Total external costs of smoking compared with alternative situation of zero smoking prevalence.	Indication of the size of the smoking problem.
Avoidable costs	Potential economic benefits from harm minimisation strategies.	Determination of the appropriate level of resources to be devoted to harm minimisation strategies.
Costs incidence	The distribution of external costs among various community groupings.	Use in mobilising support from various groups (e.g. business community) for anti-smoking campaigns.
Disaggregated costs	External costs of smoking disaggregated by categories.	Economic evaluation (cost-benefit or cost-effectiveness analysis) of smoking intervention programmes.
Budgetary impact	The impact of smoking on government revenues and expenditures.	Analysis of whether a case exists for the tobacco industry to provide compensation for smoking costs incurred by the public sector.

(ii) Prediction of the extent of future problems

Mackay and Crofton (1996) have warned: "With the decrease in smoking prevalence in developed countries, the multinational tobacco companies are now moving massive resources to boosting sales in developing countries. In some developing countries, indigenous tobacco production and consumption present major problems. Many people and governments in these countries are not yet fully aware of the risks and lack the resources to counter ruthless marketing by the industry. If not prevented, there will be appalling future increase in tobacco-related disease, disability and death." This warning is applicable to large and already powerful economies such as China and also to small vulnerable economies such as the Pacific Islands, which may require different policy combinations, albeit with the same objectives.

Even in countries in which smoking prevalence rates are falling, the external costs of tobacco are likely to be rising (see Australian evidence in Collins and Lapsley, 1996). Current estimates may also be substantial understatements of the true costs since they tend not to take account of the recent mounting accumulation of epidemiological evidence on the impact of passive smoking.

In many developing countries smoking prevalence rates are rising fast. Furthermore, in such countries health care costs are low because of the relatively low levels of health care provision. Health care expenditures can be expected to rise significantly. Currently a high proportion of all external costs in these countries is borne by private individuals and by business, rather than by the public sector. For these reasons, external costs of smoking in developing economies may currently appear to be relatively low but they will accelerate rapidly in the future (World Bank, 1993). Formal external cost predictions will dramatically demonstrate the future trends, as well as the changing incidence of costs.

The accumulating evidence, both epidemiological and economic, is so extensive that estimates of future cost burdens can already be made for developed countries. It should be perfectly possible to adjust these estimates and revise their underlying assumptions in order to assist developing countries to make their own estimates and predictions.

(iii) Policy and program evaluation

Social cost estimates are essential for program and policy evaluation. Firstly, they are required to establish base-line costs, so that the dimension of the costs of tobacco is fully recognised. Secondly, the establishment of base-line costs enables the estimation of specified outcomes against which the economic effectiveness of programs can be measured. Thirdly, through the use of social cost estimates, a range of economic evaluations including cost-effectiveness and cost-benefit analysis can be undertaken to ensure that policy decisions, both initially and subsequently, can be appropriately informed.

The production of aggregate cost estimates necessitates the estimation of the individual cost categories discussed in Section 7 above. Once aggregate estimates have been produced, there exist all the data necessary for evaluating program and policy outputs at a more micro level.

(iv) Political pressure for resources

Cost estimates have a major role in the political arena, to emphasise the economic significance of the social costs of tobacco. These costs frequently need emphasis, as the need for real resources for prevention strategies must compete with other government pressures and priorities. Prevention strategies invariably involve initial outlays, and advocates for public health programs must satisfy themselves and their funders that smoking reduction programs are cost-effective. The level of resources required for publicising, strengthening and enforcing regulatory environments is frequently at worst overlooked or at best underestimated.

(v) Litigation and legal settlements

The use of cost estimates for litigation is a purpose which is currently very topical, in view of the agreements now being considered between the tobacco companies and some US states. For example, in a recently announced case, Texas became the third state to recover public money spent treating sick smokers, settling for US$14.5 billion over 25 years (*Australian Financial Review*, 19 January 1998).

The tobacco industry, through the settlements, will also pay for anti-smoking initiatives and state research. Cost estimates have formed an integral component of these lawsuits, the most publicised of which has been the proposal for a US$368.5 billion settlement of current and prospective tobacco lawsuits by 40 States.

These settlements rest on the issue of whether State tobacco tax revenues (adjusted appropriately for general consumption tax levels borne by all goods) have covered the public sector outlays attributable to smoking. Apart from the obvious areas of health expenditures and tobacco-related research and public education, other relevant costs should include those relating to reduced public sector productivity, litter, fires and bushfires, and legislative action to reduce the prevalence of active and passive smoking. Current settlements would appear to incorporate a fairly narrow definition of tobacco-attributable costs. Countries implementing low levels of tobacco tax (like the US) would have a stronger case in this type of settlement than high tobacco tax countries.

(vi) Funding alternatives

There are a range of funding alternatives available for tobacco policy implementation. While, of course, the primary source is government, the current and potential role of Non Government Organisations (NGOs) should be recognised, especially in relation to public health awareness and Quit programs. In some locations, NGOs fund, organise and administer these programs, (for example, Pacific Tobacco and Health Project developed by the Australian Adventist Development and Relief Agency) while in other locations they provide expertise, advice, and funding support for local initiatives. Governments have the traditional sources of tax-based funding available to them, but usually resources for smoking reduction have to be allocated from already over-committed health budgets.

In Victoria, Australia, there is an example of the dedication of levies from tobacco sales being applied to tobacco control and harm minimisation through the Victorian Health Promotion Foundation. This hypothecated tax also provides sports sponsorships, replacing previous tobacco sponsorships which are now illegal.

The hypothecation of tobacco taxes for these purposes may have some political advantages for governments contemplating possible methods of funding tobacco control policies:

1. Communities may be more willing to bear particular tax increases if these increases are directly linked to popular expenditure increases. Cost-benefit analyses of these expenditures should be able to demonstrate high social rates of return.
2. It will politically be more difficult for tobacco lobbies to argue against tobacco tax increases if these increases are hypothecated to expenditures designed to reduce tobacco-related harm.
3. Hypothecated tobacco taxes (like any tobacco tax) will reduce tobacco consumption, and so tobacco-related externalities.

In the United States, the proposed tobacco company agreements would have provided funding for programmes and research. There appeared to be no provision for US-based companies to apply agreed principles and payments to their international activities.

Some policy implications of cost studies

(i) Zero tolerance of smoking or harm minimisation?

What should be the objective of public smoking policies - zero tolerance or harm minimisation? Public health policies can be seen as the equivalent of zero tolerance while the economist's concept of optimal consumption levels can be seen as akin to a harm minimisation strategy. Do these different approaches indicate a different optimal mix of policies? In practice, is there a major difference between the two approaches?

Neither side in the debate would argue for complete prohibition of tobacco consumption or sale. Aside from any civil liberty issues (which are usually vastly overstated by the tobacco lobby) the examples of drug criminalisation world-wide and alcohol prohibition in the United States indicate that the prohibition approach is likely to lead to increased social costs, as well as a different structure of costs. Health costs directly associated with tobacco consumption might fall but there would probably be substitute consumption of other drugs and there would certainly be dramatically increased costs associated with crime, policing and punishment. Both sides agree that, whatever the desired smoking prevalence rate is, governments cannot and should not achieve this rate by blanket prohibition. Zero tolerance might be the dream of public health policy but few would be deluded into believing it to be achievable.

Partial prohibitions, for example of cigarette vending machines, of the purchase of cigarettes by minors or of smoking in public areas and workplaces, are another matter altogether.

Economists would argue that zero tolerance produces resource misallocation because it leads to sub-optimal consumption levels. It may, however, be the case that optimal consumption levels are, in fact, very low and close to those which are considered achievable by public health professionals. If smokers or potential smokers behaved rationally, were fully informed about the impact upon them of smoking and were faced by public policies which internalised their external costs, tobacco consumption might well fall to low levels.

Support for this view would come from Pigou's "defective telescopic vision" — people tend to place too low a value on the future and eventually come to realise this fact. This could be one of the reasons for the zeal of many ex-smokers who regret their earlier smoking habit. Part of the explanation for this is an improved level of knowledge of the health and other impacts of active and passive smoking. But part of the explanation also lies in the belief that in earlier years their implicit time preference rate was too high. Government policies designed to correct for this defective telescopic vision would then appear to be over-correcting for current levels of external costs.

Governments themselves may well have defective telescopic vision. The longer term cost of inaction may be outweighed, in their view, by the short-term costs of action, particularly where they are faced by strong tobacco lobbies, as can be true in both developed and developing countries. The existence of estimates of current and future external smoking cost may be a means of boosting the resolve of governments facing a trade-off between short-term costs and longer-term benefits.

(ii) Lead times in policy implementation and effect

Brief reference has been made to the lead times inherent in tobacco policies. They may be illustrated as follows:

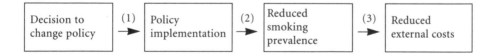

There are thus three lead times involved in the process leading from a decision to change tobacco policy through to a reduction in the external costs attributable to tobacco. Periods (1) and (2) may be relatively brief, depending upon the type of policy adopted. For example, tobacco tax increases may have a relatively rapid effect on smoking prevalence, while the accumulated effects of tobacco advertising and sponsorship may take a considerable time to dissipate after bans come into effect. However, the really lengthy lead time will be in period (3). Anti-smoking policies and programs may lead to dramatic reductions in smoking prevalence but these may not translate into reduced external costs for many years.

A very high proportion of the external costs associated with smoking result from the related mortality and morbidity. It takes years of smoking for these effects to manifest themselves in declining health and it takes years of abstinence from smoking before the deleterious health effects dissipate. Some relatively rapid reductions in external costs will occur (resulting for example from reductions in deaths and injuries from fires, in fire and bushfire property damage, and in litter, pollution and environmental degradation). However, in the main, there are few spectacular and quick benefits from tobacco policies. This contrasts with alcohol where random breath testing can lead to dramatic reductions in road accident injuries and deaths, and alcohol outlet licensing provisions which can lead to significant reductions in alcohol-related violence.

In these circumstances governments, who typically have short-term planning horizons, may struggle to see the benefits accruing to them of introducing tobacco control measures. This is particularly likely to be true if a high proportion of the external costs of tobacco impinge upon the private and business sectors of the community rather than on government. This is likely to be the case above all in developing nations with relatively under-developed health sectors.

On the other hand, the costs which governments are likely to face in the short-run are clear:

1. pressure from the tobacco industry, sometimes backed by the national governments of the parent companies;
2. identifiable job losses, while the job gains resulting from the allocation of consumption expenditures are virtually invisible;
3. reduced tax revenue, unmatched in the short-term by reduced public expenditures.

Pressures on governments to resist the introduction or strengthening of tobacco control measures are similar to those which governments face to maintain or increase protection levels. Indeed, not requiring the tobacco industry to bear its external costs can be seen as a form of protection, by way of subsidy, from internal competition for productive resources.

When governments are faced with minimising short-run costs to themselves or maximising long-term benefits to the community as a whole, their own interests are likely to prevail.

In these circumstances, external cost estimates can be used to sensitise governments and the rest of the community to the costs imposed by tobacco. Thus heavier countervailing pressures to the tobacco lobby may be brought to bear. Comprehensive tobacco external cost estimates and predictions may be an instrument for strengthening government resolve to implement stronger tobacco control policies.

Policies for developing countries

The development of tobacco control policies has been undertaken almost exclusively in developed countries. Developing countries have been slow to attempt to reduce smoking prevalence. There are various reasons for this:

1. There may be public ownership of sections of the tobacco industry, with budgetary reliance on the resulting profits.

2. Public revenue sources may be limited and there may be a reluctance to prejudice revenue collections from tobacco taxes, a particular problem if non-tax methods of reducing smoking prevalence are adopted.

3. Tobacco producing countries may be nervous about the balance of payments effect of reductions in tobacco demand. In fact, there is no reason to think that reductions in the domestic demand for tobacco will necessarily feed through to the export demand for tobacco. A reduction in domestic demand is likely to improve the balance of payments position of developing economies.

4. Developing countries may face very substantial pressure from foreign-owned tobacco companies, often backed by the national governments of the parent companies. Such pressure can be difficult to resist.

Policy responses for developing countries should relate to the particular characteristics of these countries. The first and most obvious characteristics are size and relative economic independence. As virtually all countries tax tobacco, the real comparisons need to be the cost of tobacco in terms of purchasing power parity, and the rate of tobacco tax relative to the tax on other consumer goods. These taxes need to be carefully calculated, to offset against tobacco cost estimates and to answer the frequently heard mantra, "smokers pay their own way through tax".

In Australia, it has proved effective to undertake net cost estimates, comparing outlays with receipts. Tobacco producing countries, like Zimbabwe, which are reliant on tobacco crops as a source of revenue, require their own specifically tailored policy prescriptions, and disaggregation of social costs can assist this process.

Conclusion

The objective of this paper has been to discuss some of the uses and limitations of estimates of the external costs of tobacco, in both the development of optimal policy strategies and the political environment in which public policy decisions are made.

The goal of tobacco policy must be to reduce tobacco-related death and disease and other forms of harm to society. Within this policy content, harm minimisation strategies must include reduction in harm to non-smokers as well as to reduce illness and death in smokers. Economic cost studies are able to identify both the costs of tobacco and where these costs are borne. They also provide the base data for calculations of the relative effectiveness of alternative interventions. Avoidable cost calculations, particularly when indicating the relevant time frames, can provide the basis for decisions about the appropriate level of resources to be devoted to tobacco policies.

The provision, in an appropriate form, of health information about tobacco is a prerequisite for efficient tobacco control policies. This information can be provided simultaneously by both governments and NGOs. Public health programs are usually addressed to populations while medical interventions are focussed on individual patients. Regulation, tax and public health policies are all the primary responsibility of government. It can be argued that medical interventions are not necessarily government responsibilities.

All of these strategies need to be justified by supporting analysis, particularly in government environments in which public policy decisions are increasingly dominated by advice from departments of finance or treasury. Without quantitative evidence of the nature of the problem and of the potential returns to public policies, tobacco control is likely to be seriously underfunded. In developing countries, cost estimates are particularly needed to bolster the ability and the resolve of governments to resist heavy pressure from the tobacco lobby.

The Canadian Centre on Substance Abuse has developed *International Guidelines for Estimating the Costs of Substance Abuse* (Single *et al.*, 1996) with the intention of assisting both developed and developing countries to undertake the measurement of external costs on a broadly agreed and common basis. These would facilitate international comparisons and to inform policy decisions. The *Guidelines* have probably not received the international exposure that they warrant. New research should be encouraged to include transferability of results to countries unable to afford their own comprehensive epidemiological and economic research.

If debates relating to size and extent of the effects of tobacco and the economic ramifications can be conducted in a collegial environment, contributing to new knowledge, and focusing on transferability of research, and evaluation of strategies, this will be a significant contribution to the overall objectives of reducing tobacco consumption and minimising harm.

References

Armstrong, B.K. (1990), "Morbidity and mortality in Australia: How much is preventable?", in McNeill, J. *et al.* (eds), *A Handbook of Preventive Medicine*, Edward Arnold.

Becker, G. and K. Murphy (1988), "A theory of rational addiction", *Journal of Political Economy*, 675-700.

Buck, D., C. Godfrey, M. Raw, and M. Sutton (1995), *Tobacco and Jobs. The Impact of Reducing Consumption on Employment in the UK*, Society for the Study of Addiction, Centre for Health Economics, University of York.

Collins, D.J. and H.M. Lapsley (1991), *Estimating the Economic Costs of Drug Abuse in Australia*, National Campaign against Drug Abuse Monograph Series No. 15, Canberra: Australian Government Publishing Service.

Collins, D.J. and H.M. Lapsley (1996), *The Social Costs of Drug Abuse in Australia in 1988 and 1992*, National Drug Strategy Monograph Series No. 30, Canberra: Australian Government Publishing Service.

Collins, D.J. and H.M. Lapsley (1997), *The Economic Impact of Smoking in Pacific Islands*, Pacific Tobacco and Health Project.

Courtwright, D., H. Joseph and D. Des Jarlias (1989), *Addicts who Survived: an Oral History of Narcotic Use in America*, University of Tennessee Press.

English, D.R., C.D.J. Holman *et al.* (1995), *The Quantification of Drug-Caused Morbidity and*

Mortality in Australia, 1995 Edition, Canberra: Australian Government Publishing Service.

Industry Commission (1994), *The Tobacco Growing and Manufacturing Industries*, Report No. 39, Canberra: Australian Government Publishing Service.

Kristein, M.W. (1983), "How much can business expect to profit from smoking cessation?", *Preventive Medicine*, 12:358-381.

Mackay, J. and J. Crofton (1996), "Tobacco and the developing world", in Doll, R. and J. Crofton (eds.), *Tobacco and Health*, published in *British Medical Bulletin*, 52.

Markandya, A. and D.W. Pearce (1989), "The social costs of tobacco smoking", *British Journal of Addiction*, 84.

Marshall, M. (1991), "The second fatal impact: cigarette smoking, chronic disease and the epidemiological transition in Oceania", *Journal of Social Science and Medicine*, 33.

Novotny, T.E., R.A. Romano, R.M. Davis and S.L. Mills (1992), "The public health practice of tobacco control lessons learned and directions for states in the 1990s", *Annual Review of Public Health*, 13:287-318.

Peto, R., A.D. Lopez, J. Boreham, M. Thun and C. Heath Jr (1994), *Mortality from Smoking in Developed Countries 1950-2000: Indirect Estimates from National Vital Statistics*, New York: Oxford University Press.

Richter, B.J. and G.B. Gori (1980), "Demographic effects of the prevention of early mortality associated with tobacco-related disease", in Gori, G.B. (ed.), *A Safe Cigarette: The Banbury Report*, Cold Spring Harbor Laboratory.

Senate Community Affairs Reference Committee (1995), *Report on the tobacco industry and the costs of tobacco-related illness*, Canberra: Senate Printing Unit.

Single, E., D. Collins, B. Easton, H. Harwood, H. Lapsley and A. Maynard (1996), *International Guidelines for Estimating the Costs of Substance Abuse*, Ottawa: Canadian Centre on Substance Abuse.

Stevenson, R. (1994), "Harm reduction, rational addiction and the optimal prescribing of illegal drugs", *Contemporary Economic Policy*, Vol. XII.

Warner, K.E. and G.A. Fulton (1994), "The economic implications of tobacco product sales in a non-tobacco state", *Journal of the American Medical Association*, 271:771-6.

World Bank (1993), *The World Development Report 1993: Investing in Health*, New York: Oxford University Press.

Chapter 14

Estimating Smoking-Attributable Medical Care Costs: Lessons from the US

Thomas E. Novotny

The public health approach to tobacco control necessitates careful surveillance of various indicators, problem assessment, and disease impact measurement (Novotny *et al.*, 1992). One element of disease impact measurement is the estimation of smoking-attributable economic costs (Shultz *et al.*, 1991). In addition, estimates of medical care costs have been used to drive public policy by identifying burdens placed on public budgets from cigarette smoking (Collins and Lapsley, 1997). This chapter reviews some of the methods used to estimate smoking-attributable medical care costs, summarises a recent study of smoking-attributable medical care expenses in the United States, and discusses implications for the estimation of medical expenditures attributable to cigarette smoking in developing countries.

Current estimates of smoking-attributable direct medical care expenditures

Several different approaches to estimate smoking-attributable medical care expenditures have been applied in the United States. These include simple attributable risk calculations, lifetime cost estimations, net social cost estimations, and econometric modelling.

Attributable risk (AR) calculations are prevalence-based estimates, counting the effects from both current and former smokers. These involve variations on the following formula:

$$AR = \frac{P(RR-1)}{(RR-1)+1}$$

where P is the prevalence of smoking (current or former) and RR is the relative rate of medical care utilisation for smokers *versus* non-smokers for a set of smoking-related diseases. The smoking-attributable fraction (SAF) developed from this formula is applied to categories of medical care expenditures (usually including hospital care, physician care, pharmaceuticals, home health care, and nursing home care) to calculate the smoking-attributable or preventable medical care costs that would not have been spent in the absence of smoking.

The lifetime estimate of smoking-attributable medical care costs is an incidence-based measure of present and future costs due to smoking. It involves modelling expected expenditures during different age intervals given survival, death, the probability of survival, and the probability of dying during these age intervals (Hodgson, 1992).

An individual's expected expenditures during age interval t are:

$$E(st) = E(st)P(st) + E(dt)P(dt)$$

where $E(st)$ = expenditures during age interval t

   $E(dt)$ = expenditures during age interval t if the individual dies in t

   $P(st)$ = probability of surviving through age interval t

   $P(dt)$ = probability of dying during age interval t

Expenditures are discounted to obtain present value of the stream of dollars occurring over time. This method accounts for the uneven expenditures on medical care for different age groups, especially for the increase in expenditures at the end of life. Higher medical care use among smokers may be partially offset by the higher mortality of smokers, which reduces lifetime expenditures.

Net social cost studies of smoking may include only those costs born by the smoker and by health care finance agencies for direct medical care (Barendregt, *et al.*, 1997). Life tables for different populations (smokers, non-smokers, mixed smokers/non-smokers) have been used with a dynamic model of smoking cessation over time to determine the net lifetime costs given the differential mortality for smokers and non-smokers. Without discounting, which reduces lifetime costs for non-smokers more than those for smokers due to differences in longevity, this method shows higher net social/lifetime costs for non-smokers. However, discounting future monetary values of current health expenditures in the range of 3 to 5 per cent is generally accepted by economists in estimating net costs. Thus, the study cited underestimates smoking's economic impact (Hodgson, 1998).

Net cost studies may also count the contributions by smokers to taxes paid on cigarettes and reduced demands on pension and social protection systems caused by early mortality among smokers (Manning *et al.*, 1989). Given these "death benefits" of smoking, smokers may pay their own way, in other words, not incurring any net social costs. However, such net cost studies do not count the pain and suffering, human capital losses, or burdens placed on families who lose breadwinners to premature smoking-attributable death. Neither do they count numerous other important smoking-related diseases such as fire injuries caused by cigarettes, environmental tobacco smoke-related illnesses, and paediatric illnesses caused by maternal smoking.

Econometric modelling has been used as a variant of a two-stage medical care-demand formula described by Duan *et al.* (1983). In this application, the effect of smoking history on the presence of smoking-related medical conditions (i.e. heart disease, emphysema, arteriosclerosis, stroke, and cancer) is estimated first. Second, the propensity to self-report poor health status is estimated, given smoking history, smoking-related disease status, socio-demographic and risk factor control variables, and sample selection bias. Next, for each of the medical care expenditure categories, the probability of having any expenditures is calculated as a function of smoking. Finally, the level of expenditures is estimated using a linear model of the logarithm of annual expenditures, given that there are any expenditures (Miller *et al.*, 1998). The model is described in the following figure:

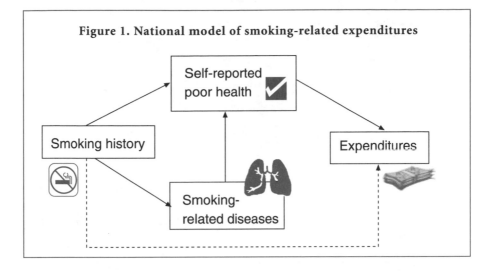

Figure 1. National model of smoking-related expenditures

This model captures a snapshot of expenditures for a given population at a given time. In the United States, the model was developed for use in analysing the National Medical Expenditure Survey-II (NMES-II), a non-institutionalised population-based panel of 35 000 individuals in 14 000 households who were interviewed four times over a period of 14 months in 1987-88. Respondents answered questions about socio-demographic factors, health insurance coverage, health status, specific health risk behaviours, use of all types of medical care services (except nursing home care), and medical expenditures for those services. The actual medical expenditures were confirmed using data from providers and insurers. The inclusion of control variables in the model helps isolate the effects of cigarette smoking. The model estimates excess expenditures (SAFs) for four medical expenditure categories and six age and sex groups (19-34, 35-64, 65 and older). For nursing home costs, the excess hospital cost fractions for those aged 65 and older were used to apply to total nursing home costs to obtain a smoking-attributable fraction of these costs. The results obtained from these models are summed.

Results of US national estimates of medical care attributable to cigarette smoking

Using the national model described above, 1993 estimates of smoking attributable mortality were calculated by applying the derived SAFs for each age-gender group to the five categories of medical care expenditures reported by the Health Care Financing Administration (Table 1).

Of concern to policy-makers is the distribution of expenditures by payer source. Because respondents to the NMES-II indicated their source of medical

Table 1. Smoking-attributable fractions and medical care costs, United States, 1993

Expenditure Category	SAF (%)	Expense (US$ billion)
Hospitals	7.5	26.9
Physicians	7.7	15.5
Nursing homes	6.6	4.9
Prescription drugs	2.6	1.8
Home health care	7.0	0.9
Total	7.1	50.0

Source: Centers for Disease Control (1994)

insurance or payments, the total costs shown above are disaggregated by payer source. More than two-fifths of total expenditures are from public sources in the United States, including Medicare, Medicaid, other state, and other Federal programmes (Table 2).

Table 2. Distribution of total medical care expenditures attributable to cigarette smoking by source of payment, United States, 1993

Payment Source	Percentage
Self Pay	21.0
Private Insurance	33.4
Medicare	20.4
Medicaid	10.2
Other Federal	9.5
Other State	3.2
Other	2.2
Total	100.0

Source: Centers for Disease Control (1994)

As an extension of the national model, an analysis of state-specific data for populations likely to be receiving publicly-funded medical care was conducted. Data sources for this analysis included smoking and other risk behaviour data from the Behavioural Risk Factor Surveillance System (BRFSS) and socio-economic data from the Current Population Survey (CPS). The BRFSS uses telephone surveys of civilian, non-institutionalised adults (18 years of age and older) to provide state-specific population-based estimates of current cigarette smoking and other risk factors. The US Bureau of the Census' CPS is a household survey of adults (15 years of age and older) which collects population-based data on socio-economic status, smoking, and other demographic variables. These last two data sets were used to model the likelihood of public medical care funding (Medicaid). For each state, 24 age-sex and medical care category models were developed (Miller *et al.*, 1998). The total SAFs for the states averaged 14.4 per cent of total Medicaid costs (ranging from 8.6 per cent in Washington DC to 19.2 per cent in Nevada). Total Medicaid expenses for all states were US$12.9 billion for 1993.

This estimate (as well as the national estimate above) is conservative for a variety of reasons. It excludes costs for illness among children exposed to smoking in households (estimated at US$4.6 billion in 1993 prices (Aligne and Stoddard, 1997)), costs of burn injuries due to cigarette-caused fires, costs of medical care for persons terminally ill or institutionalised (including military and veterans hospitals), and costs of environmental tobacco smoke-caused illnesses among adults. However, a significant limitation in the analysis is the lack of actual data on nursing home admissions and acute facility re-admissions due to cigarette smoking. As indicated, nursing home expenditures, which may be the majority of Medicaid expenditures, were estimated using the SAF for acute hospitalisations among persons aged 65 years and older.

Implications for estimating medical care costs attributable to smoking in developing countries

The estimation of direct medical care expenditures attributable to cigarette smoking is a formidable task. Data on health care costs linked to risk behaviour, health status, specific disease diagnoses, and measures of access are costly and difficult to obtain. However, smoking-attributable cost estimates are on one hand a surveillance tool or disease burden assessment, and on the other hand a potentially important piece of information for policy-makers. Thus, the estimate may be an important element in health planning and evaluation. However, such estimates are not without controversy.

For example, some studies on health care costs of smoking point out that there would be a savings in these costs in the short-term, but in the long-term, a smoke-free society would increase health costs through increased lifespans (Barendregt *et al.*, 1997). Thus, a more important consideration might be to consider a "willingness to pay" approach, given smoking's adverse effect on mortality. That is, society has decided that it is a greater good to prolong life, and thus efficient means of doing so (i.e. reducing population smoking) are goods for which money should be spent. Estimating the costs of smoking-related illness are moot exercises in this case, perhaps even misleading. Instead, analysts need only consider the costs of interventions and the cost-per-life-saved in the decision analysis that considers the benefit of tobacco control interventions.

Some additional issues in estimating costs are important to consider. First, governments have limited health care budgets, and these budgets are usually designated on a yearly basis; it would be highly unlikely that the long-term "benefits" of premature death would visibly affect these yearly budgets. If the consideration of unused pensions and social protection funds by smokers were considered, the benefit to the yearly health care budget of premature mortality is even less plausible. Second, the estimates described above severely underestimate total costs, particularly regarding terminal care costs (not included in the NMES-II data set). Decedents in the year in which death occurs may have six times the health care costs of persons not dying in that year (Hodgson, 1992). Third, the issue of discounting the present value of future losses changes the impact of lifetime cost estimates, and it should be included in such estimations.

Should developing countries invest in data sets to help determine health care costs attributable to cigarette smoking? The answer is probably yes, but not specifically to address this question. Countries wishing to assess the prevalence of behavioural risk factors will need periodic surveys of the population to monitor progress and plan behavioural interventions. Countries wishing to assess health care utilisation need data both on use patterns and on determinants of utilisation. Given the needs for econometric studies of medical care utilisation in health planning, it seems possible to at least build data systems that could link behavioural risk factor indicators, health status indicators, and medical care utilisation indicators. Modelling of these components might provide useful data for policy-makers who wish to incorporate tobacco control strategies into health finance reform. Given the burden of smoking on countries such as those of the former Soviet Union, where efforts to reform health systems might greatly benefit from reductions in smoking-attributable illness, such data sources and research on costs may well be justified. In countries where the consumption of tobacco and hence the maturity of the tobacco epidemic is not as far advanced, investments in data and research on smoking-attributable health care costs are probably not indicated. Instead, direct efforts to prevent the short- and long-term economic impact of smoking should be engaged through infrastructure development, information dissemination, price increases, advertising restrictions, and other effective interventions.

References

Aligne, C.A. and J.J. Stoddard (1997), "Tobacco and children — an economic evaluation of the medical effects of parental smoking", *Arch. Paediatric and Adolescent Medicine*, 151:648-53.

Barendregt, J.J., L. Bonneux and P.J. Van der Maas (1997), "The health care costs of smoking", *New England Journal of Medicine*, 337:1052-57.

Centers for Disease Control (1994), "Medical-care expenditures attributable to cigarette smoking — United States, 1993", *Morbidity Mortality Weekly Report*, 43:469-72.

Collins, D.J. and H.M. Lapsley (1997), *The Economic Impact of Tobacco Smoking in Pacific Islands*, Pacific Tobacco and Health Project.

Duan, W., W.G. Manning, C.N. Morris and J.P. Newhouse (1983), "A comparison of alternative models for the demand for medical care", *Journal of Business Economics and Statistics*, 1:115-26.

Hodgson, T.A. (1992), "Cigarette smoking and lifetime medical expenditures", *Milbank Memorial Fund Quarterly*, 70:81-125.

Hodgson, T.A. (1998), "The health care costs of smoking", *New England Journal of Medicine*, 338:470.

Manning, W.G., E.B. Keeler, J.P. Newhouse, E.M. Sloss and U. Wasserman (1989), "The taxes of sin: do smokers and drinkers pay their way?", *Journal of the American Medical Association*, 261:1606-9.

Miller, L.S., X. Zhang, T.E. Novotny, D.P. Rice and W. Max (1998), "State estimates of Medicaid expenditures attributable to cigarette smoking, Fiscal Year 1993", *Public Health Reports*, 113:140-51.

Novotny, T.E., R.A. Romano, R.M. Davis and S.L. Mills (1992), "The public health practice of tobacco control: lessons learned and directions for the states in the 1990s", *Annual Review of Public Health*, 13:287-318.

Shultz, J.M., T.E. Novotny and D.P. Rice (1991), "Quantifying the disease impact of cigarette smoking with SAMMEC II software", *Public Health Report*, 106:326-32.

Chapter 15

UK Smoking Targets: Policies to Attain Them and Effects on Premature Mortality

Joy Townsend

Britain has amongst the highest mortality rates in the world for all the major smoking diseases: lung cancer, ischaemic heart disease (IHD) and chronic obstructive airways disease (COAD) (World Health Organisation, 1988). The damage from these diseases is largely irreversible by the time they are diagnosed, and life expectancy short (US Department of Health and Human Services, 1989). Smoking accounts for over a third of all deaths in middle age and 18 per cent of all deaths in the UK (111 000) (Health Education Authority, 1991). A policy to reduce smoking was considered central to achieving the targets for the UK Health of the Nation strategy (Secretary of State for Health, 1992). Smoking had decreased over the previous 20 years, but it was by no means inevitable that this would continue unless there was an effective policy to counteract the effects of rising incomes, price erosion, advertising and promotion. The downward trend was likely to reverse, as was already apparent for some groups. In particular, smoking by 15-year-olds had increased from 20 per cent to 25 per cent (Lader and Matheson, 1991) and among girls aged 16 to 19 had increased from 28 per cent to 32 per cent (Office of Population Censuses and Surveys, 1991) in the late 1980s when the real price of cigarettes fell.

This chapter examines the factors related to changes in smoking and estimates the contribution made by changes in different factors to the reduction in UK smoking between 1976 and 1988. Estimates are made of the maximum likely contribution to a fall in cigarette consumption by the year 2000 from health education, advertising control, general practitioner smoking cessation advice, and public and workplace policies (Townsend, 1993). A pricing policy was estimated which, with the other policies, would be necessary to reduce smoking prevalence to one in five of the adult population, which was the government target for the Health of the Nation strategy. Predictions were made for the effect of the policy package on lives and life years saved annually (Townsend, 1993).

Consumption trends

The trends in UK cigarette consumption over the previous 20 years had each been mirrored by a trend in the real price of cigarettes in the opposite direction,

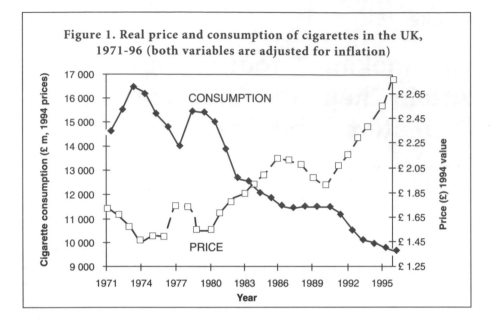

Figure 1. Real price and consumption of cigarettes in the UK, 1971-96 (both variables are adjusted for inflation)

with smoking not only decreasing when prices rose, but also rising when the price of cigarettes did not keep up with inflation (Figure 1). Similar counter-movements of smoking with relative cigarette price had been shown for France (INSEE, 1990) and Canada (Sweanor, 1991).

This relationship between cigarette consumption and changes in real price and income, has been assessed using a variety of models (Atkinson and Townsend, 1973; Godfrey and Maynard, 1988; Pekurinen, 1991) giving estimates of the price elasticity of demand for cigarettes from -0.4 to -0.87, clustering around -0.55. This means that a 1 per cent rise (fall) in relative cigarette price results in about 0.55 per cent fall (rise) in the amount smoked. These estimates have been surprisingly robust over time and place (Stone, 1945; Lewit and Coate, 1982; Worgotter and Kunze, 1986; Scott, 1991; Townsend, 1988), with higher estimates mostly for recent periods of rapid price increase (Fry and Pashardes, 1988). Higher price elasticities have been reported for low socio-economic groups (-1.3 for UK unskilled manual workers) (Townsend, 1987a; Atkinson, Gomulka and Stern, 1984) and teenagers (-1.4 in US) (Lewit, Coate and Grossman, 1981), suggesting that on average these groups reduce not only consumption but total expenditure on cigarettes when there is a price rise. Price response of teenagers had not been measured in the UK, but the substantive increase in teenage smoking from 20 per cent to 25 per cent from 1988-90 when the relative price of cigarettes was falling suggested that the UK response may be similar. Rapid price rises in Canada had been associated with a halving of smoking prevalence among those aged 15 to 19, from 45 per cent to 22 per cent, between 1980 and 1988 (Sweanor, 1991).

Most of these econometric studies analysed quantity smoked per adult or per household, as these are easier to model and estimate than actual smoking prevalence. However, for the US Lewit and Coate (1982) estimated the 'smoking prevalence' price elasticity as -0.3 (the effect on quantity per adult smoker was -0.1).

Smoking and national *per capita* income

A positive and significant relationship has been reported between smoking and real income, with an income elasticity varying from 0.1 to 0.7 (Atkinson and Townsend, 1973; Godfrey and Maynard, 1988; Pekurinen, 1991; Stone, 1945; Lewit and Coate, 1982; Worgotter and Kunze, 1986; Scott, 1991; Townsend, 1987a, 1988; Fry and Pashardes, 1988; Atkinson, Gomulka and Stern, 1984; Lewit, Coate and Grossman, 1981), so that for every 1 percentage point increase in income, smoking consumption is likely to rise by up to 0.7 per cent. A conservative estimate of 0.4 is used for the UK, which is close to estimates of the responsiveness of smoking consumption to income differences across Europe (Townsend, 1988).

Health promotion

The effects of the UK Royal College of Physicians reports on smoking and health (Royal College of Physicians, 1962) and the UK TV ban on cigarette advertising were estimated to have reduced smoking by 5 per cent in 1962, 1965 and 1971 (Atkinson and Townsend, 1973). Subsequent sustained anti-smoking information played a major part in reducing smoking in the UK. Hamilton (1972) reported for the US that health education had a significant effect over the period 1953-70 and reduced cigarette consumption by 14 per cent per year. In Australia, reductions of 6-11 per cent had been reported from New South Wales mass media campaigns (Egger *et al.*, 1983). Mass media interventions in smoking had not always been as successful, and of course success is likely to result from a subtle combination of the methodology of the programme and the receptiveness of the particular audience, and by its nature would have a large element of variation and unpredictability. But the potential effectiveness of such interventions was clear both on a national and on a local basis. School health education had resulted in a high level of awareness of the risks of smoking, and had affected attitudes to smoking (Catford, Nutbeam and Woolaway, 1984), but studies failed to show effects on the uptake of smoking by teenagers (Murray, Swann and Clarke, 1984; Cleary, Hitchcock and Semmers, 1986). Health promotion had been countered by advertising, and there was evidence that this was an important factor in promoting and reinforcing smoking among young people.

Advertising

During 1976-88 the tobacco industry spent an average of about £125 million annually advertising and promoting tobacco products in the UK. There had been much dispute about the influence of cigarette advertising on the amount smoked. The industry argued that its advertising did not recruit smokers or increase consumption, but only affected brand share. While some econometric studies had demonstrated an effect of cigarette advertisement on consumption others had not. It is difficult to model the effects of as complex an influence as advertising. McGuiness and Cowling (1975) attempted to measure advertising as a stock variable: a weighted sum of advertising over time. Their work, re-estimated by Johnston, suggested that a 10 per cent increase in advertising expenditure increased smoking by 1 per cent. Similar effects had been shown for New Zealand (Chetwynd *et al.*, 1988), and the reinforcing effects of cigarette advertising on children aged 11 to 14 had been demonstrated (Aitken and Eadie, 1990). Effects of a total advertising ban were and are uncertain, but estimates from these studies suggested a fall of about 10 per cent (Atkinson and Townsend, 1977; Laugesen and Meades, 1990; Harrison and Chetwynd, 1990). 'Before' and 'after' estimates for New Zealand (Russell *et al.*, 1979), with no concurrent price changes, suggested about a 7 per cent fall after their ban on cigarette advertising. The European Union directive to ban tobacco advertising, if adopted, might assist achievement of targets to reduce smoking of this order of magnitude.

General practice smoking cessation advice and support

Advice given on an *ad hoc* basis in general practice has been shown to be highly effective (Russell *et al.*, 1979) and cost-effective (Williams, 1985). If GPs were to give advice and counselling during normal consultations for any problem to patients who smoke, smoking prevalence might be reduced by as much as 5 per cent (Russell *et al.*, 1979). This is most effective on an *ad hoc* basis as smokers had been shown to be reluctant to attend special clinics (Sanders, Fowler and Mant, 1989); there could be economic incentives for noting cigarette consumption on patients' records and giving advice against smoking. A recent study of adolescents invited for a general practice health check (Townsend *et al.*, 1991) had shown that 60 per cent of those aged 13 to 17 who smoked were willing to make an agreement with their family doctor or practice nurse to give up smoking; this may be an effective way of reducing teenage smoking.

Smoking in public places and the workplace

It has been shown that non-smokers who experience lifetime exposure to environmental smoke have an increased risk of lung cancer of 10-30 per cent (US Department of Health and Human Services, 1986). Adults with asthma may experience substantial decline in lung functions from an hour's exposure to side-stream smoke (US Department of Health and Human Services, 1986). The Froggatt report had reviewed the evidence and identified many deleterious effects of passive smoking on respiratory function, signs and symptoms and childhood development (Independent Scientific Committee on Smoking and Health, 1988). These findings have added a new dimension to the arguments for policies on smoking in public places and in the workplace, and has been augmented by recognition of the public fire hazards of smoking which accelerated provision of smoke-free transport. Nevertheless, the UK had a long way to go to catch up with the best practices of countries like Canada, US and several states in Australia. A European Union resolution had been adopted which restricted smoking in enclosed places open to the public, including public transport. Implementation within the UK would support the proposed smoking targets.

Smoking in pregnancy

Women who smoke in pregnancy have increased risk of spontaneous abortion, antepartum haemorrhage, abruption placenta, premature rupture of membranes and premature delivery (US Department of Health and Human Services, 1989). The Independent Scientific Committee on Smoking and Health reported that smoking in pregnancy is associated with an increase in perinatal mortality of 28 per cent and of a reduction in birthweight of between 150 grams and 250 grams (Fry and Pashardes, 1988). It also concluded that there was a significant relationship between passive smoking in pregnancy and reduced birthweight.

Availability

Cigarettes and tobacco are amongst the most readily available of all products in terms of the number of places where they can be bought and the hours of availability. Although not legally available to those under 16 years of age, underage sales are widespread (Lader and Matheson, 1991; McNeil and Jarvis, 1990), and are the main source of supply for underage teenage smoking.

Recommended indicators for establishing and monitoring smoking targets

In order to establish and monitor smoking targets, appropriate indicators needed to be agreed and relevant data series identified. The indicator most frequently used in public debate is adult prevalence. In the UK this is available biennially by age, sex, socio-economic group and region from the General Household Survey (Office of Population Censuses and Surveys, 1991). There is a delay in publication of about 18 months, so the latest available figures are for smoking prevalence up to three and a half years earlier. For underage smoking (those aged 11-15), excellent detailed prevalence data, verified by cotinine assay, are collected biennially and published within a year (Lader and Matheson, 1991). From National Income Accounts there is consumers' expenditure on cigarettes and other tobacco, available quarterly (Central Statistical Office (UK), 1990b) with a maximum lag of six months. These are in current and constant prices, have the advantage of being up to date, and combine the effects of prevalence and amount smoked per smoker, both of which affect mortality and morbidity. They are in money terms which is not always easily conceptualised, so need to be converted, and are based on sales data which are not always available from the industry. Fourthly, there are customs and excise data on cigarettes released from bond (Central Statistical Office (UK), 1990a), which give probably the most accurate long-run indicator; these do not relate to immediate consumption, being affected by stocks and expectations in the short-run, but a three-year moving average would give a reliable long-run indicator. Price, being closely related to consumption, could be monitored also as a quasi indicator.

Results

(i) Factors responsible for the fall in UK smoking 1976-88

Firstly, a retrospective analysis was carried out on the previous 12 years from 1976-88. The UK National Income Accounts show a fall in cigarette smoking prevalence of 19 per cent, and in cigarettes smoked per smoker by 4 per cent, making an overall fall in cigarette consumption of 22.5 per cent over the 12 years (Central Statistical Office, 1990b). These data (which are based on sales) are used in the present estimates, and the government survey data, which are known to suffer under-reporting (Wald and Bouman, 1991), are used to indicate allocation between prevalence and consumption per smoker. Cigarette prices in real terms rose by 30 per cent over the period. Assuming a price elasticity of -0.55, this would have reduced smoking by about 17 per cent (1.3 per cent *per annum*). The 33 per cent rise in real disposable income per head, assuming an average income elasticity of 0.4, would have resulted in increased consumption of some 12 per cent (1 per cent *per annum*) (Table 1).

Table 1. Contribution of changes in price, income and other factors to the reduction in cigarette consumption, 1976-88

	Effect on no. smokers* (%)	Effect on quantity per smoker* (%)	Total reduction in cigarettes per adult* (%)
Price contribution	-13	-5	-17
Income contribution	+9	+3	+12
Residual health influences advertising trend	-14	-3	-17
Total	-19	-4	-23

Note: *Effects are multiplicative and the reduced percentages multiply rather than add to the combined effect.
Source: Table reproduced from Townsend (1993) with permission of *Addiction*.

The residual 17 per cent (1.5 per cent *per annum*) fall would be from the combined influences of changes in health education, access and other trend effects modified by changes in advertising and promotion. These influences together appear to be of the same order as that of price rises over this particular period. The decrease in smoking was due predominantly (82 per cent) to a decrease in numbers of smokers, and to a lesser extent (18 per cent) to smokers reducing their level of smoking. The relative price elasticities for smoking prevalence and smoking quantity estimated by Lewit, Coate and Grossman (1981) are used to estimate the effects of price, income and health education on smoking prevalence and quantity (Table 1).

A policy package to achieve UK smoking targets by the year 2000

The UK Health of the Nation (Secretary of State for Health, 1992) target of reducing the prevalence of adult cigarette smoking to 20 per cent was ambitious and needed to be so if the overall health targets were to be achieved. Specific target reductions were also set for underage smoking and smoking during pregnancy. There was a considerable body of knowledge available internationally on policies to reduce smoking, and British experts had played an important role in their development. The proposed target was only marginally lower than that reached in New Zealand and was above the 16 per cent smoking prevalence of professional men and women achieved in the UK (Office of Population Censuses and Surveys, 1991) both of which were substantially above the existing UK levels and so were potentially achievable. This section estimates the likely maximum impact of a policy package for health education, cessation support, cigarette advertising, and restriction of smoking in the workplace and in public places, taking into account likely increases in *per capita* real income. An estimate is then made of increases in cigarette tax necessary, in addition to the above policies, to achieve the target prevalence. If real disposable income per head grew at the same rate as during the previous 12 years (3.2 per cent *per annum*), smoking prevalence was likely to increase by 9 per cent and quantity smoked per smoker by 3.5 per cent (Table 2). As the advertising studies suggested that a ban on advertising would reduce smoking by between 7.5 (Chetwynd *et al.*, 1988; Laugesen and Meades, 1990; Harrison and Chetwynd, 1990) and 10 per cent (McGuinness and Cowling, 1975; Atkinson and Townsend, 1977) a conservative estimate of the effect of the enforcement of the European Union directive on advertising would be a fall of 7 per cent (reducing prevalence by 5 per cent and amount per smoker by 2 per cent).

Experience from the US, the UK and Australia suggested that substantial and sustained health education could reduce smoking by 10 per cent over the period (between 5 per cent and 17 per cent), reducing prevalence by 7 per cent and amount smoked per smoker by 3 per cent. Extensive general practitioner encouragement and support to 95 per cent of smoking patients to stop smoking were estimated to reduce prevalence by 5 per cent (Russell *et al.*, 1979) and amount smoked by 2 per cent. This was an ambitious coverage, but had been proposed as a target indicator (McNeil and Jarvis, 1990), and could be included as a threshold level for extra payments to general practitioners similar to those paid for immunisation targets. This did not happen. Smoking policies for public places and the workplace were important expanding areas of influence (Health

Table 2. Policies to reduce smoking prevalence to 20 per cent by the year 2000				
Factor	Policy	Reduction in no. of smokers* (%)	Reduction in cigs per continuing smoker* (%)	Total reduction in cigs per adult* (%)
Advertising and promotion	Ban	5	2	7
Health education	Sustained	7	3	10
Cessation	Smoking advice to 95% GP patients who smoke	5	2	7
Public places, workplace	Smoking restrictions	5	2	7
Income	Rise 3.2% p.a.	-9	-3	-13
Price	Raise 3% (5.25% p.a.)	27	9	34
Income	Rise 1.6% p.a.	-5	2	7
Price	Raise 55%	25	8	31
Combined package		37	14	46

Note: * Effects are multiplicative, and the reduced percentages multiply rather than add to the combined effect.
Source: Table reproduced from Townsend (1993) with permission of *Addiction*.

and Safety Executive, 1992), and extension of these policies might reduce prevalence by a further 5 per cent and amount smoked by 2 per cent.

The above effects together could reduce adult smoking prevalence to 27.5 per cent (Table 2). Progressive tax increases therefore would be necessary to achieve the full smoking target of 20 per cent. A substantial and sustained price increase was required. (If the price elasticity were -0.5, a price rise of 127 per cent or 7.1 per cent *per annum* above inflation would be required. The required price change needed to be monitored and adjusted annually.) Tax harmonisation policy within the European Union stipulated minimum but not maximum cigarette tax levels. Existing price levels within the Union varied some six-fold, and the problem of price differentials would not be substantially altered by such tax increases. The assumption of income growing at the same rate as 1976-88 was probably optimistic. If *per capita* income grew at only half that rate (i.e. 1.6 per cent *per annum*), a lower price increase would suffice. In fact, the latter rate was nearer the actual rate of income growth.

Mortality implications of the smoking targets

If effective, these policies to reduce both smoking prevalence and quantity smoked would result in lower mortality and morbidity. The mortality benefit from smoking cessation, the difference between the risks to continuing smokers and to ex-smokers, increases rapidly with time. There were also expected benefits from reduced recruitment to smoking. The relationship between smoking and the onset of disease, and between smoking cessation and the rate of decline in disease, varies among the smoking diseases. Lung cancer risk increases exponentially with years of smoking (and proportionally with cigarettes smoked per day), and at any age a person smoking for 35 years is at over three times the lung cancer risk of one smoking for 25 years (Peto, 1986). The average current smoker's relative risk of dying from lung cancer is about 16 times that of a never-smoker (US Department of Health and Human Services, 1989). After 5-9 years cessation, this reduces to six-fold, and after 15 years to about two-fold. After 20 years it is probably still slightly in excess of the risk of never-smokers. Rosenberg reported (Rosenberg, Kautman and Halmrich, 1985) from the Framingham Study that ischaemic heart disease risks of smokers reverted to those of non-smokers after five years. Cook *et al.* (1986) have suggested that the increased risk is more prolonged. The onset of chronic obstructive airways disease is very gradual, and breathlessness only becomes troublesome after considerable damage to the lung has taken place, much of which is irreversible and progressive, so the benefits of cessation tend to be more long-term (US Department of Health and Human Services, 1989). The results of the above studies and summaries were used to indicate the likely effects on mortality from the major diseases were the smoking targets achieved (Table 3). Reductions in the tar content of tobacco would further reduce mortality from lung cancer.

Table 3. UK smoking deaths avoided by the policy package

Cause	UK deaths 1998	% reduction with policy:	
		2000	*2019*
Lung cancer[a]	40 400	18	38
Ischaemic heart disease	178 300	5	8
Chronic[b] obstructive airways disease	28 900	4	35
Other smoking deaths	24 300	6	46
Totals from smoking[c]	111 000	17	46

Notes: These figures are based on 1988 mortality unadjusted for demographic change and represent orders of magnitude.
[a] Based on Doll and Peto (1977), and Cook *et al.* (1986).
[b] All deaths from the disease.
[c] 80% of lung cancer, 76 COAD, 18% IHD and 100 of other smoking deaths in 1988.

Mortality risk from all causes reduces with length of cessation. The relative mortality risks reported in the British doctors' study (Doll and Peto, 1977) are almost identical to those for the US nine states study (Hammond and Horn, 1958), and give the age-adjusted continuing smoker's risk as 1.8 relative to a never-smoker, reducing to 1.68 in the first year of cessation, to 1.3 in the 13th year and reaching the never-smoker's risk of 1.0 in the 21st year of cessation.

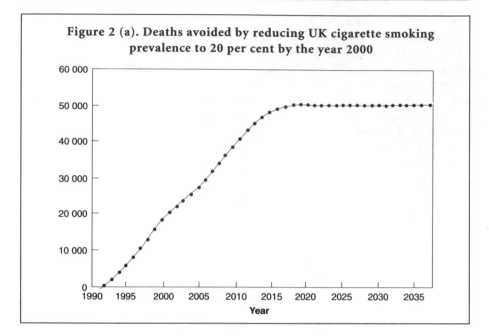

Figure 2 (a). Deaths avoided by reducing UK cigarette smoking prevalence to 20 per cent by the year 2000

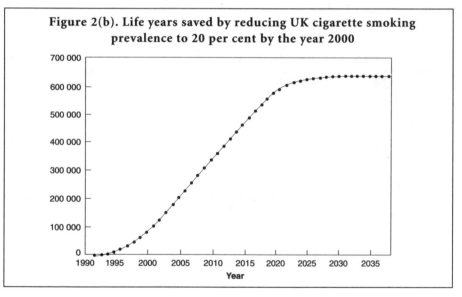

Figure 2(b). Life years saved by reducing UK cigarette smoking prevalence to 20 per cent by the year 2000

These values were used to indicate deaths from all causes avoided by the proposed policy (Figure 2). Some 19 000 (17 per cent) premature deaths per year would be avoided by the year 2000, and 50 000 (45 per cent) from 2017.

The years of life saved by these policies, based on the number of people alive each year who would otherwise have died from smoking, is indicated in Figure 2(b), assuming that the average person dying prematurely from smoking loses 12.5 years of life. An extra 84 000 people would be alive from year 2000, 500 000 from year 2017 and 645 000 from year 2032 were the smoking targets achieved. The quality of life saved by preventive action would tend to be normal for the relevant age.

The ban on advertising was not undertaken, but the government did commit itself to annual tax rises of 3 per cent above inflation, and in fact effected higher increases (probably due, it must be said, mainly to its need for extra tax revenue). As a result, smoking levels were kept at least moving towards the target, although teenage smoking rose rather than fell. There was limited smoking cessation support. Smoking prevalence was on target until 1994, but is now currently tending towards 26 per cent rather than 20 per cent. The new Labour government has committed itself to an advertising ban.

Table 4. Effect on Government Budget of a 40 per cent reduction in cigarette smoking (at 1993 prices) phased in during 1990-2000

	£ million per annum 2005-2015
Savings:	
Hospital inpatient stay (net)	40
General practitioner consultations (net)	-10
Sickness benefit (net)	300
Widows' benefit	170
Costs:	
Retirement pensions	-375
Health education	-50
Net effect (excluding tax revenue)	75
Extra tax revenue	280

Note: £1=$1.60

Conclusion

The main smoking target discussed here has been adult smoking prevalence. Smoking by lower income groups, teenagers and pregnant women tends to follow the general level and is likely to be more influenced by the above policies with some specifically targeted policies. Relative to many other European countries (Townsend, 1988), the UK already had high cigarette prices, but it also had and still has relatively high smoking mortality (World Health Organisation, 1988). Cigarettes were cheaper relative to the cost of living than they had been 40 years previously, and even cheaper relative to income changes and prices in countries such as Canada, Denmark and Norway. Raising cigarette tax effectively reduces cigarette consumption particularly by those most in need of targeting (Townsend, 1993; Lewit, Coate and Grossman, 1981). Smokers on low incomes who do not reduce their smoking may experience financial difficulties. Such problems need to be addressed, but also should be weighed against the overall benefits, particularly to families in these groups, from overall reduction in expenditure on tobacco, and reduction in childhood respiratory problems and the devastating longer-term social implications of early death or chronic disablement of parents. An unskilled male manual worker in the UK is five times more likely to die from lung cancer than a professional man, twice as likely to die of ischaemic heart disease (IHD), and more than six times as likely to die from chronic obstructive airways disease (COAD) (Office of Population Censuses and Surveys, 1986). Unskilled manual women workers are at three times the risk of dying from lung cancer, and four times the risk of dying from IHD or COAD compared with professional women or wives of professional men. Until the 1960s and the divergence in smoking by socio-economic group, there was no social group difference in lung cancer mortality, and socio-economic group 1 had the highest mortality (Townsend, 1978) from IHD. Smoking morbidity also falls more heavily on low income families. The economic effects of smoking reduction have not been addressed in this chapter, although they have been elsewhere (Townsend, 1987a; 1987b; Jones and Posit, 1989).

The effect on government revenue is likely to be approximately neutral (Table 4), the higher tax rate compensating for the reduced quantity bought and the other extra costs and savings to the government budget being approximately equal (Atkinson and Townsend, 1977). The effects on employment are likely to be beneficial, as the tobacco industry is highly capital-intensive, and alternative expenditure is likely to be on goods and services produced by more labour-intensive industries. The economic welfare effects of the policy on the individual smoker are discussed elsewhere (Townsend, 1987a; 1987b). Economic theory is based on the assumption that individuals spend their resources to maximise their own welfare, and it does not easily deal with a product like tobacco which is highly addictive, which when used in any quantity increases the risk of death and illness, and which three-quarters of its consumers are trying to stop using. This majority of smokers are looking for a non-marginal welfare gain by successfully extricating themselves from the addiction.

References

Aitken, P.P. and D.R. Eadie (1990), "Reinforcing effects of cigarette advertising on under-age smoking", *British Journal of Addiction*, 83:399-412.

Atkinson, A.B., J. Gomulka and N. Stern (1984), *Household Expenditure on Tobacco 1970-1980: Evidence from the Family Expenditure Survey*, London: London School of Economics.

Atkinson, A.B. and J.L. Townsend (1973), "Anti-smoking publicity and the demand for tobacco in the UK", *Manchester School*, 41:265-82.

Atkinson, A.B. and J.L. Townsend (1977), "Economic aspects of reduced smoking", *Lancet*, ii:492.

Catford, J.C., D. Nutbeam and M. Woolaway (1984), "Effectiveness and cost benefits of smoking education", *Community Medicine*, 6:262-72.

Central Statistical Office (UK) (1990a), *Monthly Digest of Statistics*, London: HMSO.

Central Statistical Office (UK) (1990b), *National Income and Expenditure*, London: HMSO.

Chetwynd, J., P. Cooper, R. Brodie and E. Wells (1988), "Impact of cigarette advertising on aggregate demand for cigarettes in New Zealand", *British Journal of Addiction*, 83:409-14.

Cleary, P.D., J.L. Hitchcock and N. Semmers (1986), *Adolescent Smoking Research and Health Policy*, Cambridge, Mass: Institute for the Study of Smoking Behaviour and Policy.

Cook, D., A. Shaper, S. Pocock and S. Kussick (1986), "Giving up smoking and the risk of heart attacks. A report from the British Regional Heart Study", *Lancet*, 11:1376-80.

Doll, R. and R. Peto (1977), "Mortality among doctors in different occupations", *British Medical Journal*, 1:1433-5.

Egger, G., W. Fitzgerald, G. Frape et al. (1983), "Results of large scale media anti smoking campaign in Australia: North Coast 'Quit for life' programme", *British Medical Journal*, 278:1125-8.

Fry, V. and P. Pashardes (1988), *Changing Patterns of Smoking: Are There Economic Causes?*, London: Institute of Fiscal Studies.

Godfrey, C. and A. Maynard (1988), "Economic aspects of tobacco use and taxation policy", *British Medical Journal*, 297:339-43.

Hamilton, J.L. (1972), "The demand for cigarettes: advertising, the health scare and the cigarette advertising ban", *Review of Economic Statistics*, 54:401-10.

Hammond, E.C. and D. Horn (1958), "Smoking and death rates report on forty-four months of follow up on 187 783 men", *Journal of the American Medical Association*, 116:1159-72.

Harrison, R. and J. Chetwynd (1990), "The impact of cigarette advertising on aggregate demand for cigarettes in New Zealand", in Durston, B. and K. Jamrosik (eds.), *Proceedings of the Seventh World Conference on Tobacco and Health*, Perth: Health Department of Western Australia.

Health and Safety Executive (1992), *Proposals for Work Place (Health Safety and Welfare) Regulations and Approved Code of Practice*, London: HMSO.

Health Education Authority (1991), *Health Update No. 2: Smoking*, London: Health Education Authority.

Independent Scientific Committee on Smoking and Health (1988), *Fourth Report of the Independent Scientific Committee on Smoking and Health*, London: HMSO.

INSEE (1990), Comptes Nationaux Dominique Darman, Première No. 100, August, Paris: INSEE.

Jones, A. and J. Posit (1989), "The revenue and welfare effects of cigarette taxes", *Applied Economics*, 20:1223-32.

Lader, D. and J. Matheson (1991), *Smoking Among Secondary School Children in 1990*, London: HMSO.

Laugesen, M. and C. Meads (1990), "Tobacco advertising restrictions and consumption in OECD Countries, 1960-86", in Durston, B. and K. Jamrosik (eds.), *Proceedings of the Seventh World Conference on Tobacco and Health*, Perth: Health Department of Western Australia.

Lewit, E.M., D. Coate and M. Grossman (1981), "The effects of government regulations on teenage smoking", *Journal of Law and Economics*, 14:545-69.

Lewit, E.M. and D. Coate (1982), "The potential for using excise taxes to reduce smoking", *Journal of Health Economics*, 1:121-45.

McGuinness, A.J. and K.G. Cowling (1975), "Advertising and the aggregate demand for cigarettes", *European Economic Review*, 6:311-28.

McNeil, A. and M. Jarvis (1990), "Children's purchases of single cigarettes: evidence for drug pushing?", *British Journal of Addiction*, 85:1317-22.

Murray, M., A. Swann and G. Clarke (1984), "Long-term effects of a school-based anti-smoking programme", *Journal of Epidemiology and Community Health*, 38:247-52.

Office of Population Censuses and Surveys (1991), *General Household Survey 1990*, London: HMSO.

Office of Population Censuses and Surveys (1986), *Occupational Mortality: the Registrar General's Decennial Supplement for Great Britain 1979-80, 1982-83*, Series DS No. 6, London: HMSO.

Pekurinen, M.J. (1991), *Economic Aspects of Smoking: Is There a Case for Government Intervention in Finland?*, PhD Thesis, University of York.

Peto, R. (1986), "Influence of dose and duration of smoking on lung cancer rates", in Zarridge, D.G. and R. Peto (eds.), *Tobacco: a Major International Health Hazard*, Lyon: International Agency for Research on Cancer.

Rosenberg, L., D. Kautman and S. Halmrich (1985), "The risk of myocardial infarction after quitting smoking: a report from the Framingham Study", *New England Journal of Medicine*, 313:1911-4.

Royal College of Physicians (1962), *Smoking and Health*, London: Pitman Medical.

Russell, M.A.H., C. Wilson, C. Taylor and C.D. Baker (1979), "Effective general practitioners' advice against smoking", *British Medical Journal*, 2:231-5.

Sanders, D., G. Fowler and D. Mant (1989), "Randomised controlled trial of anti-smoking advice by nurses in general practice", *Journal of Royal College of General Practitioners*, 39:273.

Scott, W.G. (1991), *Submission to the Select Committee on the Smoke Free Environment Amendment Bill (No. 2)*, New Zealand.

Secretary of State for Health (1992), *The Health of the Nation: a Strategy for Health in England*, London: HMSO.

Stone, R. (1945), "The analysis of market demand", *Journal of the Royal Statistical Society*, 108:286-382.

Sweanor, D. (1991), *Canadian Tobacco Tax Project 1985-91*, Ottawa: Non-Smokers' Rights Association.

Townsend, J. (1978), "Smoking and class", *New Society*, February.

Townsend, J. (1987a), "Cigarette tax, economic welfare and social class patterns of smoking", *Applied Economics*, 19:335-65.

Townsend, J. (1987b), "Economic and health consequences of reduced smoking", in Williams, A. (ed.), *Health and Economics*, London: Macmillan.

Townsend, J. (1988), *Price, Tax and Smoking in Europe*, Copenhagen: World Health Organisation.

Townsend, J. (1993), "Policies to halve smoking deaths", *Addiction*, 88:43-52.

Townsend, J., H. Wilkes, A. Haines and M. Jarvis (1991), "Adolescent smokers seen in general practice: health, lifestyle, physical measurements and response to anti-smoking advice", *British*

Medical Journal, 303:947-50.

US Department of Health and Human Services (1989), *Reducing the Health Consequences of Smoking: 25 Years of Progress: a Report of the Surgeon General*, DHHS Publication No. (CDC) 89-8411, Office on Smoking and Health, Center for Chronic Disease Prevention and Health Promotion, Centers for Disease Control, Public Health Service, Washington, DC: US Department of Health and Human Services.

US Department of Health and Human Services (1986), *The Health Consequences of Involuntary Smoking*, US Surgeon General, DHHS Publication No. (CDC) 87-8398, Washington, DC: Department of Health and Human Services.

Wald, N. and A.N. Bouman (1991), *UK Smoking Statistics: 2nd edition*, Oxford: Oxford University Press.

Williams, A. (1985), "Economics of coronary artery bypass grafting", *British Medical Journal*, 291:326-9.

Worgotter, G.F. and M. Kunze (1986), "Cigarette prices and cigarette consumption in Austria 1955-83", *New York State Journal of Medicine*, 3:478-9.

World Health Organisation (1988), *World Health Statistics Annual*, Geneva: World Health Organisation.

Chapter 16

Employment Issues in Tobacco Control

Rowena van der Merwe

This chapter addresses the question of output and employment outcomes associated with a decline in tobacco consumption resulting from the strengthening of tobacco control measures, and is a comparative review of studies conducted in various countries on this topic. It examines the general assumptions used to investigate the impact that declining tobacco consumption would have on a number of factors in the economy such as jobs, health care expenditure, the balance of trade and tax revenue. The chapter then reviews six studies that have examined declining tobacco consumption and jobs in Scotland, Michigan, the USA, Canada, the UK, and South Africa.

Particularly in countries where tobacco is produced, the tobacco industry has attempted to convince people that, regardless of its effects on physical health, tobacco plays an important role in the community's economic health, generating employment and contributing vital revenue to the fiscus. Stronger tobacco control measures (such as increased excise taxes, restrictions on smoking in public places and limits on advertising and promotion) that reduce smoking, and hence cigarette sales, will increase unemployment and government deficits.

However, when the industry estimates tobacco's importance in terms of jobs, they treat the resources devoted to tobacco production and sales as disappearing, if sales decline altogether. The industry focuses on the jobs directly associated with producing and selling its products. It argues that any stronger tobacco control measures will affect jobs directly associated with the industry. This is of course true, but it is not a complete picture of what would happen if stronger tobacco control initiatives were implemented. Resources would be redistributed as consumers used the same money to purchase alternative goods and services. This alternative spending could generate employment and tax revenues associated with the production, distribution and sale of the purchased goods and services.

The assumptions underlying research on tobacco and jobs

It is reasonable to assume that consumers who stop smoking reallocate their tobacco expenditure to other goods and services in the economy. Falling employment in the tobacco industry will thus be offset by increases in employment in other industries. This is the primary logical underpinning of all research on this topic, as consumers will have no less income after decreasing expenditure on tobacco products. The studies are therefore generally concerned with the multiplier effects arising from a change in personal consumption behaviour away from cigarettes and in favour of alternative goods and services.

Even if one were to assume that a portion of the reallocated resources would go to saving rather than spending, there could still be employment gains. If the consumption expenditure on tobacco were saved, this would also generate jobs in the savings industry, assuming that people do not keep their additional savings under their mattresses. Most studies reviewed in this chapter have tested for this assumption through sensitivity analyses which test different levels of savings.

The economic impact of falling tobacco consumption

Falling tobacco consumption could have a number of economic conse- quences, not only on employment but also on health care expenditure, tax revenue, and the balance of trade. Most studies have isolated these economic impacts to specific areas. This chapter focuses on the employment component, but other areas in the economy are important too. Ideally, therefore, some overall analysis of all the costs and benefits of different levels of tobacco expenditure should be undertaken. Most studies on tobacco and jobs, however, focus on employment and do not include a full cost-benefit analysis of the industry, although some of the potential economic effects of falling tobacco consumption may best be addressed through such an analysis.

(i) Job losses

As mentioned above, with an expenditure switch from tobacco it is probable that jobs will be created in other industries. Therefore, jobs in tobacco manufacturing alone will not provide a good indicator of the employment effects of reduced consumption. The effect of reduced consumption on retail jobs will depend on their dependence on tobacco sales; in general, however, if spending on tobacco is reduced, people will spend more in retail outlets on other goods and services, even if some expenditure is deferred through saving. It is often strongly argued that advertising companies dependent on tobacco monies will suffer revenue losses and hence employment losses following a fall in tobacco consumption. However, even if the fall in tobacco consumption is the result of a partial or complete ban on advertising, consumers will switch spending to other product markets, which in turn will prompt an increase in spending on advertising in these markets.

(ii) Reasons for employment losses in tobacco manufacturing

The obvious explanation for a decline in tobacco manufacturing employment would be that it is due to a fall in consumption. It is also possible, however, that the decline in employment is due to productivity improvements introduced by the tobacco industry. It is probable that an increase in excise tax may result in the industry introducing productivity or quality improvements, based on the hypothesis that a tax on a commodity results in production shifts towards characteristics of the commodity not subject to the tax. This may improve the quality of the good, and the production process. For example, a tax levied on cigarettes may induce manufacturers to produce a 'slow-burning cigarette', which supposedly increases the quality of the cigarette and improves the production process. The 'slow-burning' characteristic of the cigarette is not subject to the tax (Barzel, 1976). This productivity or production improvement may also result in job losses: for example, Pieda (1991) showed that much of the employment loss in the UK tobacco industry during 1980-90 was due to productivity improvements.

(iii) Health care expenditure

A reduction in smoking will result in behavioural changes which will have economic consequences. A nation-wide decrease in tobacco use would reduce illness and increase the trend toward an ageing population profile in the long-term, which in turn would force changes on the health care system. The most obvious would be the increasing demand for specialists in geriatric medicine and for long-term care services. Other effects of a decline in tobacco consumption would be a substantial reduction in demand for physicians specialising in pulmonary medicine or oncology. Similarly, the need for neonatologists would fall, as would the need for neonatal intensive care units. Over the following decade or two, while the need for treatment of serious chronic disease in the young and middle-aged would decrease, the number of elderly patients with chronic diseases might increase (Warner, 1987), although recent evidence suggests that avoidable mortality in middle-age need not translate into higher morbidity in older age. Hodgson (1992) suggests that smokers have higher lifetime medical care expenditure than people who have never smoked, although there is still some debate on this matter.

Health care costs are not, however, addressed in most studies of the employment aspects of tobacco control. The omission of tobacco-related health care activity — jobs, incomes, and tax revenues — results in a short-term underestimation of the economic impact of the tobacco industry, and a long-term overestimation (because in the long-run other health care services will develop). Tobacco-related health care expenditure will decline only gradually, since current tobacco-related diseases reflect the cumulative effects of past decades of smoking. Therefore, just as in the case of tobacco product expenditures, reduced spending on tobacco-related health care could be redistributed to other spending within the economy that would generate "replacement" employment.

(iv) Tax revenue

For many governments, tobacco taxation is a significant and useful source of revenue raised with relative ease from consumers. Governments are likely to react to the loss in revenue by either decreasing expenditure, which would result in government job losses, or (more realistically) by drawing increased tax revenue from other goods and services. The latter would occur naturally as consumer expenditure is switched to other goods on which taxes are collected.

If it is assumed that the decrease in smoking is brought about not by excise taxes, but by other regulatory actions such as an advertising ban, then consumers would definitely have as much money as before to spend on other goods and services besides cigarettes. So long as the money is not all saved, which is a reasonable assumption, then demand for other products will rise accordingly. The loss of jobs in tobacco products will then to a degree be counterbalanced by new jobs created in the industries supplying new consumer demands. Alternatively, if it is assumed that the cessation of smoking is brought about by excise tax increases, then new jobs will also be created so long as the government spends the additional tax revenues. For the number of new jobs to offset the lost jobs, consumers and governments must spend their extra income instead of saving it or using it for deficit reduction. There is then every reason to believe that the economy can respond to the decline in cigarette consumption by generating at least as many jobs in other industries as were lost in tobacco production (Allen, 1993).

It is often the case that a combination of increased excise tax and other regulations causes a decline in consumption. Because demand for cigarettes, particularly in the short-term, is relatively price-inelastic (i.e. relatively unresponsive to price changes), it is likely that in the short-run cigarette tax revenue will increase. The additional government funds could generate employment via increased spending on public services.

If government was to seek alternative sources of revenue to replace cigarette tax revenue which is likely to decrease in the long-term due to declining consumption, this might shift the tax burden to previous non-smokers. However, if the new revenues from other sources compensated for the loss of the former cigarette tax yield, then consumers as a whole would bear no additional tax burden. Thus even a hypothetical (and highly unlikely) complete demise of the tobacco industry would create a governmental revenue shortfall only if the excise tax revenue was not replaced with an equal-yield revenue source.

Studies examining tobacco and jobs have made certain assumptions to test different ways in which government may react to the possible long-run loss in revenue from tobacco taxes. Usually the studies assume that in the short-run there is no change in government expenditure, or that in the longer-run government will either react by decreasing government expenditure, or by seeking alternative tax bases, or by some combination of the above.

(v) The balance of trade

As a result of a fall in local tobacco consumption, the tobacco industry may increasingly focus on export markets. Finding these foreign markets means that the decline in local employment in the industry will to some extent be mitigated. This will be the case for cigarette manufacturing, and for primary production in tobacco-growing countries. For example, this policy of targeting export markets has been evident in South Africa during 1996-97, with primary producers making greater efforts to become less dependent on local markets. Because domestic demand was shrinking while international tobacco prices were rising during this period, there was strong incentive for South African producers to increase exports to overseas markets.

International studies

This chapter reviews six different studies that look at the effects of decreased tobacco consumption on employment using several of the above-mentioned assumptions. The tobacco industry has also made estimates of the job losses that would result from a decline in consumption. These typically take into account only the people directly employed in the industry, and do not consider that money no longer spent on cigarettes will be spent elsewhere in the economy. Hence, these studies show only how tobacco expenditure supports jobs in the tobacco industry itself, whereas in actuality if expenditure on tobacco products dropped the money involved would not disappear from the economy.

(i) Scotland

McNicoll and Boyle (1992) estimated the impact on the Scottish economy of a reduction in spending on cigarettes in Glasgow in 1989. Specifically, they looked at the multiplier effects on economic activity in Scotland if the citizens of Glasgow were to reduce or eliminate their expenditure on tobacco. The money not spent on tobacco was assumed to be spent on other goods and services according to consumers' existing (average) expenditure patterns. Therefore, lost jobs would be replaced by new jobs created in other industries. The study was based on the use of input-output tables which show the interdependencies between industrial sectors and sub-sectors in the economy, and how the changes in one industry affect the level of output in other industries. Two alternative situations in a given base year were compared using a static approach, assuming that there would be no change in government expenditure (and hence that tax revenue changes would not affect the Scottish economy). Their results suggest that if everyone in Glasgow had stopped smoking in 1989 there would have been a net gain of nearly 8 000 jobs in Scotland.

(ii) Michigan

Warner and Fulton (1994) used a dynamic rather than a static model, allowing the adjustment of the economy to hypothetically decreasing tobacco expenditure to occur over a number of years. A dynamic model can simulate the full impact of all important influences on the economy. A regional economic model of the United States (Regional Economic Models Inc. (REMI) dynamic regional forecasting model) was used in the case of the (non-tobacco producing) state of Michigan. Two scenarios were examined: a complete and instantaneous cessation of tobacco expenditure, and a more realistic gradual acceleration in the rate of decline in tobacco consumption during the period 1992-2005. It was assumed that expenditure switched from tobacco to other goods and services would conform with the average consumer's existing spending pattern, while declining excise tax revenue was offset by increases in other government taxes together with reduced government spending (and hence employment).

The results suggested that Michigan would have experienced a net gain of 5 600 jobs in 1992, and by the year 2005 would have gained a further 1 500 jobs. Job losses would have occurred in the retail, wholesale and government sectors. However, these losses would have been outweighed by employment creation in all other industries (services, manufacturing, transport, communication, public utilities, finance, construction, and mining). Labour income was also estimated to be greater without tobacco, by $226 million in 1992 and $112 million in 2005. The higher earnings would have been due to the change in the balance of industrial sectors from lower-paying to higher-paying industries, with competitive pressures driving up earnings because of increases in demand in an economy of Michigan that would have been stronger overall.

(iii) The US

In 1996, the Michigan study (Warner and Fulton, 1994) was extended to include the whole of the United States to assess whether declining tobacco product sales significantly reduced employment across all the tobacco producing and non-tobacco producing states during 1993-2000 (Warner *et al.*, 1996). The study used the same macroeconomic computer simulation model of Regional Economic Models Inc. (REMI) to assess employment effects, with domestic tobacco expenditures eliminated or reduced and the equivalent spending redistributed according to consumers' normal spending patterns. Being a dynamic model, inter-regional trade flows and feedback effects could be simulated.

The results showed that the tobacco-producing region of the US, the South-East, would have suffered net job losses, but with every non-tobacco producing region enjoying a net gain in jobs, all non-tobacco regions collectively would have gained enough employment to completely offset the losses. By the year 2000 the absence of tobacco spending would have meant a net gain of 133 000 jobs in the US economy. Under the more realistic scenario of doubling the downward trend in tobacco consumption, the net gain in US employment would have been 19 719 jobs. The study concluded that, contrary to the tobacco industry's claims, reductions in spending on tobacco products would boost employment in all of the non-tobacco regions, and would not diminish employment in the tobacco-producing region by as much as the industry estimates.

(iv) Canada

Allen (1993) argued that although the Canadian government believed that they had to choose between health or jobs, this was not true. Canadians could have good health without losing out on employment. Firstly, with Canadian cigarette consumption dropping slowly, those jobs that had to be shed could, through careful planning, be subsumed within normal workforce attrition. Secondly, technological changes had caused many of the job losses and would continue to do so, regardless of the health policy that the government pursued. Thirdly, the most potent cause of falling consumption was increased excise taxes, and the government revenues that were raised through these taxes would be spent to maintain public services which in turn would create new jobs.

The study developed these arguments by analysing employment changes and rates of return earned in the industry. Allen argued that the tobacco manufacturing companies had been able to maintain profits that were among the highest in the country. In addition, real hourly wages earned by cigarette manufacturing workers were much higher than average earnings of Canadian workers. Tobacco growers also earned on average much more than non-tobacco farmers.

Allen therefore argued that tobacco control policies aimed at reducing consumption, primarily government taxes, would have a negligible adverse effect on employment. Firstly, much of the employment decline in tobacco manufacturing had already occurred. Even if Canadian production was shifted abroad, there would be significant cost savings in supplying the Canadian market from abroad. Canadian plants were much smaller and less efficient than American plants. This rationalisation through the North American Free Trade Agreement was in any case inevitable. Secondly, the jobs in distribution would remain even if production were shifted elsewhere. And thirdly, Allen argued, the economy would tend to self-correct, generating new jobs to replace those lost in tobacco production.

(v) The UK

A study by Buck *et al.* (1995) used a static model of the UK, as a sufficiently detailed dynamic model of the various industries was not available. The model compared what the economy would look like at a particular point in time, if 40 per cent of tobacco expenditure was switched to other forms of spending. It did not predict how the economy would react over the long-run.

The assumption that consumers would spend their money according to average consumption expenditure patterns was also challenged. It was assumed that with a marginal increase in income, in the short-term, expenditure on essential items such as housing would change very little, while expenditure on luxury items such as recreational goods and services would change more. Four patterns of changed consumer spending were thus tested, spending according to: average consumers (the standard assumption); all non-smokers; all former smokers; and recent stoppers (the more realistic assumption). The spending patterns from these groups are summarised in Table 1.

It was also assumed that the government would react to lost revenue by either reducing expenditure, or more likely increasing consumer taxes to replace lost revenue. Different goods and services are taxed at different levels, and re-

Table 1. Spending patterns of smoking, non-smoking, former-smoking, and recent-stopper households in the UK

Functional category	% net household expenditure (excluding tobacco and miscellaneous)			
	Smokers	Non-smokers	Former smokers	Recent stoppers
Food	21.1	20.3*	21.0	18.6*
Alcoholic drink	6.2	3.5*	3.7*	4.3*
Clothing and footwear	6.7	6.3	6.1*	7.8*
Housing	22.0	25.6*	25.1*	19.1*
Fuel and power	7.4	7.2	6.9*	5.3*
Household goods and services	5.7	5.7	5.8	6.5
Transport and communication	12.4	11.9	11.8	14.8*
Recreation and education	9.4	10.0*	10.3*	12.5*
Other goods and services	9.3	9.5	9.2	11.1*
Total	100.0	100.0	100.0	100.0
Number of households	3003	4043	1580	359

Note: * Indicates that percentage of total expenditure on this category is significantly different from the percentage spent by smoking households at the 95% level.

Source: 1990 Family Expenditure Survey in Buck et al. (1995)

allocated expenditure to the different industries in Table 1 would bring in different tax revenues.

Results showed a smaller net increase in jobs when it was assumed that governments increased other consumer taxes, as opposed to reducing expenditure. All categories showed net increases in jobs, except if released expenditure were spent according to non-smokers' spending patterns, which was not assumed to be the realistic assumption, and is not either the standard assumption. If ex-smokers spent freed money as recent stoppers and government increased other consumer taxes in response (the more realistic assumptions), there would be a net increase of 115 000 full-time equivalent jobs (Table 2).

(vi) South Africa

A study by Van der Merwe (1997) examined empirically the output and employment effects if stronger tobacco control policies resulted in reduced consumption in South Africa. In a developing country, taxation is usually a more potent mechanism to reduce consumption than in developed countries, because consumers of cigarettes tend to be more price-sensitive (Chapman and Richardson, 1990). In South Africa excise taxes were increased during the 1990s, and a commensurate fall in consumption suggested that this was indeed the more important policy tool. Yet, given high unemployment in the country, policy-makers were keen to pursue this public health policy in a way that would minimise job losses.

The study used input-output methodology and a Social Accounting Matrix

Table 2. Predicted changes in full-time equivalent jobs if there was a 40% reduction in consumption in the UK

Assumptions about how released tobacco expenditure spent	*Government reaction to lost revenue*	
	Reduction in expenditure	*Increase in other consumer taxes*
According to existing patterns[1]	6 382	889
As non-smokers	-14 834	-22 133
As all former smokers	3 742	-3 771
As recent stoppers[2]	124 705	115 688

Notes: 1. Assumption of other studies, e.g. Warner *et al.* (1996) and McNicoll *et al.* (1992).
2. Assumption that recent stoppers spend higher proportion of income on other goods and services, transport, recreation and education, which is more labour-intensive.

with four expenditure scenarios to estimate output and employment effects. For three of the scenarios, the basic underlying assumption was that, in 1995, South Africans did not spend anything on cigarettes — obviously an extreme case. However, since the models are essentially linear, the implications of specified reductions in South African smoking can be approximately interpolated from the results. The fourth scenario assumed an accelerated decline in 1995 consumption patterns. The analysis showed that net employment effects would be positive, if consumption expenditure switched from tobacco to other goods and services in the economy.

The results suggested that a reduction in consumption of cigarettes would lead to a net increase in economic activity in the following ways:
1. in terms of Scenarios 1 and 2, between 9 000 and 34 000 jobs would be created if cigarette purchasing had ceased completely in 1995 and consumers then spent their money as average consumers do;
2. under Scenario 3, 50 000 jobs would be created if cigarette purchasing had completely ceased in 1995 and the money was then spent in a way that resembles ex-smokers' expenditure patterns, as in the study by Buck *et al.* (1995);
3. in Scenario 4, 3 500 jobs would be created if the rate of decline in cigarette consumption had doubled in 1995.

The results of this study are discussed more fully in Chapter 20.

Economic structure, employment losses and implications for an optimal policy mix

The tobacco industry has internationally emphasised its role as an employer and revenue generator, and (particularly in countries suffering a high rate of unemployment) this political appeal may have found many supporters. However, absent from this notion (and underlying most of the above analysis) lies the fact that economies are generally dynamic in their response to expenditure switching. The above-mentioned studies unequivocally showed net positive outcomes for employment when consumption expenditure on tobacco was switched elsewhere.

The negative side-effects of the switch are the problems of transition and differential levels of productivity in the tobacco industry. The short-term costs associated with the transition to a society of lower tobacco consumption are, however, already being experienced in many countries. Much of the transition has been pre-empted by the tobacco industry through cost rationalisation programmes and productivity improvements. The dislocation for the newly unemployed naturally constitutes very significant social and economic costs within any economy, and given the gradualness of the transition to a lower tobacco-consuming society these costs will be spread over time. In the primary sector, for example, this would probably mean that "fewer of the children of today's tobacco farming families would grow up to be tobacco farmers" (Warner, 1987, p.2083), and not that thousands of present-day tobacco farmers would become instantly unemployed.

The input-output approach underlying the type of study reviewed above highlights the significance of the underlying economic structure and systemic sectoral inter-linkages. With respect to tobacco, economic structures may be divided into three generic types:
- Type One: all tobacco consumed is locally produced;
- Type Two: local consumption exceeds local output, hence tobacco is imported to meet the shortfall;
- Type Three: the economy is a net exporter of tobacco.

In principle, constraining the tobacco industry has both negative and positive economic impacts; this is particularly so with respect to job creation. Generally, a hypothetical elimination of the tobacco industry in economies of Types One and Two is expected to have positive job creation effects for the economy as a whole. Type Three economies might well face the reverse. This is particularly so in economies where the major share of output is exported. Given the sectoral inter-linkages, the larger the share of exports out of local production, the more likely that constraining the industry would entail some job losses in the short term.

For example, in the US study, the tobacco-producing South-East region would have sustained net losses in employment, suggesting that the sectoral composition of an economy is paramount to the employment outcomes that will result. Whether a country or region is a net importer or exporter of tobacco would affect its employment outcomes.

In terms of the global tobacco control debate, it would therefore be useful to conduct similar research in other countries in order to assist policy-makers in making realistic assessments of the outcomes of their policy decisions. In many countries studied thus far, as shown in this chapter, policy outcomes in terms of output and employment need not be negative. In fact, it is conceivable that for the majority of countries that either produce and consume or import and consume tobacco, a decline in the domestic market will have very little effect on employment. In countries which rely heavily on tobacco production for a sustained export market, this may not hold true. It is indeed expected that such economies may suffer net negative repercussions in terms of the employment effects of a fall in tobacco exports. This may for example be the case in

Zimbabwe, an economy heavily dependent on its agrarian sector and tobacco exports (see Chapter 21).

In terms of an optimal policy mix, it is therefore conceivable that a country implementing a package of tobacco control policies (increased excise taxes, advertising regulations, bans on smoking in public places), may even simultaneously achieve positive, economic outcomes in terms of output and employment. The optimal mix of tobacco control policies may generate optimality in its economic outcomes too. This may be expected in countries that primarily produce for their own consumption or import tobacco. For countries that are tobacco exporters, the optimal mix of policies for tobacco control at the outset will be very different, given the different economic structure, and the outcomes for employment that result may therefore not necessarily produce positive outcomes.

The final consideration though is that, regardless of the political or economic implications of tobacco-related employment, the primary focus should be on health, not employment. The principal contribution of the tobacco industry, which is continually understated, is not as a source of employment or revenue, but it's role as a source of illness and premature death.

While all these studies are primarily concerned with the question of job losses, it should be noted that the decline in tobacco usage has other implications for the economy. In particular, less cigarette smoking will lead to a healthier workforce. The decline in sickness will raise the productivity of labour. The avoidance of premature death will preserve the skills and talents of experienced workers. Reducing tobacco consumption will conserve human resources and cannot but improve economic performance (Buck *et al.*, 1995).

References

Allen, R.C. (1993), *The False Dilemma: the Impact of Tobacco Control Policies on Employment in Canada*, National Campaign for Action on Tobacco: Ottawa.

Barnum, H. (1994a), "The economic burden of the global trade in tobacco", *Tobacco Control*, 3:358-61.

Barnum, H. (1994b), "The economic burden of tobacco — a World Bank analysis", *Smoking Prevention*, Newsletter 26, European Bureau for Action on Smoking Prevention: Brussels.

Barzel, Y. (1976), "An alternative approach to the analysis of taxation", *Journal of Political Economy*, 84:1177-97.

Buck, D., C. Godfrey, M. Raw and M. Sutton (1995), *Tobacco and Jobs: The Impact of Reducing Consumption on Employment in the UK*, Society for the Study of Addiction, Centre for Health Economics, University of York: York, England.

Chapman, S. and J. Richardson (1990), "Tobacco excise and declining tobacco consumption: the case of Papua New Guinea", *American Journal of Public Health*, 80:537-40.

Hodgson, T.A. (1992), "Cigarette smoking and lifetime medical expenditures", *The Milbank Memorial Fund Quarterly*, 70:81-125.

McNicoll, I.H. and S. Boyle (1992), Regional economic impact of a reduction of resident expenditure on cigarettes: a case study of Glasgow, *Applied Economics*, 24:291-6.

Pieda, P.L.C. (1991), *The Economic Significance of the UK Tobacco Industry*, Pieda: London.

Van der Merwe, R. (1997), *An Empirical Analysis of the Output Effects of Cigarette Taxes in South Africa and the Regional Impact*, paper presented at the Tenth World Health Conference on Tobacco or Health, Beijing, 24-28 August.

Warner, K.E. (1987), "Health and economic implications of a tobacco-free society", *Journal of the American Medical Association*, 258:2080-6.

Warner, K.E. and G.A. Fulton (1994), "The economic implications of tobacco product sales in a nontobacco state", *Journal of the American Medical Association*, 271:771-6.

Warner, K.E., G.A. Fulton, P. Nicolas and D.R. Grimes (1996), "Employment implications of declining tobacco product sales for the regional economies of the United States", *Journal of the American Medical Association*, 275:1241-6.

Chapter 17

Behavioural Management of Tobacco Addiction: What Does Social Marketing Offer?

Amy Seidel Marks

It is ironic that the very tools used by the tobacco industry to make cigarettes into the single most profitable legal consumer product sold (Pertschuk, *et al.*, 1992; Wallack and Montgomery, 1992) can also be used to combat the smoking pandemic unleashed by tobacco products (Mackay, 1998). The tools referred to are those of marketing, a discipline comprising theories, conceptual frameworks and practices derived from the social and statistical sciences and from business experience. Through the steady and often brilliant use of marketing, tobacco companies have made smoking a socially acceptable behaviour to billions of people in the twentieth century. And their responses to tobacco control efforts draw heavily upon marketing strategy. It is helpful then to reflect upon what assistance marketing has to offer the tobacco control movement itself, as it works to ensure that the twenty-first century heralds the emergence of a tobacco-free global society.

This chapter discusses insights from marketing which offer guidance for how tobacco control advocates can influence people's tobacco usage. First it defines social marketing and compares it with the other behavioural management tools of law and education (Rothschild, 1998). Next, attention is given to what social marketing can contribute to the development of an optimal tobacco control policy mix. Lastly, as a means of illustrating just one way in which social marketing can assist policy development, a model is presented of how people decide about smoking, which is derived from social marketing and psychological research. Tobacco control policy seeks to stop people from adopting or relapsing into a smoking lifestyle. This is in direct opposition to tobacco industry efforts to induce non-smokers to smoke and to keep smokers from quitting. It is, therefore, important for policy-makers to understand the process by which people decide about tobacco usage. Research findings suggest that this involves a "tobacco addiction cycle". The cycle is comprised of stages that a person moves through when he or she changes from being a "non-smoker" into a "new smoker", then becomes a "committed smoker", then typically becomes a "smoker trying to stop", and, for a fortunate few, becomes a "reformed smoker" who, unfortunately, is liable to start the cycle all over again. By identifying how members of a society fall into the stages of the addiction cycle, policy-makers can design mixes of interventions that speak to the segment of people at each stage in a way that optimally influences them to move away from smoking and toward a non-smoking lifestyle. Mixing interventions that target smaller segments of the population with society-wide interventions enables each level of intervention to amplify the effect of the others, and optimises the impact of tobacco policy expenditures.

Social marketing as a tool of behaviour management

The application of marketing to tobacco control work and to other public health and social development endeavours is typically referred to as "social marketing" because certain things change about how marketing is used. Just what is different is discernible from examining the definition of social marketing provided by one of the leaders of thought in the field, Alan Andreasen (1994, p.110): "Social marketing is the adaptation of commercial marketing technologies to programmes designed to influence the voluntary behaviour of target audiences to improve their personal welfare and that of the society of which they are a part."

This definition highlights the fact that social marketers differ from other marketers in that they take a prescriptive, focused ethical stance toward what the outcomes of their efforts should be. Social marketers constrain themselves to trying to influence behaviours that contribute to individual and collective welfare. The specification of what constitutes individual and collective welfare is usually derived from "state-of-the-art" standards and norms of the arena of impact. In public health, the standards and objectives articulated by social institutions such as the World Health Organisation and national departments of health define the ethical focus and outcomes that social marketers seek to foster.

The focus on *voluntary* behaviour is also significant. First of all, it is not enough to just influence ideas and beliefs — the outcome social marketers aim for is behaviour change (Andreasen, 1995). In addition, social marketing focuses on influencing people to freely choose to undertake the target behaviour or stop a harmful behaviour. This focus on voluntary behaviour differentiates it from other options for influencing behaviour also used in tobacco control. Michael Rothschild (1998) has offered a comparison amongst such options. He has developed a behaviour management framework that differentiates amongst three approaches to altering behaviour that causes social problems: education, marketing, and the force of law. This framework suggests conditions under which a public policy-maker might select from the three categories of tools. Key conditions are whether the target is prone to, resistant to or unable to adopt the behaviour public policy seeks to advocate. This chapter will define the three different approaches, and briefly describe the conditions under which they apply.

Education refers to "messages of any type that attempt to inform and/or persuade a target to voluntarily behave in a particular manner, but do not on their own, provide direct and/or immediate reward or punishment" (Rothschild, 1998, p.3). This approach is particularly effective when reaching people who are "*prone to change*" because they have the motivation, opportunity and ability to behave as desired and will respond to educational information alone. It is also effective when people don't have the ability to change, whether or not they have the motivation and opportunity to do so.

Policy-makers can also use the *force of law* to manage public behaviour. This refers to "the use of coercion to achieve behaviour in a non-voluntary manner (for example, military conscription), or to threaten with punishment for non-compliance or inappropriate behaviour (for example, penalties for drunken driving, or littering)" (Rothschild, 1998, p.4). Law is of use when people are "*resistant to change*" through lack of motivation. In fact, it becomes the primary tool in instances where people refuse to change even though they have the opportunity and ability to do so (Rothschild, 1998, p.30).

In the middle ground is *marketing*, which involves "offering reinforcing choices in the target's environment which invite voluntary exchange" (Rothschild, 1998, p.4). Marketing is most effective when it is possible to offer benefits to a person that outweigh those derived from the problem behaviour so as to motivate change. At the heart of the marketing concept is a mutually satisfying voluntary exchange of values. Marketing is particularly appropriate when a person is "*unable to change*" due to lack of opportunity, because it can reconfigure the environment to provide opportunity. In addition, it can be used in other instances where the person is unable to change or resistant to change because of a lack of ability and/or motivation (Rothschild, 1998, p.30).

According to Rothschild, marketing shares certain characteristics with education, but is distinct from it: "Education and marketing are similar in that both propose a free choice behaviour change. In addition, marketing offers a timely and explicit payback while education can offer only a vague uncertainty of future potential payback, and is unable to reinforce directly . . . the target needs to search for it. Marketing adds choices to the environment, while education informs and persuades with respect to choices that already exist" (Rothschild, 1998, p.5).

Each is relevant to a different context: "Education should be used when explicit exchange is possible or necessary and/or when the target is prone to behave appropriately without the development of an exchange: marketing should be used when the target is unlikely to behave as desired without receiving something (tangible or intangible) in return." (Rothschild, 1998, p.8)

Marketing also shares certain characteristics with law, but is distinct from it: "Law is similar to marketing in that both offer exchanges in the target's environment; marketing's offerings, though, are presented with free choice which is rewarded, while the force of law generally imposes sanctions for non-compliance with the proffered choice" (Rothschild, 1998, p.5).

Rothschild provides a succinct summary of how the three approaches work: education conveys "promises", marketing offers "carrots", and the force of law is a "stick".

How then does social marketing fit into this framework? Andreasen's (1995) definition of social marketing specifies that it is geared toward soliciting exchanges that enhance individual and the society's welfare. The implications are that when tobacco control policy-makers use marketing for social welfare purposes to influence people to not start smoking and to stop using tobacco, they are practising a specific form of marketing — social marketing. Tobacco companies are not constrained to such purposes and can be said to practice marketing. Marketing will be used as the generic term of which social marketing is a sub-set, with the understanding that, when the purpose is for tobacco control, social marketing is implied by the generic term.

It is interesting to note which approaches tobacco control policies and intervention programmes typically draw upon. Certainly, tobacco control examples of all three types can be cited:

education — brochures describing the health risks of smoking;

marketing — a discounted insurance premium for non-smokers; and

law — a sales ban making cigarette sales to minors illegal and punishable.

However, it is apparent that a large proportion of tobacco control effort in recent years falls under the category of force of law. This is understandable, given the addictive nature of tobacco and addicted smokers' resistance to changing their behaviour, as well as young people's inability to take seriously the long-term, intangible threat of illness and death. Actually, though, it is only in the past few years that tobacco control advocates have achieved significant enactment of laws to curb tobacco distribution, sales and promotion and raise the price through excise taxes. Laws for reducing the exposure of non-smokers to second-hand smoke are only now beginning to emerge. Previously, for decades, the emphasis was placed on educating smokers and non-smokers through warnings about health hazards, but this failed to adequately reduce the spread of smoking and consequent increase in tobacco-related morbidity and mortality.

Clearly, the "stick" is needed to curb smoking by those who are unwilling to change or are highly predisposed to start. Much credit is due those who have helped put tobacco control regulations and laws into place. More support is needed for such efforts in the next few years, particularly in the countries of the South. This is particularly important because of the need to shift public perception away from belief that smoking is normal and to foster belief in non-smoking behaviour as the social norm. Jacobson, Wasserman and Anderson (1997, p.90), in their review of the tobacco legislation and regulation in the US, noted that " . . . to the extent that laws and regulations stimulate or validate changing cultural norms, it is important not to abandon the force of law in maintaining the desired goal of reduced tobacco use".

However, effort *also* needs to be put into providing people with "carrots" and "promises" to entice them to be non-smokers. This is particularly true for certain sectors of the broader society for whom laws are not enough.

For example, laws can backfire in their effect on some people. Young people who use smoking in order to experience rebellion and communicate resistance to authority may feel even more positively about tobacco just because the "establishment" and its laws condemn smoking (Siegel and Biener, 1997). Marketing and education should also be used by policy-makers if they are to reach more than the (non-existent) "average citizen". This is because people vary in their perceptions of and response to tobacco. Where law is most effective for one sector of the society, marketing or education may be better for another sector. In other words, not everyone is a recalcitrant smoker or an impressionable, social-acceptance-seeking youth that must be coerced to reduce smoking by laws constraining access or usage. Large numbers of people, particularly in developing economies, have never seriously contemplated personally smoking, and even those who smoke have some negative feelings about it. Many are therefore predisposed to respond to less-coercive tobacco control measures. Education by itself might be enough: some people could be confirmed in not smoking simply by hearing messages about the costs and hazards of tobacco. Marketing might work best for others: already addicted smokers might become motivated to stop by marketing efforts that offer benefits for not smoking such as reduced insurance premiums. Still others who are drawn toward smoking but have not yet tried it, may be inspired to never start if *both* educated about its hazards *and* offered a social marketing option. The latter would be something where not smoking provided tangible benefits greater than that of smoking. An example of this "something" could be membership in an investment scheme for a child's education that is open only to a non-smoking guardian. Social marketing provides the mechanism for identifying the need for, conceptualising, developing and implementing such a scheme.

Thus, all three tools need to be used in public policy management. Rothschild's (1998) behavioural management framework offers insights into the unique capacities of each tool and under what circumstances it is best used. However, it is not enough to focus on using each tool on its own. A fundamental principle underlying the concept of the behaviour management framework is that policy-makers should construct a strategic mix of the tools so that an optimal overall impact on the public problem is achieved. Tobacco control policy development, therefore, needs to utilise all three tools in society-wide interventions. Laws, education programmes through the national education and health departments, and national media, as well as creative marketing initiatives such as a public health system-based cessation programme should be co-ordinated so that each increases the impact of the other.

In addition, tobacco control policy-makers should identify how segments of the population differ from each other in their response to tobacco and then develop a strategy that is a unique mix of the tools for each segment. These targeted intervention mixes, that configure the tools strategically together to "speak" uniquely to each segment, need to be designed to be complementary to society-wide interventions so as to amplify overall policy impact. Thus, spending a portion of the national tobacco control budget on well-designed, complementary targeted interventions can actually optimise the impact of *all* expenditures.

The focus of this chapter is on social marketing, so discussion now turns to what it can offer tobacco control policy-makers. Even though education is not discussed to the same degree in this text, whereas the role of law is covered in other chapters, it is hoped that the points raised here will highlight the importance of using all three tools of behavioural management so that an optimal tobacco control policy mix is achieved.

What does social marketing have to offer an optimal policy mix?

Social marketing has several ways in which it can inform the formulation and implementation of tobacco control policy.

(i) Understanding what tobacco companies do

First of all, social marketers come from the same discipline as tobacco marketers and are uniquely placed to identify what needs to be counteracted by tobacco control policy. In others words, "it takes a marketer to know a marketer", even though this might be painful to social marketers who feel marketing should be used for human welfare! Social marketing expertise can help public policy-makers predict, research and identify how the tobacco companies sell cigarettes and other tobacco products. Specifically, public policy-makers need to understand what marketing strategies and tactics are used to influence people to use tobacco. Social marketers can also use the science and "art" of marketing to project what the tobacco industry will do to respond to public policy interventions. That information, as well as social marketers' strategic planning expertise, should be a basis for the development of policy-makers' tobacco control strategies and tactics.

For example, marketing research can identify the extent to which youth in a region acquire cigarettes from vending machines, and what other access methods they may turn to in the event of a ban on them using vending machines. This information can be used to motivate the regulation of vending machines. It can also help in the formulation of other strategies to curb young people's efforts to get cigarettes from alternative routes in the event of a ban. Social marketing distribution theory would also suggest ways to market the regulations to vending companies and retailers so as to preclude illegal youth access.

(ii) Segmenting the public

People differ with regard to their attitudes toward a health hazard such as tobacco, but forces shaping public policy can cause policy-makers to ignore these differences. Policy-makers are often pushed to reach the greatest number of people for the least cost because of factors such as limited budgets, an assumed mandate to "serve all the people all the time", and the belief that a majority or "average" opinion exists. In addition, public servants typically find it politically necessary to make trade-offs in brokering political opposition to the development of an intervention. However, there are too many cases where political horse-trading has resulted in such a jumble of compromises that the intervention lacks programmatic focus and strategic clarity, and results in the minimal possible impact. Too many a public campaign is a "buckshot" approach that aims at a mythical "average" person, but "hits" only a small number while spewing expenditures everywhere.

Marketing research can help move beyond a purely society-wide focus to also identify and target key segments within the population, such as those who are more at risk of smoking or more predisposed to not smoke. Segmentation of effort can enhance effectiveness and even increase efficiency. A broader "buckshot" approach, such as a mass media campaign spreading the same tobacco control message to everyone, may not speak adequately to attitudes and beliefs held by sub-segments. Although it may be cost-efficient in terms of implementation (and cost per person), it may have low effectiveness and influence only a small portion of people. Research grounded in social marketing concepts and strategy can identify what divisions exist in the body politic concerning tobacco. Separate segments can be identified, clarifying the nature of the people comprising each one, and their propensity to smoke and attitudes about it. Interventions can then be tailored that speak to a particular segment's mindset toward tobacco, and more efficiently and effectively influence its members to adopt a tobacco-free lifestyle.

Although separate interventions for each segment may be prohibitively expensive in comparison to a single society-wide intervention, this does not preclude targeting one or more of the most critical segments so as to complement the impact of the broader intervention and increase overall effectiveness. In addition, the research can reveal essential underlying perceptions shared amongst most segments that can inform the mass media intervention's content.

(iii) Tailoring interventions to different orientations to tobacco

Once a way of segmenting people according to their relationship to smoking is found, emphasis needs to be placed on convincing those who already wish to smoke not to do so. This is the antithesis of the tobacco industry's focus on convincing them to smoke. However, it is not enough to just work on those who want to smoke. Indeed, laws and regulations to that effect already exist in many countries. One must also speak to those who are inclined NOT to smoke and reinforce their orientation. In addition, tobacco control advocates must speak to those who have not really considered the issue, and give them the information, attitudes and skills they need to withstand the pressure from tobacco company messages. Policy-makers need to immunise them against the tobacco industry's efforts and social influence (Pechmann and Ratneshwar, 1994). This is of particular importance for vast sectors of the populations of developing economies.

Social marketing offers tools for achieving these ends. It provides insights and methods for segmenting people according to their responses to tobacco, so that collections of people sharing similar tobacco orientations can be identified. Interventions can then be tailored to the people in each segment. The content of an intervention would relate to the particular pattern of attitudes held by the people in its target segment. The targeting of segments is in contrast to using a single, society-wide intervention that speaks to an "average" attitude. This "average" attitude may in fact be held by only a small subset (i.e. segment) of the whole population.

Tailoring interventions means that a segment of the population can be efficiently targeted with messages, programmes and policies that correlate with the members' mindset toward rejecting tobacco and inspire them to move toward a tobacco-free lifestyle. Social marketing offers the concepts and practices needed to design these interventions as well as to orchestrate and implement them. These include " . . . functions such as market research, product positioning and conception, pricing, physical distribution, advertising, and promotion (hence the mnemonic 'four Ps' — product, price, place and promotion). The 'social product' might be a consumable object (such as a contraceptive device), a practice (a one-time act or more complex behavioural repertoire), or even an abstract belief, attitude, or value (like social justice)" (Walsh *et al.*, 1993).

(iv) Configuring the behavioural management tool mix

Lastly, social marketing efforts could be designed to *co-ordinate* with educational and/or legal interventions so as to amplify the effects of all of them. For example, social marketing research has suggested that health-related instruction in schools may work in tandem with tobacco control advertising to "immunise youth so they do not come to believe the myth that smoking has desirable psycho-social consequences" (Pechmann and Ratneshwar, 1994, p.248). The researchers speculated that " . . . our anti-smoking ads may have been particularly effective because these ads made more salient subjects' negative preconceptions about smokers, which were beliefs presumably attributable at least in part to anti-smoking school programs" (Pechmann and Ratneshwar, 1994, p.248).

These findings imply that the effects of an educational campaign using mass media advertising could be amplified if it were co-ordinated with a social marketing programme that provided tobacco control education to children in their schools. Teachers would be motivated to use the materials because they would save time and effort. Further motivation could be created by, for example, giving the teacher a chance to win a prize by submitting the children's projects on learning points in the curriculum. The research findings also raise the possibility that adherence to a law banning sales of cigarettes near schools could be bolstered through educational programmes in the schools, as well as social marketing interventions targeted at parents, shopkeepers and even cigarette hawkers. Using and co-ordinating several behavioural management tools can increase the impact of each. In addition, mixing a society-wide intervention, such as a mass media advertising campaign, with other interventions that target specific segments can amplify the effects of all and optimise the impact of tobacco policy expenditures.

In summary, public policy-makers must decide what behavioural management tool to use when, but different tools are appropriate for different consumer needs and circumstances. It is therefore important to understand how people differ with regard to their relationship with tobacco and to speak to people differently, in their "own terms". Issues such as how a person feels about tobacco smoking, how accessible it is to him or her and how able he or she feels to use or refuse it will determine how to best use education, marketing and law, singly or together, to enable him or her to reject it. Discussion now turns to a specialised field within marketing for an understanding of how people relate to tobacco. The chapter concludes with this illustration of just one area in which social marketing can inform tobacco control policy development.

The tobacco addiction cycle

The field of consumer behaviour, which draws heavily on the social sciences, identifies various psychological conditions or states that people move through when they purchase and use products. This section begins by applying a generic consumer behaviour model of decision-making to tobacco consumption. Cigarettes are used to illustrate the points made in this paper, but other tobacco products fit into the patterns discussed.

(i) Smoking as a lifestyle

The left-hand side of Figure 1 shows steps that someone who has never used cigarettes can go through on the way to becoming a smoker. At the top and bottom of the diagram *non-smoking* and *smoking* are each referred to as a *lifestyle*. The word "lifestyle" implies that tobacco usage has an impact on a smoker's life experience that is deeper and more complex than simply buying an object, using it and throwing away its remnants (Solomon, 1994). Cigarettes and other tobacco products have been shown to be highly addictive, so that a user becomes dependent on them (Heishman, Kozlowski and Henningfield, 1997). Such dependency means the smoker feels compelled to use the product and therefore organises many other aspects of his life around purchase and consumption behaviour.

A few brief examples are provided to illustrate how smoking influences a person's lifestyle so that it supports the consumption of cigarettes (Solomon, 1983). These examples are extrapolated from findings about what is the typical consumption behaviour of "fast-moving consumer goods" (Peter and Olson, 1996; Schiffman and Kanuk, 1997; Solomon, 1994). Smokers tends to shop regularly at places that give reliable access to their preferred brand of cigarettes, buy at a frequency to keep the nicotine level in their bodies at an optimum, and arranges their expenditure patterns so as to pay for this habit. They organise their daily schedule and behaviour around smoking, and where it is prohibited, such as in a workplace, must go out of their way to take a "smoke break". In those instances, smokers tend to socialise with each other and the habit can affect whom they know and count as friends. Frequently, smokers have product-induced coughs and other symptoms that affect them in the morning, and are more prone to respiratory infections and other illnesses that cause them to lose workdays. Chronic illnesses arising from tobacco usage themselves entail lifestyles, popularly referred to by such words as "asthma sufferer" or "heart patient", etc. Additionally, consumer research has shown that product usage or ownership affects the degree to which a person pays attention to information in the environment about the product (for example, Peter and Olson, 1996), which suggests that smokers' usage of the media and related thinking patterns are affected by their consumption of cigarettes.

(ii) Not smoking as a lifestyle

Just as cigarette users have a smoking lifestyle, so non-smokers can be said to have a lifestyle based on not using cigarettes. Many non-smokers claim to be oblivious to smoking and would say that smoking does not consciously affect

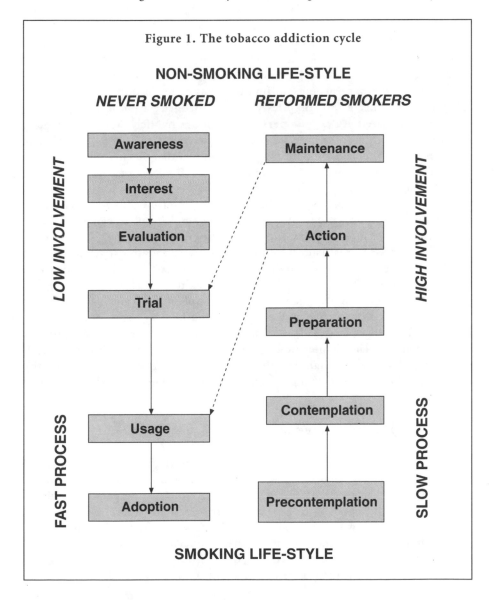

Figure 1. The tobacco addiction cycle

what they do or how they live. In that case they may be said to function in a smoke-free way. However, many other non-smokers' lives are affected daily by others' smoking and this influences their lifestyle. People who don't like to be exposed to smoke consciously and unconsciously design their day around avoiding uncomfortable levels of exposure to tobacco smoke. Avoiding tobacco smoke can affect where one shops, with whom one socialises, and even work efficiency and comfort in public places. In short, non-smokers, by virtue of not using tobacco products, have patterns of life they do not share with smokers, and which frequently are shaped by efforts to avoid tobacco exposure.

The concept of lifestyle also means that people use socially recognised symbols such as clothing styles, language and possessions to communicate identity and meanings about self-worth to others (Solomon, 1983). Tobacco companies have spent billions in the last century to make their products social icons that people use to communicate who they are or want to be. Much of advertising content tries to link different "personalities" or lifestyles to different brands of cigarettes, so people can find one that expresses just what they want to be and say. Thus, a smoking lifestyle has embedded within it a deeper-level usage of the cigarette to express personal meanings publicly. For many people, the addictive nature of the product is both biochemical and psychological. The cigarette is a fundamental building block of identity. Asking them to stop smoking is also asking them to lose an element of core meaning in their lives.

Non-smokers are often swimming against the stream of social trends by not using and even opposing icons that have become powerfully condoned and used in the culture. It is only in recent years that non-smokers have been given social icons such as no-smoking signs and no-smoking sections that they can use to express their preferences. They have had to endure an arduous struggle in using those icons, because they communicate socially negative meanings for large numbers of people. This is only gradually starting to change.

The concept of lifestyle means that when someone who has never smoked becomes a smoker or when a smoker ceases smoking, he or she goes through a process of lifestyle change. This is far more complex than just buying a product or not buying it. The chapter now turns to the stages that consumer research suggests people go through in lifestyle change. The discussion starts by examining the stages of changing from a non-smoking lifestyle to one of smoking.

(iii) How someone who has never smoked becomes a smoker

The left-hand side of Figure 1 shows that a multi-stage process of change occurs when someone who has never smoked becomes a smoker. This process will be discussed in terms of how it might apply to a young person under 18 years of age. The stages shown here are characteristic of several "hierarchy of response" models that have been developed by consumer researchers to explain the psychological steps entailed in purchase behaviour (Kotler, 1997). These models do not imply that every person moves through all the stages shown, but rather that the sequence of events is typical for many purchase decisions.

Most of these models are based on the notion that decisions to try, use, and adopt a product or service first entail a "cognitive" or learning stage. In this model, the young person becomes *aware* of the product through passive exposure to information in the environment and to smokers. Thus, the increasing amount and kinds of tobacco promotion, whether through advertising or things like sports sponsorships, ensure that increasing numbers of children in most urban centres in the world and even in large portions of the rural areas are exposed from the earliest ages to various forms of persuasive messages to smoke (Wallack and Montgomery, 1992). In addition, children's passive exposure to the product increases as the incidence of smoking in society increases.

Most consumer response models indicate that a person then moves on to an "affective" stage of the process. Figure 1 shows the person to feel enough *interest* in the product to pay attention to advertising and other kinds of information sources and learn about it. Tobacco advertising can draw children into this deeper level of response to smoking. For example, a US study found that over half of the 3 to 6-year-old children studied were able to match the Joe Camel tobacco character with cigarettes (Mizerski, 1995).

Figure 1 then shows that the person moves to *evaluation*, which is a kind of "mental trial" to see whether it is personally relevant and, if so, what brand or form is preferred (Schiffman and Kanuk, 1997). Advertising seems to play a role in assisting teenagers to evaluate cigarette brands at this stage. Pollay *et al.* (1996) found teenager advertising elasticity to be about three times higher than an adult's, consistent with the finding that teenagers' brand choices are highly concentrated on the ones most advertised. This suggests that, contrary to tobacco industry claims, adolescents use advertising, and not just peer smoking behaviour, in evaluating the relevance of smoking to their own selves (Boddewyn, 1987).

The final phase of most consumer response models is "behavioural", in which the person acts on the beliefs and attitudes he developed in the previous stages. First he or she *tries* the product in a limited, experimental way, and goes through a pattern of *usage* and then *adopts* it as a regular part of his lifestyle. Research has found that "even limited exposure to cigarettes during [early adolescence] substantially raises the probability of regular smoking in adulthood" (Hine *et. al.*, 1997) with conversion rates from trial being as high as 75 per cent. This suggests that the time span between trial and adoption might be very small and that a period of uncommitted usage is omitted in at least some cases. One of the criticisms levelled towards the tobacco industry is that it has increased the level of nicotine in brands so as to induce addiction after only a few cigarettes (Kelder and Daynard, 1997). This would collapse the stages into a trial step followed almost immediately by adoption.

It must be noted that the decision-making stages shown in Figure 1 are not being presented as the final word in consumer behaviour. Indeed, numerous rival models and psychological processes have been proposed that are more complex and model deeper dynamics of the mind and motivation (for example, Hine *et. al.*, 1997). In addition, it is important to note that different sequences of the stages of response have been proposed. One such suggestion uses the Foote, Cone and Belding model of product categories to suggest that cigarettes fall into a product category that evokes a powerful affective, emotional level of response (Vaughn, 1980). The immediacy of this response can lead people to first mimic the behaviour of others, and only then create emotional and rational justifications for their behaviour. That response sequence would be "behaviour" to "affect" to "cognition", which is the opposite of what is shown in Figure 1. This idea fits well with the popular notion that peer influence is an overpowering force that can supersede even strong antismoking beliefs a youth may hold (Hine *et al.*, 1997). The point being emphasised is that, although consumer researchers have learned a lot about the psychological response process a person experiences in moving from a non-smoking to a smoking lifestyle, even more has yet to be discovered. Figure 1 simply tries to illustrate that a process occurs and that understanding its dynamics is important.

(iv) Stages of change from smoking back to not smoking

The right-hand side of Figure 1 is, in effect, a mirror image of the left-hand side because it represents the reversal of the process just discussed. However, the fact that different steps are shown suggests that the road back to non-smoking for a smoker is much rougher than the one that lead to the smoking. Smoking is an addictive behaviour because tobacco contains nicotine, a drug "as capable of producing addiction as heroin, cocaine, or alcohol" (Heishman, Kozlowski and Henningfield, 1997, p.15). Addiction to nicotine involves physical dependence on cigarettes such that stopping smoking elicits a withdrawal syndrome. Withdrawal brings about symptoms so intolerable as to cause the abstainer to revert back to smoking to get rid of them. The cigarette, as tobacco companies themselves have admitted, is a "nicotine delivery system" of a drug that hooks the user into a deep level of dependency from which it is hard to break free.

Prochaska and DiClemente developed a model of the structure underlying people's intentional efforts to change their own addictive or problem behaviours. Their team's studies over two decades have identified a consistent pattern of critical stages that underlie such behaviour changes and are precursors to success (for example, DiClemente, Prochaska, Fairhurst, Velicer, Velasquez, and Rossi, 1991; Prochaska, DiClemente and Norcross, 1992). The basic constructs of their "Stages of Change" model are shown on the right-hand side of Figure 1. These are briefly explained below and some are illustrated with examples from the experience of Prochaska, DiClemente and Norcross (1992) with smoking cessation treatment programmes.

Precontemplation is a condition in which the person has no intention to change the problem behaviour, and actually does not see it as a problem. Prochaska, DiClemente and Norcross (1992, p.1103) measure it by "asking whether the individual is seriously intending to change the problem behaviour in the near future, typically within the next six months", with those saying "no" being classified in this category.

Contemplation is when a person is aware that a problem exists and is "seriously thinking about overcoming it but [has] not yet made a commitment to take action" (Prochaska, DiClemente and Norcross, 1992, p.1103). People can remain in this stage for long periods, with one group of smokers studied being there for the whole two years of the project and showing no movement at all. The mindset is typified in the statement, "Yes, I know. I am not ready yet" (Prochaska, DiClemente and Norcross, 1992, p.1103). Contemplators give serious consideration to problem resolution and actively evaluate the pros and cons of smoking versus those of the process of overcoming the addiction and those of being a non-smoker.

Preparation is a transitional phase between contemplation and action and entails seriously intending to take action very soon. Small tentative actions are taken to prepare for the real change effort. DiClemente *et al.* (1991) found that smokers at this phase would try such things as smoking five cigarettes less a day or delaying the first one of the day by half an hour.

Action is when a person makes significant, overt efforts to change the behaviour through a considerable commitment of time and energy. Prochaska, DiClemente and Norcross (1992) classify a smoker as being in this stage only if he reaches a certain degree of change in previous behaviour. For example, they would not classify someone who cuts down on smoking by 50 per cent and changes to low tar cigarettes as taking action, but rather as being in preparation for action. Their experience, like others, with smokers who reach this level is that they almost always revert back to smoking after the first attempt to take action. "With smoking . . . successful self-changers make an average of from three to four action attempts before they become long-term maintainers" (Prochaska, DiClemente and Norcross, 1992, p.1104). The arrow in Figure 1 from this stage back to the usage condition on the left-hand side indicates the tendency for those taking action to revert back to usage and then become trapped once again in a smoking lifestyle.

Maintenance is reached when a person works on keeping the behaviour change stable and preventing relapse. It is not a static stage, but instead is "a continuation, not an absence of change" (Prochaska, DiClemente and Norcross, 1992, p.1104), that in some cases lasts a lifetime. It is a constant state of working on preventing a relapse. The arrow in Figure 1 from this stage back to the trial condition on the left-hand side shows that reformed smokers are vulnerable and, through something as small as "just a little puff of yours, please", can slip back down into a smoking lifestyle.

Several important insights emerge from this model. First of all, actions are hard to bring to the maintenance stage and frequently result in failure. However, the vast majority of such relapsers cycle back to the earlier stages of contemplation or preparation and, having learned something, try again. In fact, Prochaska, DiClemente and Norcross (1992) posit a spiral-like, iterative pattern to exist whereby regression to an earlier stage means the individual starts the process over again, but usually from a stronger base.

Both because of this iterative pattern of change in cessation and because of the very high involvement it necessitates, the process of smoking cessation is typically much slower and more intensive than that of starting smoking. Figure 1 shows that, relative to each other, the path from not smoking to smoking is a faster one than that of cessation. Because it involves a less intense degree of cognitive and affective functioning, in a psychological sense, the time between the interest and adoption phases may actually be collapsed. A teenager that decides smoking is of interest may jump almost immediately to full adoption because it is part and parcel of the overall lifestyle he or she aspires to and then adopts.

Implications of the tobacco addiction cycle for tobacco control policy

Looking at addiction as the cyclical process shown in Figure 1 highlights the importance of identifying just where a person is in the cycle. The four implications for tobacco control policy development, which were discussed in Section 3, also apply here and are briefly illustrated below.

(i) Understanding what tobacco companies do

Tobacco companies base marketing decisions on this type of information. Therefore, tobacco control policy-makers can also use a model like Figure 1 to understand tobacco marketing and develop strategies and tactics to counteract it. For example, Figure 2 is a typical analytical framework used for teaching a masters-level marketing course that is based on a portion of Figure 1. It illustrates the importance, when marketing a product, of knowing how many people are at each of the consumer response stages shown on the left-hand side of Figure 1. Cigarette companies undoubtedly use similar segmentation frameworks when developing their marketing efforts.

Figure 2 shows that although a large number of people may be aware of a product or brand, the numbers decrease as some people progress through the stages of response because others never move on. Thus, in this hypothetical example, a marketer may only reasonably be able to expect that 5 per cent of the whole market will regularly use and repurchase the product. However, the diagram shows that this 5 per cent base of loyal customers has resulted from at least 90 per cent of the market being made aware of the product, 60 per cent becoming interested, 30 per cent personally evaluating its feasibility for their own use, 20 per cent trying it, and 8 per cent using it a few more times before 5 per cent settle into the habitual use that is adoption. This kind of model can help tobacco companies to analyse the behaviour of customers that are loyal to a particular brand. It does not model people who are brand-switchers, but similar frameworks have been developed for that kind of consumption behaviour (for example, Lilien, Kotler and Moorthy, 1992).

Figure 2 is also useful for tobacco control thinking, in that it can be applied at a product category level, as opposed to brand level, to analyse the aggregate adoption of regular cigarette consumption. (Obviously, the 5 per cent adoption rate shown is not an accurate number for most countries' addicted smoker segment!) Such modelling can help policy-makers understand the dynamics of

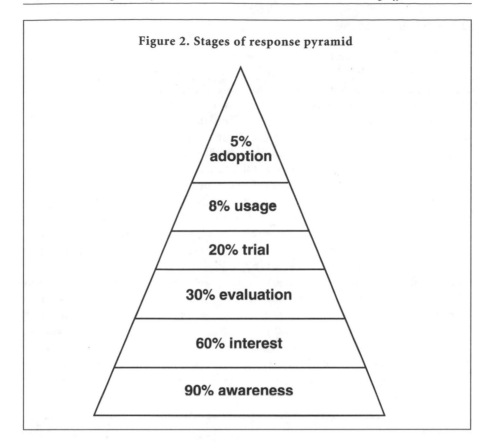

Figure 2. Stages of response pyramid

5%
adoption

8% usage

20% trial

30% evaluation

60% interest

90% awareness

the tobacco market and how tobacco companies seek to influence consumption.

Information about what stage consumers are in can be a powerful tool for a tobacco company's strategic decision-making and action. For example, it provides insights into what results marketers should aim for and what expenditures to make to achieve them. After doing the research to gather and estimate the numbers shown in Figure 2, one is better able to identify what is a reasonable target number to aim for at each level *and* what is a reasonable end result from the process. A tobacco company's marketers could seek to increase the final 5 per cent brand loyal percentage shown in the pyramid to 7 per cent, but it would mean adjusting the numbers in one or more of the stages preceding it. This could only happen by increasing the effectiveness and or amount of marketing efforts that create awareness, interest, evaluation, etc. That costs money, and managers must decide whether the probable financial returns from the marginal increase in regular users (2 per cent) would justify the amount of additional expenditure needed. Thus, understanding how people move through the stages of response is a tool for optimising the outcomes of tobacco marketing efforts. The model in Figure 2 is but a simple example of the wide range of mathematically-based decision-modelling approaches marketing can offer public policy development (Lilien, Kotler, and Moorthy, 1992).

(ii) Segmenting the public

This also holds true for tobacco control policy development. The stages of response on the left-hand side of Figure 1 can be used to segment the population. Tobacco control strategies could then be developed for the people at each stage to inhibit or reverse their movement toward smoking.

Likewise, the stages of change model on the right-hand side of Figure 1 provides a sound basis upon which to segment the population of smokers in terms of their readiness not to smoke. Prochaska, DiClemente and Norcross (1992) found in repeated studies over the years that people at one stage of the change process did not respond to influence not to smoke in the same way as people at different stages. They had numerous experiences with people being offered well-designed and administered cessation programmes at minimal cost, only to see tiny numbers sign up for them and large percentages then drop out. They discovered that for the groups they worked with in the US, "the vast majority of addicted people are *not* in the action stage". On average they have found that "10-15 per cent of smokers are prepared for action, approximately 30-40 per cent are in the contemplation stage, and 50-60 per cent are in the pre-contemplation stage" (Prochaska, DiClemente and Norcross, 1992, p.1105). They also found that the amount of progress people made in cessation programmes was dependent on the stage they were in. Figure 3 shows the relationship that emerged from one study. Those who had progressed to the preparation stage of change showed the most success in keeping off cigarettes over 18 months.

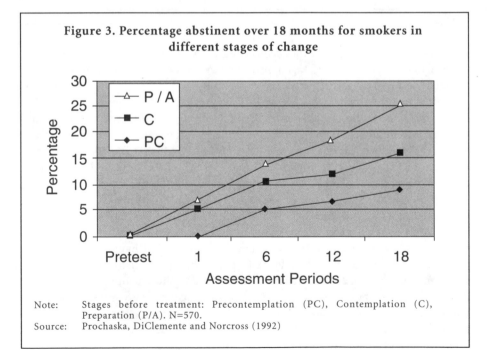

Figure 3. Percentage abstinent over 18 months for smokers in different stages of change

Note: Stages before treatment: Precontemplation (PC), Contemplation (C), Preparation (P/A). N=570.

Source: Prochaska, DiClemente and Norcross (1992)

The researchers concluded that "To treat all of these smokers as if they were the same would be naive. And yet, that is what we traditionally have done in many of our treatment programmes" (Prochaska, DiClemente and Norcross, 1992, p.1105). In general, tobacco control policies and interventions could more effectively influence more people not to smoke by segmenting the public according to stages in the tobacco addiction cycle.

(iii) Tailoring interventions to different orientations to tobacco

The purpose of segmentation is to develop different interventions for different segments, each tailored to fit the readiness of people in that stage to move toward not smoking. For example, Prochaska, DiClemente and Norcross (1992) investigated what kinds of psychotherapeutic techniques are most applicable at each stage of change. Table 1 is their integration of findings about the different intervention processes which were most used by people at the different stages in their efforts to stop smoking or lose weight.

Table 1. Stages of change in which particular processes of change are emphasised

Precontemplation	*Contemplation*	*Preparation*	*Action*	*Maintenance*
Consciousness raising				
Dramatic relief				
Environmental re-evaluation				
	Self-re-evaluation			
		Self-liberation		
			Reinforcement management	
			Helping relationships	
			Counter-conditioning	
			Stimulus control	

Source: Prochaska, DiClemente and Norcross (1992)

The researchers concluded that matching particular interventions to key client characteristics, such as what stage of change a person is in, increases the success of treatment: "Probably the most obvious and direct implication of our research is the need to assess the stage of a client's readiness for change and to tailor interventions accordingly" (Prochaska, DiClemente and Norcross, 1992, p.1110).

This research focused upon individuals' efforts to change themselves. However, the principles it uncovered also apply to public policy-makers' efforts to change the public's behaviour and reduce tobacco usage. Designing different interventions for different stages in the cycle of tobacco addiction would enhance the success of tobacco control efforts.

To do so, policy-makers need to understand: (1) how the public is segmented *vis-à-vis* the stages within the tobacco addiction cycle; (2) what the characteristics are of the people in each segment; and (3) what the basic needs and wants of people in each segment are that must be met before they can move further toward not smoking. Research based on the social sciences is needed to determine these issues and help in the design of interventions. Social marketing can provide this research and apply it to intervention design and management.

This is, in fact, what tobacco companies do — they are masters at marketing. They use a wide range of marketing interventions to meet the needs and wants of people at each stage of response to tobacco and influence them to move further along the process toward smoking. They also inhibit people in their efforts to quit by providing ubiquitous cues to smoke through advertising and promotion, and ensuring ready access to cigarettes through intensive distribution policies. Figure 4 sheds light on how marketing knowledge helps tobacco companies know which of three promotional tools will be most effective in convincing people to smoke. It shows how each tool differs in effectiveness at each stage of response in terms of the amount of change achieved for the budget spent.

The figure illustrates that advertising tends to be the most cost-effective tool for creating awareness amongst large numbers of people. However, its effectiveness diminishes as people get closer to trying a product, and the most cost-effective tool for inducing trial is personal influence through face-to-face selling. Figure 4 also shows that sales promotions, such as coupons or contests, are even more cost-effective for moving people to adoption by offering immediate incentives for repurchase and money-saving "reasons to buy".

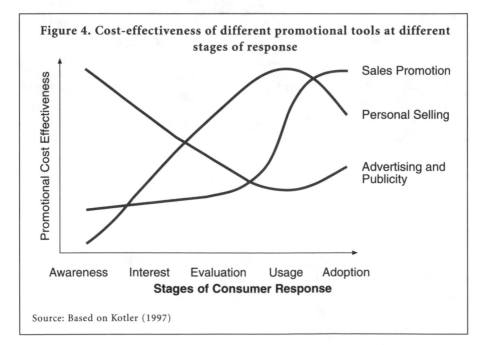

Figure 4. Cost-effectiveness of different promotional tools at different stages of response

Source: Based on Kotler (1997)

(iv) Configuring the mix of behaviour management tools

Social marketing insights are also useful for deciding which behaviour management tool should be used. For example, the role that advertising is shown to have in Figure 4 in creating product awareness, suggests that advertising can influence people's perception of the degree to which smoking is widespread and a social norm (Belch and Belch, 1995; Solomon, 1994). Consequently, in countries where smoking is not yet widely practised by large sectors of the population, a law banning tobacco advertising could be expected to decrease the rate of growth in awareness and, through a domino effect, decrease the rate at which the subsequent stages of product adoption are reached. Such a drastic, but singular policy action taken at the initial stage of people's movement toward smoking could then reduce the amount of more cost-intensive interventions needed when people reach the later stages of the tobacco addiction cycle. An estimate of those cost savings, not to mention the reduction in human suffering, could justify using the force of law even though it elicits extensive political and commercial opposition.

A case in point is South Africa, where the Minister of Health has called for a ban on tobacco advertising in her country (Zuma, 1998). One effect of such a ban would be to counteract tobacco company targeting of Black women who comprise about 39 per cent of the population, (Central Statistical Services, 1995), even though (or perhaps because) the norm is for Black women not to smoke. Such a ban would prohibit the industry from exposing South Africans to an advertising barrage of advertising images of Black women smoking, thus decreasing the degree to which the impression is created that such behaviour is a norm for Black women. It would, of course, also minimise advertising influences to smoke on people at every other stage of the addiction cycle.

Social marketing can also be used to configure an effective mix of behaviour management tools. For instance, for young people in the stage of evaluation (see Figure 1) to decide not to use tobacco, they need to perceive that abstention offers more benefits than smoking. As mentioned earlier, this is hard for youth to do because they tend not to appreciate the intangible and long-term health benefits of rejecting smoking, and opt for the immediate social and physical "benefits" of tobacco use. A social marketing strategy would aim to correct this imbalance by making the benefits of abstention tangible and of more value than those of smoking. Additionally, social marketing strategy would further suggest targeting a sub-division of the evaluation segment, in order to cost-effectively reach the whole segment. Such a sub-segment is youth opinion leaders, who are key determinants of their peers' social behaviour.

What is interesting is that the need to target opinion leaders may be more urgent if an advertising ban exists. This is because tobacco companies can be expected to also target them through sponsoring such things as web-sites based on topics of youth interest, designer clothing, and social events. Much of the money that the industry cannot put into advertising would be used for such promotions, and tobacco control would need to counteract this. An example of a social marketing intervention to pre-empt such industry marketing would be educational financial aid packages that are only eligible to non-smokers. Effective implementation of such a programme would necessitate close collaboration with educational departments and institutions, so that pre-existing financial offerings can be incorporated into this programme in order to reduce its cost. This intervention would still be expensive, and complex to develop and administer, but the cost may be justified. The percentage of young people that it will deter from moving out of evaluation into cigarette trial, usage and adoption could be estimated and used to gauge the marginal public health benefits. The estimate would need to account for how a targeted intervention like this would limit the impact of tobacco industry marketing. For example, if tobacco control policy were to link with financial-aid funding programmes aimed at Black women in South Africa, it might even forestall tobacco companies from becoming major benefactors of Black educational institutions and Black students, a strategy they have followed in the US (Robinson *et al.*, 1992). Even if they pursued it in South Africa, a tobacco control financial-aid programme could lessen its effectiveness. In short, tobacco control policy development needs to focus on configuring all three behavioural management tools — social marketing, education and law — so as to amplify the impact of each one and optimise overall tobacco control expenditures. Social marketing offers strategic tools for the creation of an optimal tobacco control policy mix.

In summary, the process view of the tobacco addiction cycle reveals that it is necessary for those seeking to manage tobacco behaviour to know at what stage of the cycle a person is in, so as to design and deliver interventions that cost-effectively move him or her forward in the process. Tobacco companies focus on moving people toward a smoking lifestyle and on interrupting the cessation process so that they return to smoking. Tobacco control focuses on moving people through cessation to a non-smoking lifestyle and on interrupting the adoption process so people remain non-smoking. Each can use similar approaches and methods to achieve their very different results: while the tobacco industry uses marketing, public health policy-makers have recourse to social marketing.

References

Andreasen, A. (1994), "Social marketing: its definition and domain", *Journal of Marketing and Public Policy*, 13:108-14.

Andreasen, A. (1995), *Marketing Social Change: Changing Behavior to Promote Health, Social Development, and the Environment*, San Francisco: Jossey-Bass.

Belch, G.E. and M.A. Belch (1995), *Introduction to Advertising and Promotion: An Integrated Marketing Communications Perspective, Third Edition*, Chicago: Irwin.

Boddewyn, J.J. (1987), *Why Do Juveniles Start Smoking?* (2nd Edition), New York: International Advertising Association.

Central Statistical Services (1995), *Mid-Year Estimates: 1991-1995*, Pretoria: CSS.

DiClemente, C.C., J.O. Prochaska, S.K. Fairhurst, W.F. Velicer, M.M. Velasquez and J.S. Rossi (1991), "The process of smoking cessation: An analysis of precontemplation, contemplation, and preparation stages of change", *Journal of Consulting and Clinical Psychology*, 59:295-304.

Heishman, S.K., L.T. Kozlowski and J.E. Henningfield (1997), "Nicotine addiction: implications for public health policy", *Journal of Social Issues*, 53:13-34.

Hine, D.W., C. Summers, K. Tilleczek and J. Lewko (1997), *Journal of Social Issues*, 53:35-52.

International Tobacco Initiative (1996-97), *(Draft) Annual Report*, Ottawa: International Tobacco Initiative.

Jacobson, P., J. Wasserman and J. Anderson (1997), "Historical overview of tobacco legislation and regulation", *Journal of Social Issues*, 53:75-95.

Kelder, G.E. Jr. and R.A. Daynard (1997), *Journal of Social Issues*, 53:169-86.

Kotler, P. (1997), *Marketing Management: Analysis, Planning, Implementation, and Control* (9th Edition), New Jersey: Prentice Hall.

Lilien, G.L., P. Kotler and K.S. Moorthy (1992), *Marketing Models*, Englewood Cliffs, NJ: Prentice Hall.

Mackay, J. (1998), *Reflections of a Public Health Advocate on Marketing's Role in the Great Cigarette Debate*, paper presented to the Marketing Department, University of Science and Technology, Hong Kong, 13 February.

Mizerski, R. (1995), "The relationship between cartoon trade character recognition and attitude toward product category in young children", *Journal of Marketing*, 59:58-70.

Pechmann, C. and S. Ratneshwar (1994), "The effects of antismoking and cigarette advertising on young adolescents' perceptions of peers who smoke", *Journal of Consumer Research*, 21:236-51.

Pertschuk, M. and the Advocacy Institute Staff (1992), *New Opportunities, New Threats: Some Strategic Implications of the Changing Public Policy Environment for Tobacco Control — A Work in Progress* (Version 1.0), a report of the Advocacy Institute.

Peter, J.P. and J.C. Olson (1996), *Consumer Behavior and Marketing Strategy* (4th Edition), Chicago: Irwin.

Pollay, R.W., S. Siddarth, M. Siegel, A. Haddix, R.K. Merritt, G.A. Giovino and M. Eriksen (1996), "The last straw? Cigarette advertising and realized market shares among youths and adults, 1979-1993", *Journal of Advertising*, 60:1-16.

Prochaska, J.O., C.C. DiClemente and J.C. Norcross (1992), "In search of how people change: applications to addictive behaviours", *American Psychologist*, 47:1102-14.

Robinson, R.G., M. Barry, M. Bloch, S. Glantz, J. Jordan, K.B. Murray, E. Popper, C. Sutton, K. Tarr-Whelan, M. Themba and S. Younger (1992), "Report of the Tobacco Policy Research Group on marketing and promotions targeted at African-Americans, Latinos, and Women", *Tobacco Control*, 1:S24-30.

Rothschild, M. (1998), *Carrots, Sticks, and Promises: A Conceptual Framework for the Behavior Management of Public Health and Social Issues*, Working Paper Series, Madison, WI: University of Wisconsin.

Schiffman, L.G. and L.L. Kanuk (1997), *Consumer Behavior* (6th Edition), New Jersey: Prentice Hall.

Seftel, H. (1992), "Health Consequences of Passive Smoking", Paper presented at the Seminar on Tobacco-Free Workplaces, 17 November, Johannesburg.

Siegel, M. and L. Biener (1977), "Evaluating the impact of state-wide anti-tobacco campaigns: the Massachusetts and California tobacco control programs", *Journal of Social Issues*, 53:147-68.

Solomon, M.R. (1983), "The role of products as social stimuli: a symbolic interactionism perspective", *Journal of Consumer Research*, 10:319-29.

Solomon, M.R. (1994), *Consumer Behavior* (2nd Edition), Boston: Allyn and Bacon.

Steyn, K. (1996), *Comprehensive Tobacco Control Research Programme for South Africa*, Chronic Diseases of Lifestyle Programme, Medical Research Council, Pretoria: Medical Research Council.

Vaughn, R. (1980), "How advertising works: a planning model", *Journal of Advertising Research*, 20:26-38.

Wallack, L. and K. Montgomery (1992), "Advertising for all by the year 2000: public health implications for less developed countries", *Journal of Public Health Policy*, 13:204-23.

Walsh, D.C., R.E. Rudd, B.A. Moykens and T.W. Moloney (1993), *Health Affairs*, Summer:104-19.

Yach, D. and G. Martin (1993), "Tobacco consumption: determinants and deterrents", *Continuing Medical Education*, 11:813-24.

Zuma, Minister N. (1998), Opening address to the conference on *The Economics of Tobacco Control: Towards an Optimal Policy Mix*, 18 February, Cape Town.

Chapter 18

How Tobacco Farming Contributes to Tropical Deforestation

Helmut Geist

The global shift and its consequences

Since the late 1970s, for the first time in history, commercial growing and curing of tobacco has shifted predominantly into the developing world, mostly for reasons of low-cost production and open access to common natural resources. Since then, substantial concern has been raised that commercial tobacco farming has profound ecological implications due to changes in land-cover caused by deforestation, besides the inherent consequences of modern agriculture *per se* (Boesen and Mohele, 1979; Chapman and Wong, 1990; Goodland, Watson and Ledec, 1984; Goodman, 1995).

In 1993, when tobacco production reached a peak of 8.4 million tons per annum, 81 per cent of the world's land under tobacco was located in the tropical and subtropical zones. Most tobacco-growing areas are located in regions of semi-arid to semi-humid climate such as tree savannahs, dryland woodlands and fringe rain forests, all of them having a dry season long enough to allow for harvesting and curing of the crop. These geographical areas not only constitute fragile natural environments to a considerably higher degree than temperate regions, but also show comparatively high rural population densities in the face of low development potential.

The specific requirements of tobacco growing, such as its uniquely high labour intensity, the need for fresh (virgin) soils, and (in particular) the use of wood as a "free good" to cure and store tobacco, underpin this global shift in location. Immediately after harvest, and regardless of the variety of tobacco grown, picked green leaves have to undergo the farm-based process of curing. This involves drying them in order to obtain the characteristic taste, aroma and colour of tobacco, and to preserve the leaf for storage, packing, transport and further processing. Curing can either be done naturally by exposing the leaves to sun or air, or by generating artificial heat in closed tobacco barns. In 1993, 62 per cent of world tobacco was artificially cured, by either flue curing (in which heated air is passed through the leaves) or fire curing (in which wood smoke is introduced during the drying process). Flue-cured tobacco (Bright, Virginia) accounts for 99 per cent of all artificially-cured tobacco, and also constitutes the bulk of tobacco used for the manufacture of American and Virginia blend cigarettes. Of the land planted with flue-cured tobacco, 74 per cent is located in low-income developing countries, where there is hardly any alternative to wood as a source of energy or construction material.

It is the main purpose of this chapter to test the frequently-quoted statement, made in 1992 by US Surgeon General Novello, that "deforestation associated with tobacco curing cannot currently be considered a significant negative externality" (Campbell, 1994; ITGA, 1995, p.1; ITGA, 1996, p.1). The evidence shows that this can no longer hold true in light of the relationship between tropical dryland deforestation and tobacco farming. The chapter starts by moving from a global perspective to a continental perspective, focusing on the African continent, which contains the world's largest and more-or-less contiguous dryland forest area (called *miombo*). This continental perspective provides a framework from which a national, sub-national and local perspective is developed, using Malawi (a leading tobacco producer in both the African and global contexts) as a case study.

From a global perspective to a continental and national view

A multi-country consultancy report covering the mid-1980s and considered to be "the definitive study on the use of wood by the tobacco industry" (ITGA, 1995, p.3) states that "it is important to note that a high proportion of the tobacco growing areas in developing countries lie within parts of the world identified by FAO as being in wood-deficit or prospective wood-deficit situations" (Fraser, 1986, p.6). With special reference to tobacco, the report further concludes that the "area of all types of forest in most African and Asian countries is now below the level at which it is capable of meeting the current and future fuelwood demand on a sustainable basis. This means that accelerating deforestation can be expected, with potentially serious ecological consequences. So long as wood is treated as a 'free good' and its price does not reflect its replacement cost, the destruction of the forest will continue" (Fraser, 1986, pp.21,32).

While little is presently known about China (the world's largest producer of tobacco, especially flue-cured tobacco), it is also admitted in the most recent report of the tobacco industry that for the artificial curing of tobacco "(w)ood in log form is important in Africa (other than Zimbabwe and South Africa); (in) Latin America — principally Brazil, Argentina, and Chile; (and in) Asia — Pakistan, India, Sri Lanka, Myanmar, Cambodia, Laos, Malaysia, and the Philippines" (ITGA, 1997, p.3). The report provides a global map which draws information on the distribution of flue-cured tobacco growing areas from Universal Leaf Tobacco Co. data and on the fuelwood supply deficit areas in developing nations from FAO sources. From this map, it can clearly be seen that for most of the developing countries (excluding China, due to lack of data) containing semi-arid to semi-humid tropical ecosystems (i.e. excluding rain forests), there is a spatial correlation between areas growing flue-cured tobacco and fuelwood deficit (Fraser, 1986).

A striking feature of the map is a unique concentration of areas growing flue-cured tobacco suffering fuelwood deficit in Africa, south of the Equator, an ecozone called *miombo* woodlands. Most of the *miombo*-like dryland forests (and some areas of semi-evergreen forests) and woodlands in Latin America and Asia, such as campos cerrados and (deciduous) tree savannahs, have already been eliminated and transformed into agrarian or even degraded (desertified) land. By contrast, however, African *miombo* still covers huge areas, even in densely populated regions (Hannah *et al.*, 1994; Williams, 1994). From here, recent (and some historical) evidence shows how tobacco farming constitutes a significant social driving force governing land-use and land-cover change, resulting in deforestation of dryland tropical ecosystems (Geist, 1998; Spada and Scheuermann, 1998).

To date, most attention has been focused on land-use and land-cover changes in tropical rain forest areas, i.e. biodiversity losses and deforestation, while much less attention has been paid to the widespread changes occurring in tropical dry forests and woodlands. A majority of rural people in tropical countries depend on the latter ecosystems for their livelihoods (Campbell *et al.*, 1996), and they are arguably the "most endangered major tropical ecosystem" (Janzen, 1988). These ecosystems cover approximately 7.7 million km^2, 42 per cent of tropical forest land, with the bulk (5.5 million km^2) situated in Africa, more than half of which occurs in the *miombo* region of South-East Africa (3.4 million km^2). The definition of "forest" excludes areas of more than 20 per cent open ground.

Miombo is a vernacular word that has been adopted by ecologists to describe those woodlands dominated by trees in the genera *Brachystegia*, *Julbernardia* and *Isoberlinia*. This ecosystem extends from Tanzania and Congo in the North, through Zambia, Malawi and Eastern Angola, to Zimbabwe and Mozambique in the South, and features a hot, seasonally wet climate. The soils are predominantly infertile, being derived from acid crystalline bedrock. *Miombo* forms the largest more or less contiguous block of deciduous tropical woodlands and dry forests in the world (Desanker *et al.*, 1997; Millington *et al.*, 1994). Since the mid-1980s, around 90 per cent of the growing and curing of tobacco in continental Africa has occurred in countries covered to varying degrees by *miombo* woodlands. Taking into account changes in the dynamics of tobacco growing and production in relation to forest cover changes during 1990-95, three groups of "*miombo* and tobacco" countries can be differentiated (see Table 1):

• a small group of major tobacco producers (Zimbabwe, Malawi, and Tanzania), having 25-48 per cent of their respective country surface under *miombo*, and producing a combined total of about 75 per cent of the overall African tobacco crop;

• a small group of minor tobacco producers (South Africa, Kenya, and Uganda), having less than 7 per cent of their respective land surfaces under *miombo*, and producing in combination about 8 per cent of African tobacco; and

• a group of seven minor tobacco producers (Angola, Rwanda, Zambia, Congo/Zaire, Mozambique, Burundi, Congo-Brazzaville), being until recently mainly war-torn countries with unsettled economic environments, having large tracts (up to 60 per cent) of their respective land surfaces under *miombo*, and producing in combination about 4 per cent of African tobacco.

Country	Miombo			Forest cover change*		Tobacco production			Tobacco area		
	Surface (1986)	(% of total)	As % of country	1990-95		1989/91	1995	As % of Africa	1989/91	1995	Total change
	(km²)			(1000 ha)	(% of total)	(1000 ton)	(1000 ton)		(1000 ha)	(1000 ha)	(%)
Zimbabwe	100 858	3.0	25.3	-50	-0.6	146	198	42.0	63	82	+30
Malawi	54 119	1.6	41.9	-55	-1.6	100	129	27.4	102	130	+28
Tanzania	443 484	13.2	48.0	-323	-1.0	13	28	5.9	25	32	+28
South Africa	77 409	2.3	6.3	-15	-0.2	32	22	4.7	24	14	-42
Kenya	5 164	0.2	0.9	-3	-0.3	10	10	2.1	4	4	0
Uganda	16 282	0.5	6.8	-59	-0.9	4	7	1.5	5	8	+60
Angola	600 304	17.9	49.5	-237	-1.0	4	4	0.9	8	8	0
Rwanda	4 427	0.1	22.9	-2	-0.2	3	4	0.9	3	3	0
Zambia	447 858	13.3	59.9	-264	-0.8	5	3	0.6	4	3	-25
Congo/Zaire	1 035 936	30.9	45.9	-740	-0.7	3	3	0.6	6	6	0
Mozambique	463 507	13.8	60.4	-116	-0.7	3	3	0.6	3	3	0
Burundi	12 699	0.4	47.4	-1	-0.4	4	1	0.2	4	1	-75
Congo	66 185	2.0	19.5	-42	-0.2	2	1	0.2	n.d.	n.d.	n.d.
Botswana	1 528	0.1	0.3	-71	-0.5	0	0	-	0	0	-
Namibia	1 581	0.1	0.2	-42	-0.3	0	0	-	0	0	-
Swaziland	4 690	0.1	26.1	0	0	0	0	-	0	0	-
Gabon	20 864	0.6	8.0	-91	-0.5	0	0	-	0	0	-
Total	3 356 895	100.1	27.6	-2 111	-0.6	326	413	87.6	247	291	+18
Africa				-3 748	-0.7	378	471	100	327	376	+15

Table 1. Miombo woodlands, forest cover change and tobacco development in continental Africa, 1990-95

Note: * Annual loss of all natural forest, 1990-95
          n.d.: no data.
Sources: Millington et al. (1994); FAO (1997a; 1997b).

With regard to this differentiation, two observations are pertinent at this point. Firstly, the area in Africa under tobacco expanded by 15 per cent overall during 1989/91-95 (and by 18 per cent overall for countries of the *miombo* region). In comparison, the area under tobacco expanded by nearly 30 per cent in the major producing countries, i.e. double the amount of the overall African rate. Most of the increase in tobacco production by the major producers was due to expansion of the growing area, and not to intensification of cultivation. Secondly, while the average annual forest depletion rate for Africa had been 0.7 per cent (0.6 per cent per annum for the countries of the *miombo* region), the major tobacco producers showed an overall average annual depletion rate of 1.1 per cent, i.e. nearly 60 per cent higher than the overall annual average depletion rate for Africa, and more than 80 per cent higher than the overall annual average depletion rate for tobacco producers in the *miombo* region.

Countries with *miombo* woodlands that are not tobacco producers show an overall average annual forest depletion rate of 0.3 per cent, considerably lower than the depletion rates of minor and major tobacco producers, *viz.* 0.5-1.1 per cent. Strikingly, the overall average annual forest depletion rate of the leading tobacco producers is higher than the overall depletion rate of non-tobacco-growing countries by a factor of 3.7. However, descriptive comparisons and statistical and spatial correlations are not sufficient to establish causal relationships at these global and continental levels of data compilation and analysis; this topic is explored in the following section.

From a continental perspective to a national view

In order to isolate and identify the inter-linkages of tobacco and forest depletion in such a way that causal relationships are distinguished, a national and sub-national perspective has to be adopted, making use of an innovative mix of models and methods. Out of the group of major tobacco producers in the *miombo* region of Africa, Malawi is being used as an example, being noteworthy for two reasons. Firstly, the differing growing areas in the country provide insight into the whole range of tobacco farming cycles (i.e. early, mature and declining). Secondly, the environmental as well socio-economic data situation in Malawi allows for a consistent integration of sub-national results on a national scale, along a sufficiently lengthy time-scale, *viz.* around 100 years.

Because deforestation as a scientific phenomenon has not yet been elucidated to a satisfactory degree (Williams, 1994), it is not surprising that annual forest depletion rates for specific countries are often specified from as low as 1.6 per cent (FAO, 1997b) to as high as 3.5 per cent (SGS Silviconsult, 1994). Making use of satellite imagery to compare and analyse land use and land cover data for 1972/73 and 1990/91, in combination with ground checks of biomass assessment, it is found that forest cover in Malawi has declined from 45 per cent to 25 per cent of the land surface area during this period. Moreover, the dominant *miombo* species (such as *Brachystegia*) show the highest amount of decline in flat areas suitable for land clearance and large-scale farming; for example, there has been a decline of up to 85 per cent of forest cover in

Southern Mangochi District (see Table 2). It should be noted that calculation of annual forest depletion rates is not possible with this methodology.

Table 2. Forest cover change in Mangochi District of Southern Malawi by type of vegetation and geomorphic situation, 1972/73-90/91

	1972/73		1990/91		1972/73-90/91	
	hectares	%	hectares	%	hectares	%
Evergreen forest	470	0.1	481	0.1	+11	+2.3
Brachystegia:						
in hilly area	252 325	37.4	223 115	33.1	-29 210	-11.6
in flat area	190 556	28.2	29 009	4.3	-161 547	-84.8
Plantation:						
Eucalyptus	0	0.0	+351	0.1	+351	new
Logged areas	0	0.0	+4 817	0.7	+4 817	new
Sum (forest)	443 351	65.7	252 956	36.9	-195 234	-44.0
Sum (all surface)	675 007	100.0	675 007	100.0	(—)	(—)

Source: Geist (1997a); Government of Malawi, Ministry of Forestry and Natural Resources/ Department of Finance (1993).

During the 1972/73-90/91 period, the area under tobacco increased from about 54 000 hectares to 117 000 hectares, while tobacco production increased from 33 000 tons to 113 000 tons. Tobacco-related consumption of wood resources can be assessed given empirically-derived rates of the annual use of wood for curing different varieties of tobacco (and also for storing tobacco, in the case of sun- and air-cured varieties). These rates of wood use can be expressed either in stacked cubic metres (stm³) or in kilograms of solid wood per ton of tobacco. For ordinary furnaces, for example, rates of wood use would be 22 stm³ per ton of flue-cured tobacco and 5 stm³ per ton of burley tobacco; for improved furnaces, rates would be 12 stm³ and 2.5 stm³ respectively (Gossage, 1997).

Using data published in the *National Forest Policy Review* in 1993, a statistical correlation can be distinguished (Table 3): while tobacco production increased by 88 per cent during 1983-92, the total amount of wood used for curing (and storing) tobacco increased by 30 per cent (Misana, Mung'ong'o and Mukamuri, 1996). The lower rise in wood use in relation to tobacco expansion was due mainly to shifts in the pattern of crop varieties, and also to improvements in furnace technology, especially in flue curing. In 1986, the total demand for wood by the tobacco industry (including uses other than curing and storing) was estimated to be 23 per cent of the estimated total national wood demand of 9.4 million cubic metres (Misana, Mung'ong'o and Mukamuri, 1996; SGS Silviconsult, 1994).

A more recent study of large commercial tobacco farms in Malawi assessed the use of wood for curing and storing of tobacco, and for the domestic use of resident farm workers, tenants, and their families. It was found that in 1995/96

Table 3. Tobacco production and uses of wood for curing and storing of tobacco in Malawi by variety of tobacco grown, 1983 and 1992

	Tobacco production (t)		*Wood use per ton (m^3)*		*Total wood consumed (m^3)*	
	1983	*1992*	*1983*	*1992*	*1983*	*1992*
Burley	41 600	99 200	4	4	166 100	396 900
Flue-cured	21 700	25 700	19	14	411 500	360 000
Fire-cured	8 400	10 300	17	17	142 500	175 400
Sun/air-cured	700	1 000	1	1	700	1 000
Oriental	200	400	1	1	200	400
Total	72 600	136 600	(-)	(-)	721 000	933 700

Source: Misana, Mung'ong'o and Mukamuri (1996), based on data provided by the Forest Policy Review (1993)

"(o)f the total overall wood requirement of tobacco estates of nearly 1 670 000 stacked cubic metres per year, estates produce for themselves or buy in from legitimate sources only around 900 000 stm³, with the remaining 770 000 stm³ or 46 per cent of their total requirement being obtained mostly from customary land outside the estates" (Gossage, 1997, p.32). Given an overall national deforestation rate of 100 000 hectares per year (estimated from satellite imagery (Table 2) rather than from FAO figures (Table 1)), "the net deforestation caused by the tobacco estates outside their boundaries is likely to be around 10 000 hectares per year. Malawi clearly has a serious problem with deforestation, and the tobacco estate sub-sector contributes significantly to this" (Gossage, 1997, p.31f).

Considering only large commercial flue-cured and burley tobacco farms, and excluding smallholder farming and wood used for fire curing and sun/air curing of tobacco, the deforestation caused by tobacco estates can thus be estimated to be as high as 10 per cent of overall annual national deforestation within any given time period. If the (conservative) figures of the FAO are taken, deforestation by the tobacco estate sub-sector alone could be as high as 18 per cent of overall national depletion. For comparison, and to confirm the range identified, it is claimed that in the Southern Africa region as a whole, "more than 1 400 sq km of indigenous woodland is cleared annually to supply fuelwood for tobacco curing" (Booth and Clarke 1994, p.137). This amounts to 12 per cent of the overall annual deforestation in the region, excluding other tobacco-related uses of wood like polewood for constructing barns and the firewood requirements of resident workers and their families on tobacco estates.

Several interacting variables (such as land clearance for the expansion of agricultural land due to population pressure) are commonly cited to explain the dynamics of tropical deforestation; however, this methodology is poor in explanatory power, and provides a weak basis for formulation of policy measures. By contrast, analysis of the contribution of tobacco farming to tropical deforestation (in terms of land-cover transformation, biodiversity losses, and related problems such as soil erosion and land degradation) is clearly within the ambit of scientific analysis and policy management.

From a national perspective to a regional and local view

Moving further down the spatial scale, sub-national (and even local) shifts in tobacco farming during the course of time can be traced from analysis of land use information based upon remote sensing data, in combination with historical documents and land development and other reports. By distinguishing three transects of Malawian territory, three diverging patterns of the tobacco farming cycle can be identified, each having and requiring a different regional policy approach (see the 1:250 000 maps of the Land Resources Evaluation Project (LREP), in combination with, for example, Erhard (1994) and Wilshaw (1994)):
1. the Shire Highlands in the South had long been the core area of tobacco farming from about 1890 to the middle of the 20th century, with a tobacco auction established in the late 1930s;
2. the major tobacco producing area has now shifted into the central region around Kasungu, with a tobacco auction being established in the late 1970s in Lilongwe, the capital of Malawi;
3. recent expansion of tobacco farming has occurred in the Northern region, with a tobacco auction established in Mzuzu.

By tracing the spatial boundaries of *miombo* woodlands and tobacco areas in 1991/92, it can be seen that in the Southern region nearly all woodlands have been eliminated, with tobacco farming having reached the end of the production cycle. Most of the rural areas in the South have already exceeded their agrarian and ecological carrying capacities, and even if maximum possible afforestation efforts were taken, the supply of firewood will not be guaranteed within the foreseeable future. Instead, a food security programme has recently been initiated in the heavily populated and natural-resource-depleted former tobacco growing areas of Blantyre District.

In the Central region, limits to the expansion of tobacco production have obviously already been reached in certain areas where, for example, woodlands are used up on customary land, and tobacco estates are established close to (and are starting to encroach upon) forest reserves, national parks and game reserves; this can also be observed in the Namwera highlands (Geist, 1997a). In the Northern region, an on-going colonisation of virgin forests is evident from the spatial pattern of tobacco and woodland demarcation. The region is still densely forested, thus providing plenty of easily accessible wood as a 'free good' to tobacco farmers. These three land-use and land-cover transects show a historical shift of tobacco farming into areas which can be characterised as the "frontier of colonisation" or "pioneer frontier" of tobacco, as the tobacco estates push the forest boundary back and eliminate natural woodlands (see Geist (1998) for Africa in recent times, and Goodman (1995) for considerations on a global scale in a historical perspective).

A considerable part of Malawian tobacco expansion has been driven by integrated rural development projects (among others), as can be seen at a local level in the Mlomba area of Liwonde Agricultural Development Division (LWADD), situated in the Nsanama Extension Planning Area (EPA) area of Kawinga Rural Development Programme (RDP) in Southern Machinga District. In this case, aerial photographs taken in 1960 and 1995 can be compared with sketch maps from LWADD tobacco estate files and ground checks in the form of social surveys (Geist, 1998; Spada and Scheuermann, 1998). During the early 1980s the establishment of marketing facilities and the construction of a tarmac road considerably raised the commercial value of what could be called a hinterland area. Consequently, influential tobacco farmers, mostly members of the political and economic elite, came into the area, taking immense tracts of land and removing indigenous woodlands, transforming smallholder farming land use hitherto governed by customary law, and even encroaching upon parts of forest reserves. (A similar trend holds true for the adjacent Namwera RDP to the North, where cultivable land under tobacco estates grew from 0.1 per cent in 1910, to 10.4 per cent in 1974, to 44.7 per cent in 1985, and to a further 56.4 per cent in 1995 - see Geist, 1997a).

In Mlomba area, a fuelwood project (initially financed by the World Bank) has been cut into the Eastern slope of the Rift Valley, which was formerly part of the Liwonde Forest Reserve. This area provided fuelwood during the early tobacco farming phase of Southern Kawinga RDP; it now offers a supply of fast-growing eucalyptus from plantation forestry to the nearby (and now well-established) tobacco estates (Geist, 1986; World Bank, 1985). The Rural Development Project, which was funded by GTZ (the German Agency for Technical Co-operation) and the German Bank for Reconstruction and Development, was started in the late 1970s and was aimed at raising smallholder incomes through maize farming within the developmental framework of the National Rural Development Plan (NRDP). In 1991, the project had been terminated ahead of schedule, since it was obvious that neither the project's objectives nor its implementation had allowed for the integration of the (competing) maize and tobacco sub-sectors; it was clearly a failure, and no measures were at hand to stop deforestation and land degradation (Geist, 1986; Heydon, 1984; Kock *et al.*, 1991).

During the drought of 1992, this development area, having been transformed into a prime area of burley farming, contained approximately 10 000 farm families. An estimated 45 per cent of these did not have maize to harvest, 50 per cent had a little maize to last them 1-2 months, and only about 5 per cent enjoyed a normal maize harvest, so that food aid provided by international donor agencies became an urgent priority (UNICEF and CSR, 1992). As a general rule, the socio-economic vulnerability of societies in tobacco growing areas becomes particularly obvious during periods of crisis, i.e. when ecological conditions worsen and food prices in local markets become unstable (Goodland, Watson and Ledec, 1984; Goodman, 1995).

Conclusion: "Where there is no electricity . . ."

This chapter has moved from a global perspective to a continental one and then to the national level to evaluate evidence on a regional and local level of tobacco-related tropical dryland deforestation. This procedure, as well as the available data, will undoubtedly have to be verified for a significant proportion of other tobacco growing areas and societies to obtain a methodologically proper point of view. The heuristic key to interpreting social and environmental results in a coherent manner will probably be found through analysis of data at the national, regional, and local level, within a systematised format and a flexible time-scale (which allows for differing stages of the farming cycle). However, even at the present state of analysis, evidence from the *miombo* woodlands of continental Africa, as verified in the Malawian case, gives no reason to reject the hypothesis that tobacco farming leads to deforestation, or to deny that there are significant resource externalities to tobacco farming (Geist, 1998). The following concluding observations illustrate how environmental policy analysis of tobacco farming can be impeded by rhetorical arguments as well as one-way streets of research methodology.

Clearly, specific fuelwood demands resulting in large-scale deforestation are also associated with urban fuelwood markets, other specialised fuelwood-using rural industries, and the firewood demands of rural households. For rural industries other than tobacco farming, rough estimates of fuelwood use are given by Booth and Clarke (1994): for example, 1 m³ of wood is sufficient to provide heating and cooking for one person for a year, to smoke one ton of fish, or to burn 3 000 bricks (one-third of the bricks needed to build a standard rural house). In the case of Malawi (as well as other developing countries), there is a special focus upon the impact of rural household fuelwood demands on deforestation, for example: "(a)lthough woodfuel is used for curing tobacco, the main use is for cooking in homes by 90 per cent of Malawi's population . . . who live in rural areas where there is no electricity, and woodfuel is the only means to subsist" (ITGA, 1996, p.2).

However, the focus upon rural domestic households has "obscured the larger and politically more difficult issue of deforestation arising from agricultural land clearance, the rapid expansion of the estate sector, and the use of woodfuel for tobacco curing". Further, compared to the effects of other demands, "rural household demands have probably had a minor impact on deforestation. Indeed, some analysts have suggested that supplies of woodfuels to meet rural household demands are in substantial surplus . . . (since) a large range of woody biomass types can be used for rural domestic woodfuel: brushwood, crop residues, coppiced or pollarded branches from farm trees and so on ... (which) are not appropriate for other woodfuel-using sectors" (Dewees, 1995, p.147).

There are repeated claims that, for example, up to 100 per cent of the tobacco farmers in Kenya and Congo/Zaire, up to 80 per cent in Uganda, and up to 70 per cent in Zimbabwe have woodfuel plantings for flue-curing (ITGA, 1997). It is also claimed that the "typical percentage of farmland devoted to woodfuel planting" is 20 per cent in Tanzania and Kenya, 10 per cent in Malawi, etc. (ITGA, 1996, p.2; ITGA, 1997, p.7). These assertions, which should be treated as recommendations or as part of a land agreement (usually not followed up, however, due to poor law enforcement or benign neglect) are inconsistent with empirical data on the actual areas under trees. As in the Malawian case, a nation-wide social survey among nearly 600 tobacco estate farmers states that "(o)nly around 3 per cent of the total estate land was . . . under plantation forestry" (Gossage, 1997, p.29), and a regional survey among more than 100 estate farmers of the Namweran highlands shows that 75 per cent of the tobacco estates had far less than the required covenant (Geist, 1997a). About the same holds true in the Tanzanian case of the Southern Songea highlands, one of the major global fire-cured tobacco growing areas, where among nearly 200 farmers, not 20 per cent, but merely 1.4 per cent of the overall farmland of tobacco growers was found to be under trees (Geist, 1997b).

Major "confusion" seems to have been created by the introduction of "specific fuel consumption" (SFC) as the prevailing means of measuring wood use by the tobacco industry (Fraser and Bowles, 1986a; 1986b; 1986c; Baguely and Inglis, 1990a; 1990b; Inglis and MacDonald, 1991). SFC signifies "(t)he weight of fuel consumed in curing 1 kg of cured tobacco leaf, expressed as kg fuel/kg tobacco" (Fraser 1986, p.37). Instead of using absolute types of measurement like cubic metres of stacked wood or kilograms of solid wood (as had been the practice in earlier studies, which could be translated into straightforward environmental costs of afforestation projects, for example, by Goodland, Watson and Ledec (1984)), the adoption of a relative type of measurement not only hides the real (and absolute) dimensions of forest removal (by simply relating the use of wood to the weight of tobacco cured), but also blocks any further cost accounting for policy analysis.

For example, a SDDF (Southern Division (Dark) Fire-cured) tobacco-growing smallholder in the Namwera highlands of Southern Malawi, consumes about 8 cubic metres of firewood per year and farm, and due to a small hectarage (and output) the SFC amounted to 16 (kilograms of wood per 1 kg of cured tobacco) in 1995/96. A commercial flue farm of the same area proves to have only half of that SFC (8 kg/kg,) but consumes more than 600 cubic metres of firewood per year and farm due to a large hectarage (and production output). Thus, the paradox arises that among about 8 000 tobacco farmers in the Namweran highlands, a mere 3 per cent of the farms, growing flue-cured tobacco on large tracts of land, consume more than 80 per cent of all the wood used in the area, though they show a low SFC when compared to the wood use of small-scale tobacco farmers.

Moreover, from a methodological point of view, the method of assessing SFC refers to the "consumption of fuelwood at one particular time in the curing season" (LTS International Ltd, 1991, p.2), which is the equivalent of one loading of the barn or one curing charge, respectively. Therefore, the total and absolute amount of all wood used for all curing of all tobacco harvested cannot be accounted for.

Finally, there is a commonly held conviction that wood is used neither for naturally cured tobacco like burley, oriental, or other air/sun-cured varieties, nor for sustaining large numbers of local residents, especially on modern farms (agribusiness enterprises). For the majority of peasant farmers, however, there are hardly any alternatives to wood as a source of energy or construction material.

References

Baguely, M. and C. Inglis (1990a), *Report on Fuelwood Consumption and Plantantion Establishment Survey for Tabacalera Hondurena*, Edinburgh: LTS.

Baguely, M. and C. Inglis (1990b), *Report on Fuelwood Consumption and Plantantion Establishment Survey for the Nigerian Tobacco Company Ltd*, Edinburgh: LTS.

Boesen, J. and A.T. Mohele (1979), *The Success Story of Peasant Tobacco Production in Tanzania: the Political Economy of a Commodity Producing Peasantry*, Centre for Development Research Publications, Uppsala: SIAS.

Booth, A. and J. Clarke (1994), "Woodlands and forests", in Chenje, M. and P. Johnson (eds.), *State of the Environment in Southern Africa*, a report by the Southern African Research and Documentation Centre in Collaboration with IUCN (The World Conservation Union) and the Southern African Development Community, Harare and Maseru: SARDC, IUCN and SADC.

Campbell, J.S. (1994), *Tobacco and the Environment: the Continuous Reduction of World-wide Energy Source Use for Green Leaf Curing*, Harare: CORESTA

Campbell, B.M., P.G.H. Frost and N. Byron (1996), "Miombo woodlands and their use: overview and key issues", in Campbell, B.M. (ed.), *The Miombo in Transition: Woodlands and Welfare in Africa*, Bogor: CIFOR.

Chapman, S. and Wong W.L. (1990), *Tobacco Control in the Third World: a Resource Atlas*, Penang: IOCU.

Desanker, P.V., P.G.H. Frost, C.O. Justice and R.J. Scholes (1997), *The Miombo Network: Framework for a Terrestrial Transect Study of Land-use and Land-cover Change in the Miombo Ecosystems of Central Africa*, International Geosphere-Biosphere Programme Report No. 41, Stockholm: IGBP and ICSU.

Dewees, P.A. (1995), "Forestry policy and woodfuel markets in Malawi", *Natural Resources Forum*, 19:143-152.

Erhard, A. (1994), *Malawi: Agrarstruktur und Unterentwicklung*, Innsbrucker Geographische Studien 22, Innsbruck: University of Innsbruck.

FAO (Food and Agriculture Organisation of the United Nations) (1997a), *Production Yearbook 1996*, Vol. 50, FAO Statistics Series No. 135, Rome: FAO.

FAO (Food and Agriculture Organisation of the United Nations) (1997b), *State of the World's Forests*, Rome: FAO.

Fraser, A.I. (1986), *The Use of Wood by the Tobacco Industry and the Ecological Implications*, Edinburgh: IFSC.

Fraser, A.I. and R.C.D. Bowles (1986a), *The Use of Wood by the Tobacco Industry in Malawi*, Edinburgh: IFSC.

Fraser, A.I. and R.C.D. Bowles (1986b), *The Use of Wood by the Tobacco Industry in Kenya*, Edinburgh: IFSC.

Fraser, A.I. and R.C.D. Bowles (1986c), *The Use of Wood by the Tobacco Industry in Zimbabwe*, Edinburgh: IFSC.

Geist, H. (1986), "Subsistenzwirtschaft und Weltmarktproduktion in einer peripheren Region Malawis", *Zeitschrift für Wirtschaftsgeographie*, 30:27-51.

Geist, H. (1997a), *Tobacco Growers of Namwera RDP/Malawi: a Study of Social and Environmental Change*, Analytical draft report, Düsseldorf.

Geist, H. (1997b), *Tobacco Growers of Songea District and their Miombo Environment (Ruvuma Region/Southern Tanzania)*, Preliminary results, Düsseldorf.

Geist, H. (1998), "Tropenwaldzerstörung durch Tabak. Eine These erörtert am Beispiel afrikanischer Miombowälder", *Geographische Rundschau*, 50.

Goodland, R.J.A., C. Watson and G. Ledec (1984), *Environmental Management in Tropical Agriculture*, Boulder: Westview Press.

Goodman, J. (1995), *Tobacco in History: the Cultures of Dependence*, London and New York: Routledge.

Gossage, S.J. (1997), *Land Use on the Tobacco Estates of Malawi: Report of the Land Use Survey of Tobacco Estates in Malawi 1996*, Lilongwe: ELUS.

Government of Malawi, Ministry of Forestry and Natural Resources (1993), *Forest Resources Mapping and Biomass Assessment for Malawi, Kinema and Lilongwe*, Satellitbild and Ministry of Forestry and Natural Resources.

Hannah, L., D. Lohse, C. Hutchinson, J.L. Carr and A. Lankerani (1994), "A preliminary inventory of human disturbance of world ecosystems", *Ambio*, 23:246-50.

Heydon, D. (1984), *Balanced Estate and Smallholder Development*, final report, Eschborn: GTZ.

Inglis, C. and C. MacDonald (1991), *Report on Fuelwood Consumption and Plantation Establishment Survey for the Bangladesh Tobacco Company*, Edinburgh: LTS.

ITGA (International Tobacco Growers' Association) (1995), *Tobacco and the Environment*, Tobacco Briefing, No. 4/95, East Grinstead: ITGA.

ITGA (International Tobacco Growers' Association) (1996), *Deforestation and the Use of Wood for Curing Tobacco*, Tobacco Growers Issues Papers No. 5, East Grinstead: ITGA.

ITGA (International Tobacco Growers' Association) (1997), *The Use of Woodfuel for Curing Tobacco*, East Grinstead: ITGA.

Janzen, D.H. (1988), "Tropical dry forests: the most endangered major tropical ecosystem", in Wilson,

E.O. and F.M. Peter (eds.), *Biodiversity*, Washington, DC: National Academy Press.

Kock, W., R. Hayata, H. Werner and G. Payr (1991), *Malawi: Liwonde Agricultural Development Division (LWADD): Progress review and evaluation: Draft report: Vol.1: Executive summary and main report*, Eschborn and Lilongwe: GTZ.

LTS International Ltd (1991), *Assessment of the Specific Fuel Consumption for Flue Curing Tobacco*, Edinburgh: LTS.

Millington, A.C., R.W. Critchley, T.D. Douglas and P. Ryan (1994), *Estimating Woody Biomass in Sub-Saharan Africa*, Washington, DC: World Bank.

Misana, S.B., C. Mung'ong'o and B. Mukamuri (1996), "Miombo woodlands in the wider context: macro-economic and inter-sectoral influences", in Campbell, B.M. (ed.), *The Miombo in Transition: Woodlands and Welfare in Africa*, Bogor: CIFOR.

SGS Silviconsult (1994), *Support to the SADC Forestry Sector Co-ordination Unit (SADC-FSTCU): Project Appraisal Mission: First Draft Report*, Oxford: SGSS.

Spada, H. and M. Scheuermann (1998), "The human dimensions of global environmental change: social science research in Germany", in Ehlers, E. and T. Krafft (eds.), *German Global Change Research 1998*, Bonn: GNCGCR.

UNICEF (United Nations International Children's Emergency Fund) and CSR (Centre for Social Research) (1992), *Emergency Assessment of the Effects of Drought in Selected EPAs*, Lilongwe and Zomba: UNICEF and CSR.

Williams, M. (1994), "Forests and tree cover", in Meyer, W.B. and B.L. Turner II (eds.), *Changes in Land Use and Land Cover: a Global Perspective*, Cambridge, UK: Cambridge University Press.

Wilshaw, C. (1994): *A Century of Growth: Malawi's Tobacco Industry 1893-1993*, Blantyre: Central Africana.

World Bank (1985), *Malawi: Wood Energy Project: Phase 2*, Eastern Africa Projects Department, Southern Agriculture Division, Washington, DC: World Bank.

Chapter 19

Does Tobacco Growing Pay? The Case of Kenya

Pamphil H.M. Kweyuh

The history of tobacco growing in Kenya

The initial entry of British American Tobacco (BAT) into what eventually became Kenya goes back to the turn of the 20th century. It was then simply a marketing firm importing and selling tobacco, largely to British colonial consumers. But in 1928, owing to rising demand for tobacco, particularly the traditional *kali* (Kiswahili for "harsh") around the shores of Lake Victoria in East Africa, BAT constructed a corrugated iron factory at Jinja, along the Nile river. Increasing demand after World War II prompted the firm to reconstruct the Jinja factory in 1948. The following year, a stronger BAT acquired the East African Tobacco Company based in the British sister colony of Tanzania, which for the following 15 years became the main operating company of the BAT Group in East Africa.

In the early 1950s, as demand in Kenya grew, BAT decided to build another factory in Nairobi. This plant was opened in 1956, and full-scale production began the year after. The Rift Valley Cigarette Company, which operated a factory in Nakuru, 180 km from the Kenyan capital Nairobi, was acquired by BAT in 1956. In July 1966, Rothmans entered the Kenyan market, but sold out to BAT Kenya the following year.

However, political changes that had begun with the achievement of independence by the three East African countries (Kenya, Uganda and Tanzania) during the early 1960s forced the BAT Group to split into three separate entities. In addition, the proclamation of the "Ujamaa" (socialist) republic in Tanzania, and the take-over of power in Uganda by Idi Amin, caused Kenyan authorities and firms increasing unease over their dependence on goods and services from the other two countries. Until the mid-1970s, BAT Kenya was almost entirely dependent on Tanzanian and Ugandan tobacco.

In 1973, Kenya produced less than 100 tons of tobacco, although it had been grown in the central areas of Sagana and Kitui since the 1930s, and in Embu since the 1950s. In 1975, therefore, when BAT Kenya began active promotion of tobacco growing, the crop could for practical purposes be said to be alien to the country, although the smoking habit was increasingly firmly entrenched. BAT's promotion of tobacco growing entailed the provision of all production inputs, including fertilisers and pesticides, assisting with barn construction, and the provision of field technical staff.

Within only three years, growers (whose numbers had already risen to 7 000) encouraged by the production package had pushed annual output to 2 100 tons. By 1982 there were 9 000 farmers producing 5 100 tons per year, while one of the all-time best harvests, 11 600 tons, was reaped in 1988. Thereafter, drought and harsh economic realities took a heavy toll: while grower numbers rose by 800 during 1989-91, the area under the crop fell by 500 ha to 3 912 ha, while leaf deliveries nearly halved from 10 368 to 6 425 tons.

During 1992-94 deliveries to BAT Kenya continued to fall markedly, due to intense competition from a new entrant, Mastermind Tobacco Kenya Limited, whose potential as a rival was grossly underestimated by BAT Kenya. The founder of the new firm, a former top manager of BAT Kenya, apparently exploited the weaknesses he perceived in BAT to create a near-rebellion among BAT Kenya's hitherto compliant farmers.

Mastermind Tobacco appears to have done great planning. When they entered the market, they had no outgrowers and merely rode the wave of liberalisation which the government was under great pressure to allow. Soon, Mastermind was buying tobacco produced with BAT financial and input advances. Worse still, the farmers were not repaying BAT, and from an amount of just KSh5 million (KSh60 = US$1 in Feb 1998) the amount of outstanding loans had soared to KSh54 million at the end of the 1994/95 season.

BAT Kenya, which enjoys a sophisticated lobbying capacity as well as 20 per cent ownership by the National Social Security Fund (NSSF), a state corporation, moved swiftly to address this situation. Firstly, the Minister for Agriculture, Livestock and Marketing zoned tobacco growing areas into BAT Kenya and Mastermind "spheres of operation". It soon became apparent that this zoning tended to favour BAT Kenya, and Mastermind, using friends in government and a group of rebellious farmers, forced the Ministry to soften its approach.

The result was the gazetting of "Tobacco Growing By-Laws, 1994" by the Minister. These stipulated *inter alia* that no one should engage in the purchase and manufacturing of tobacco, unless he or she had sponsored the growing of the crop. The by-law included other far-reaching provisions (which are, however, difficult to enforce), including:

- a requirement that tobacco sponsors plant 1 800 trees per hectare of fire-cured tobacco and 3 000 trees per hectare of flue-cured tobacco;
- a list of applicable fertilisers and pest control methods;
- the limitation of purchasable categories of tobacco to 20 classifications.

Most of these provisions were in direct response to the trouble Mastermind was seen as having fomented in the tobacco industry. While the situation was stabilised, albeit temporarily, the crisis had exposed BAT Kenya's exploitation of farmers.

Chasing a mirage — Kenyan tobacco profits that never are

A standard defence advanced by the tobacco industry has been its benefit to farmers and countries. Indeed, in the early 1990s alone, the International

Tobacco Growers Association (ITGA) produced four glossy publications with such titles as *Tobacco Trade or Aid?*; *Tobacco Farming: Sustainable Alternatives? (Volumes 1 and 2)*, and *Tobacco In Developing Countries.*

Kenya features prominently in Volume 2 of *Tobacco Farming*, which makes extremely generous claims about the revenue accruing to the country's growers. It says, for instance, that Kenyan tobacco farmers achieved average gross margins (gross profit) per hectare of KSh23 431 for Burley, KSh19 220 for flue-cured, and KSh5 922 for fire-cured tobacco in 1990. However, BAT Kenya's own publication, *The Economic Impact of the Tobacco Industry in Kenya*, published a year after the ITGA data was allegedly compiled, states that:
1. the mean income from tobacco per hectare was KSh15 393;
2. the mean value farmers attached to their land was KSh12 000.

The author established from baseline surveys that in 1994, tobacco farmers' average net income was around KSh7 000, with actual gross income being what ITGA presents as the net income (Kweyuh, 1994). Gustin Otieno, a tobacco farmer for 12 years, stopped growing the crop after he realised that his actual yearly profit was almost nil: "I worked on my two-acre tobacco farm with my wife and six relatives to get the work done. When I began to cost their labour, I found that my annual profit was KSh50," he says. Otieno also notes that he spent his tobacco "profits" buying maize for his family, food they were unable to produce for themselves due to their tobacco workload.

Why do many farmers continue growing tobacco at a loss?

This was in fact the question the tobacco industry posed when *Tobacco Growing in Kenya* was first published. While independent tobacco control researchers were genuinely concerned to find an answer to this question, the reality is that the tobacco industry knows the reasons why farmers are "addicted" to growing the crop. The Kenyan case study, and another in Uganda (Aliro, 1993), discern three principal reasons:
1. the farmers have taken production loans from BAT which they are often unable to repay; if they abandon the crop, they are in contractual default and risk bankruptcy;
2. most supplementary or alternative crops have neither sponsors nor a ready market, and many farmers say they would "rather the devil we know than the angels we do not know";
3. the history of commodity marketing boards in Kenya and Uganda has been fraught with greed, mismanagement and fraud, resulting *inter alia* in long delays in payments to farmers;
4. farmers face serious post-harvest problems with many crops, such as perishability and unreliable delivery systems, while tobacco is non-perishable, delivery centres are close to farmers, and in some cases tobacco sponsors assume responsibility for picking and transporting the crop.

Tobacco's lesser-known costs and losses

A researcher in South Nyanza on a donor-funded development research initiative had targeted tobacco in her survey, but found the story of one Norah

Kaguhya so compelling, she called it a "nightmare". Soon after Mrs Kaguhya inherited a tobacco farm from her husband, she began suffering from chest pains and shortness of breath, and was finally forced to go to hospital. She could not believe it when the doctor told her that she had the symptoms of a heavy smoker and should stop smoking immediately; she had never smoked a cigarette in her life. Her story highlights the overlooked production costs of tobacco which cost farmers in developing countries dearly.

According to Dr George Ochieng', Suba District Clinical Officer, "Curing tobacco irritates the lungs, causing inflammation as a result of inhaling a lot of smoke". According to Ochieng', tobacco farmers involved in the process complain of recurrent chest infections, which improve after they stop farming the crop. BAT recommends 12 000 flue-cured or 15 500 fire-cured tobacco plants per hectare, which translates into 18 000 and 22 000 leaves respectively on the average 0.5 hectare farm that a farmer cultivates in the district.

Furthermore, tobacco-growing is highly labour-intensive. Nursery preparation and tending, seed-bed preparation, application of chemicals, watering two to four times a day, weeding, ridging, transplanting, pesticide application, sucker removal (topping) three times, harvesting, curing, tying leaves, and leaf-by-leaf inspections, leave the farmer little time to do anything else. A study of labour utilisation in tobacco growing in nearby Migori District, one of Kenya's tobacco-producing hubs, found that the high labour requirements of tobacco growing prevented farmers from planting food crops for personal use, which they then had to purchase (Ageng'o). The high labour input required farmers to specialise in tobacco and ignore other crops, the study noted, while the failure of farmers to cost labour and other inputs caused them to over-estimate their profits.

"We give tobacco priority because it gives us some income," says Wilson Alumasa, of Sigiria. "But it means we have to buy maize because we are too busy planting tobacco during the long rains to farm other crops." Ben Mumo, Area Leaf Manager at Oyani, concedes that while the crop is labour-intensive, "we don't cost the labour since it's the farmer who does the work". In fact, it is self-serving that BAT does not calculate labour costs, because labour is of necessity provided largely by women and children, who then abandon their traditional roles of caring for the family, including growing food. In addition, preliminary research points to poor performance in school and high drop-out rates among children from tobacco-growing areas.

District statistics indicate that BAT Kenya's farmers in Migori District last year produced 3 000 tons of tobacco worth KSh7.7 million, up from KSh5.7 million the previous year. Divided by 1 000 farmers, this amounts to an average of KSh7 700 (US$120) per farmer. BAT contracted 500 hectares under fire-cured and 1 084 ha under flue-cured tobacco in the district last year. Mumo notes that the industry has benefited from farmers defecting from the troubled sugar sector, where harvests have been delayed.

While BAT achieved an after-tax profit of US$3.82 million for the first half of 1997, contributed US$22.7 million to the country's foreign exchange earnings during 1997, and boasts a new state-of-the-art machine which produces 4.34

million packed cigarettes a day, Migori farmers complain that the company's profits are not trickling down adequately. For the last three years, Wilson Alumasa has achieved a net KSh3 000 (US$50) annual profit, after the multinational has received its loan repayment, from the 0.75 hectare tobacco plot he cultivates with his wife. This income is 50 per cent below the level considered "absolute poverty" by the World Bank.

Input over-supply

To counter the negative health effects of harmful chemicals used in tobacco production, BAT also sells farmers protective overalls, gumboots and gloves on loans to be recovered from farmers' final dues after sale of their tobacco leaf. *The Economic Impact of the Tobacco Industry in Kenya* says fertilisers constitute the biggest production cost, rising to nearly 50 per cent for Burley crop. Yet the same publication, in a section dedicated to "cost-cutting" issues (which it correctly points out are pressing), says that BAT Kenya's field staff have tended to oversupply farm inputs. A major concern is that Dieldrin, listed among the Pesticide Action Network's blacklisted "Dirty Dozen", was among the chemicals being supplied to farmers as recently as 1996. The economic and health costs of pesticide poisoning are not even calculated, let alone the long-term environmental impact.

Oongo (1997) reports widespread chemical poisoning in South Nyanza: "The problem is that medical care is no longer free and the firms do not have a health insurance scheme for farmers. Treatments from various tobacco growing-induced ailments is eating deeply and, at worst, killing peasants." Samson Amasinde works with his wife and three children on three acres of tobacco he has been planting since 1976. While he says that tobacco growing has helped him "pay school fees", he adds that this year, he is unable to afford protective gloves "because I already have a big loan" for tobacco inputs from BAT. "I will work without the gloves until I begin to see the effect of the chemicals," the father of six says. While low profit margins are discouraging farmers from taking advances for safety equipment such as gloves, BAT does not provide masks to protect farmers from respiratory tract infections which afflict farmers like Norah Kaguhya. "We have not yet been able to bring those here to Oyani," explains Mumo.

Deforestation and the increasing cost of wood

While fire-cured tobacco can be dried with twigs because heating is direct, flue-cured leaves require heat at a given intensity to generate the steam that dries up the leaves, delivered over a period averaging a week; hence a heavy demand for woodfuel. Having exhausted local trees, and with a BAT-sponsored reforestation programme being little more than a public relations initiative at present, farmers are having to hire animal traction to collect wood, or to buy it at a cost as high as KSh200 for a bundle that would cure about 10 kilograms of tobacco leaf. While the long-term economic and environmental impact of deforestation has not yet been calculated, Oongo (1997) suggests that the cost of buying wood for curing is already a major cause of tobacco's diminishing returns.

What next for Kenya's tobacco farmers?

Tobacco farmers not only in Kenya but the whole of East Africa will need urgent supportive interventions. The plan of action should include:

1. financial assistance to offset loan arrears that have left farmers in virtual servitude to tobacco firms; and
2. production and marketing support for supplementary crops.

For farmers who continue growing tobacco, the 1994 By-Laws will need to be turned into a comprehensive law, covering all socio-economic and agricultural aspects of the crop. While the government is moving away from price controls, an exception to these free market policies should be made in the case of tobacco to protect farmers' interests.

There will also be a need to create a tobacco growers co-operative or association. This should not be an insurmountable obstacle, as Kenya's top agricultural products, including coffee and tea, are already grown almost exclusively through co-operatives and/or farmers' associations. But as Chapman and Wong (1990) note, BAT has been opposed to the emergence of a co-operative, which it sees as posing a threat to its activities: "According to our sources . . . BAT (K) effectively bribed those involved [in the formation of a co-operative] to the point where the co-operative approach was no better than BAT (K)'s approach." BAT senior management insist they are totally opposed to co-operatives as these would increase overheads, but the true situation is that BAT fears a stronger, united opposition to its exploitative policies.

The onus of establishing a workable centralised purchasing and negotiating system lies with members of parliament, and central and local government; however, there is as yet no sign of them responding to this urgent need. There also appears a rationale in discontinuing BAT Kenya's direct production advances, and leaving the job to the open market, where farmers would go to any supplier or bank and take advances, most probably with BAT's guarantee. In this way, they will be able to get only what they have determined as genuinely needed. In any case, they have been working the land for years, and BAT should stop posing as the omniscient expert on tobacco. Further, BAT should withdraw its field staff, and leave technical issues to a combination of agronomists funded through a co-operative and the existing government agricultural extension officers.

How and when these suggestions can be put into force is unknown, for there is no political or company will to change the existing situation, and, as pointed out above, farmers remain poignantly weak and dependent on BAT Kenya.

References

Ageng'o, H. (undated), *Analysis of Labour Utilisation in Tobacco*, mimeo, Nairobi: University of Nairobi.
Aliro, O.K. (1993), *Uganda: Paying the Price of Growing Tobacco*, PANOS Monitor Publication, London/Kampala: PANOS.
Chapman, S. and Wong W.L. (1990), *Tobacco Control in the Third World: a Resource Atlas*, Penang: IOCU.
Kweyuh, P.H.M. (1994), "Tobacco growing in Kenya — the socio-ecological losses", *Tobacco Control*, 3(3), Autumn.
Oongo, E. (1997), untitled paper written for the *Tenth World Conference on Tobacco or Health in Beijing*, unpublished mimeo.

Section 3

Country Case Studies in Tobacco Control

Chapter 20

The Economics of Tobacco Control in South Africa

Rowena van der Merwe

This chapter analyses the impact of the stronger tobacco control measures implemented in South Africa since the early 1990s (particularly increased cigarette taxation and restrictions on tobacco advertising) in terms of their effects on cigarette consumption, the fiscus, economic output, employment and trade. It is based on key research findings of the Economics of Tobacco Control Project established at the University of Cape Town in 1996 to investigate demand, supply and socio-economic issues relating to tobacco control in South Africa.

South African policy towards the tobacco industry has undergone significant change in recent years, and this has led to a divergence of policy concerns. On the one hand, the government professes commitment to discouraging consumption of tobacco products in order to reduce avoidable illness and death. On the other hand, the government is very sensitive to the potential for jobs losses in the tobacco industry through increased tobacco control measures. The tobacco industry has attempted to convince the public in general and policy-makers in particular that, regardless of its effects on physical health, tobacco plays an important role in the community's economic health, generating employment and contributing vital revenue to government coffers. Because South Africa suffers high unemployment, this argument carries much political weight.

Similarly, the South African government is under pressure from claims that more stringent tobacco control measures will result in increased cigarette smuggling and illicit trade. Following the Budget Speech of the Minister of Finance in March 1997, an open letter to the government from the Tobacco Institute of Southern Africa (TISA) claimed that increasing excise duties on cigarettes would not materially affect overall consumption, but would lead to "increased contraband activity, reduced government income, and job losses" (*Sunday Times*, 1997). These claims by TISA have had a deterrent effect against the addressing of tobacco morbidity and mortality by public policy through stronger tobacco control measures, such as increased excise taxes or restrictions on tobacco advertising and promotion.

In a developing country like South Africa, excise taxation is a more potent mechanism to reduce consumption than in developed countries, because consumers of cigarettes tend to be more price-sensitive in developing countries (Chapman and Richardson, 1990). The government therefore needs to define an optimal taxation policy on cigarettes that will maximise revenue generation from this source, while at the same time constraining consumption and thereby promoting public health. However, this objective should preferably be achieved without reducing overall economic output, exacerbating unemployment or inducing illegal trade in tobacco products. Besides a tax component, an optimal mix of tobacco control policies would also incorporate regulation of tobacco product advertising, and other health promotion measures. Such policy initiatives need to be formulated not only within the socio-economic environment of South Africa, given the structure of the tobacco industry and the economy, but also within the prevailing socio-political environment.

It is important to recognise the critical role played by political support in the formulation of optimal tobacco control policy. While it may have been politically expedient in a new fledgling democracy to prioritise other health needs, tobacco control has been high on the agenda in South Africa. The Minister of Health has provided much of the impetus behind some noteworthy changes of policy in this arena. Since December 1994 South Africa has enjoyed requirements for health warning messages in tobacco product advertising, and for warning labels on cigarette packs, that are among the most stringent in the world, and a comprehensive ban on tobacco advertising is to be tabled in Parliament in the near future. In early 1998 excise duty on cigarettes was increased to about 50 per cent of the average retail price. Future strengthening of tobacco control policies will require similar political support.

Statistical trends in the South African tobacco industry

(i)   The structure of the tobacco industry

Four local cigarette producers manufacture virtually all the cigarettes consumed in South Africa (27.5 billion in 1996); cigarettes imports are not significant. Table 1 details the market shares and main brands held in 1996 by the major manufacturers; a new entrant launched in 1997 (Japan Tobacco) is not included.

Table 1. The major tobacco companies in South Africa, 1996	
Company (main brands)	*Market share (%)*
Rembrandt (Rothmans, Stuyvesant, Dunhill, Cartier)	85
United Tobacco (Benson & Hedges)	12
RJ Reynolds (imports from USA)	2
Mastermind Tobacco (exports to rest of Africa)	1
Source: *Cape Business News* (1996a)	

The industry therefore has a highly oligopolistic structure, with a few players dominating production, and significant barriers to entry as a result. Nevertheless, the entrance of a new competitor such as Japan Tobacco into such a difficult market structure suggests that profit margins in the industry are very attractive.

(ii) Price, tobacco tax and consumption

Indices of price and consumption, and the proportion of price made up by excise tax, are presented in Table 2 for 1970-97.

Table 2. Indices of real retail cigarette price and *per capita* cigarette consumption, and excise tax as a percentage of retail cigarette price in South Africa, selected years 1970-97 (1970 = 100)

Year	Price	Consumption	Excise tax as % of retail price
1970	100	100	46
1975	92	120	46
1980	77	135	40
1985	69	140	31
1986	68	140	28
1987	64	147	26
1988	63	151	27
1989	64	148	24
1990	66	151	22
1991	70	165	24
1992	71	135	22
1993	73	119	20
1994	72	119	28
1995	81	105	24
1996	85	95	32
1997	90	78	39
1998*	n.a.	n.a.	50

Notes: n.a. = not available
Sources: Central Statistical Services (South Africa) (annual); South African Reserve Bank (quarterly); Tobacco Board (South Africa) (annual); Reekie (1994); * Department of Finance (South Africa) (1997)

The index of the real price of cigarettes declined noticeably during this period, from 100 in 1970 to a low of 63 in 1988. Concurrently, excise taxes also declined markedly as a proportion of the retail price of cigarettes, from 45 per cent in the 1970s to 20-24 per cent in the early 1990s, showing that they have not kept pace with inflation. Not only did government not optimise revenue from this source, but by allowing a steady decline in tobacco taxes it in effect encouraged consumption. Not surprisingly, the index of cigarette consumption increased from 100 in 1970 to a high of 165 in 1991. Since 1995, however, the South African government has committed itself to a stronger taxation policy, and has introduced increases in duty that have brought the effective cigarette tax rate to 50 per cent of the retail price in 1998.

Converting nominal cigarette price data to 1990 rands (R), the real average price of a pack of 20 cigarettes in 1970 was about R2.60 (US$1 = R3.50 in 1990).

By 1995 this had declined to R2.03, after a low of R1.48 in 1991. Despite this, the percentage of retail price made up by excise taxes declined during 1970-95 by a disproportionately greater amount, from 46 to 20 per cent. This suggests that the industry's profit margin per cigarette also increased during this period.

(iii) Smoking prevalence

Approximately 34 per cent of the South African population smoked in 1995, nearly 7.6 million people. The majority of these smokers are male, and almost half of South African households have smokers (Table 3).

Table 3. Prevalence of smoking in South Africa, 1995

Population group	Percentage
Whites	35
Indians	36
Coloureds	59
African	31
Men	52
Women	17
Total population	34

Source: South African Institute of Race Relations (1997)

(iv) Employment

Figure 1 charts employment in tobacco manufacturing during 1945-95.

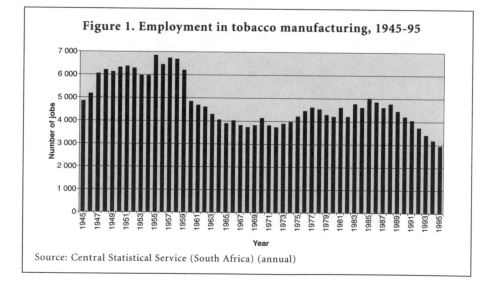

Figure 1. Employment in tobacco manufacturing, 1945-95

Source: Central Statistical Service (South Africa) (annual)

There was a considerable decrease in employment during the 1960s, followed by a steady increase until the early 1980s, and a decline from the late 1980s onwards. During 1985-95 employment in the industry declined by an average annual rate of 5.6 per cent. Since consumption began to decline only from 1991, the prior decrease in employment must have been the result of other causes such as production improvements and the resulting efficiency gains.

(v) Wages

It might be expected that employees in an industry experiencing declining demand would earn low or falling wages; this has not, however, been the case for South African tobacco workers. Since the early 1990s, employees in the tobacco industry have been amongst the most highly-paid workers in the South African manufacturing sector. During 1990-95, real average monthly wages in the industry were 25-35 per cent higher than average manufacturing wages (Central Statistical Services (South Africa), 1995). Over this period their average real wages increased by 10.6 per cent, whereas average real wages in manufacturing increased by only 4.4 per cent. Of the 29 Standard Industrial Classifications covered by South Africa's Central Statistical Services, workers in tobacco product manufacturing were the eighth-highest earning group.

Why are South African tobacco workers so well paid? The answer is two-fold. In the first place, the falling excise tax component in retail price and increasing demand experienced in previous decades clearly signalled increasing profitability in the industry, which would have enabled them to pay higher wages. In addition, the recent (and, of course, high profile) increases in tobacco tax have provided camouflage behind which cigarette manufacturers can institute increases in their own prices that are less perceptible than usual, which they have done. The resulting boost to the profits of tobacco companies naturally enables them to pay higher wages. Secondly, employers have little incentive to resist demands for higher wages since these help maintain employee morale in the face of workforce cuts and increasingly critical public scrutiny of the industry; this in turn makes it possible for the cigarette industry to continue attaining productivity gains without alienating their labour force.

The price elasticity of demand for cigarettes and potential tax revenue

(i) The price elasticity of demand

Several statistical studies in South Africa have estimated the impact of higher prices on cigarette consumption. Price elasticity of demand measures the responsiveness of consumption to price changes, all other factors remaining constant. Reekie (1994) found an elasticity of -0.87 for South Africa, while Van Walbeek (1996) estimated a value of -0.66 from the same data, suggesting that Reekie's estimate is too high. The statistical and empirical fit of Reekie's model was also criticised by Abedian and Dorrington (1994).

Table 4. Comparison of price elasticity estimates for cigarette consumption for selected countries

Date	Reference	Country studied	Elasticity estimate	Comments
1980	Fujii	USA	-0.45	1929-73 Time-series
1982	Lewit and Coate	USA	-0.42	1976 Health Interview Survey gives elasticity by age and sex
1984	Leu	Switzerland	-0.50	1954-81 Sales data
1985	Bishop and Yoo	USA	-0.45	1954-80 Time-series aggregate data
1985	Radfar	UK	-0.23 (SR) -0.39 (LR)	1965-80 Quarterly aggregate sales data
1988	Godfrey and Maynard	UK	-0.56	1956-84 Aggregated sales data
1990	Chapman and Richardson	Papua New Guinea	-0.71 -0.50	1973-86 Excise elasticity for cigarettes/non-cigarette tobacco
1993	Keeler et al.	California	-0.3 to -0.5 (SR) -0.5 to -0.6 (LR)	1980-90 Monthly time-series consumption data
1994	Sung, Hu and Keeler	11 US states	-0.40 (SR) -0.48 (LR)	1967-90 Panel data
1994	Reekie	SA	-0.877	1970-89 Time-series consumption data
1995	Tremblay and Tremblay	US	-0.4	1955-90 Time-series
1996	Van Walbeek	SA	-0.32 (SR) -0.53 (LR) -0.66 (SR) -1.52 (LR)	1972-90 Tobacco Board data 1971-89 Reekie's data
1996b	Economics of Tobacco Control Project	SA	-0.57	1970-95 Time-series consumption data, integrated supply and demand
1997a	Economics of Tobacco Control Project	SA	-0.59 (SR) -0.69 (LR)	1970-95 Time-series consumption data

Source: Economics of Tobacco Control Project (1997a)

The Economics of Tobacco Control Project (1996b) found a price elasticity of -0.57 using simultaneous equation modelling which integrated supply and demand within the South African tobacco market. Using cointegration analysis and single equation modelling, a later study by the Project (Economics of Tobacco Control Project, 1997a) found a price elasticity estimate of -0.59 in the short-run and -0.69 in the long-run.

For most developed countries the short-run price elasticity of demand is around -0.4, that is, a 10 per cent increase in price leads to a 4 per cent decline in consumption. To provide an international comparative perspective for South African price elasticity estimates, Table 4 provides a survey of these estimates similar to Zimring and Nelson (1995). It is evident that for most developing countries, including South Africa, price elasticity appears to be slightly higher than in developed countries, suggesting a greater sensitivity to price. Like the results from Papua New Guinea (Chapman and Richardson, 1990), it appears that the estimates in South Africa are more price-elastic than in developed countries. This underscores the fact that in developing countries, excise taxes are a more potent weapon for governments to reduce consumption than other non-tax measures. The level of excise tax is therefore an important and practical instrument for the control of consumption, particularly as the prevalence of smoking is highest among lower-income groups in South Africa.

(ii) Potential tax revenue

The price elasticity of demand estimate is important because it helps determine the optimal level of cigarette tax. Apart from its role as a source of government revenue, excise tax is the single most important constraining influence on cigarette consumption in South Africa. The government therefore has an incentive to find a level of cigarette tax which reduces consumption (and so benefits public health and saves health care resources), without damaging the industry to the extent that consumer taxes can no longer be levied on this product.

This section presents the results of a simulation intended to establish an optimal tobacco tax revenue for South Africa using calculated estimates of price elasticity of demand and income elasticity of demand (Economics of Tobacco Control Project, 1996b). It revealed the revenue foregone by government due to its failure to maximise the excise tax opportunities available from cigarettes (Figure 2). The simulation involved maximisation of government revenue from excise tax on cigarettes, subject to the constraint that increasing cigarette tax increases the retail price of cigarettes, which in turn reduces quantity demanded. The optimisation was solved using -0.57 as a price estimate and 1.57 as an income estimate. The simulation did not consider the probable effects of reduced consumption on tobacco industry production, corporate tax revenue and employment, nor did it include future savings in health care expenditure from a lower incidence of smoking-related diseases. These issues would best be incorporated into a comprehensive cost-benefit analysis of the industry, which is beyond the scope of this chapter.

Figure 2 shows that excise taxes were near their optimal level until 1972, after which tax rates did not maintain their real value, causing increasingly significant levels of potential excise tax revenue to be foregone. To illustrate, had the government attempted to optimise excise tax revenue from cigarettes, it could have extracted an additional R1 869 million (in 1995 rands) in 1995 alone.

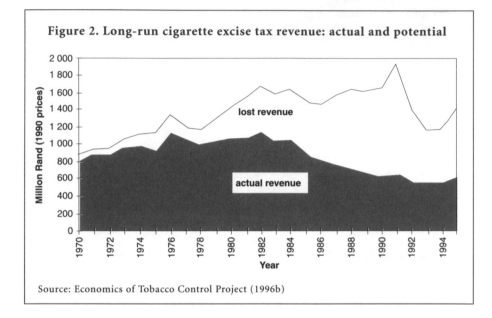

Figure 2. Long-run cigarette excise tax revenue: actual and potential

Source: Economics of Tobacco Control Project (1996b)

In 1995, excise tax made up approximately one-quarter of the R3.50 average price of a pack of cigarettes in South Africa. In March 1998 the effective cigarette tax rate was increased from 24 per cent to 50 per cent of retail price, therefore a much larger proportion is now going to government coffers. Table 5 details the estimated composition of the average price of a pack of cigarettes (R5.50) in 1997.

Table 5. Estimated breakdown of retail cigarette price, 1997

Recipient	% of retail price
Farmer	5
Manufacturer	23
Wholesaler	6
Retailer	14
Government (excise duty)	52

It could be argued that, in view of the relative price-inelasticity of demand, there is still scope to increase excise taxes above the current 50 per cent of selling price. Historically, every increase in excise tax during the last 25 years has led to an increase in tax revenue, even during the 1970s when the tax was around 45 per cent of retail price, confirming that the revenue-maximising level of cigarette tax has not yet been reached. It certainly was not reached in 1997, when the tax was 39 per cent of retail price, and the excise revenue collected from tobacco products was R1 748 million (1.2 per cent of total government revenue), up from R1 232 million (1.1 per cent of government revenue) in 1995. The revenue-maximising level of cigarette tax does not seem to have been reached in 1998 either; the optimal tax rate may be well above the current 50 per cent of retail price.

Tobacco regulations in South Africa

(i) Tobacco industry advertising

In addition to the debate surrounding cigarette taxation, the role of advertising has also been hotly debated in South Africa. The industry has persistently argued that cigarette advertising influences only the market shares of, and switching among, cigarette brands, without affecting the overall level of demand for cigarettes. Reekie (1994) found cigarette advertising expenditure to have no significant impact on demand for cigarettes in South Africa, which provided support for TISA's claims in this regard and has helped to deter government from the regulation of tobacco product advertising. In contrast, the Economics of Tobacco Control Project (1996c), using both simultaneous- and single-equation econometric analysis of demand, found that cigarette advertising has a significant impact on demand in South Africa: a 1 per cent increase in the growth of advertising expenditure will increase growth in demand for cigarettes by 0.18-0.24 per cent. This finding is consistent with research in other countries showing that tobacco industry advertising stimulates tobacco consumption (Fujii, 1980; Hu *et al.*, 1995).

For years the South African debate on tobacco advertising failed to produce conclusive policy decisions; tobacco product advertising and promotion were until recently largely unregulated. However, in the course of 1998 the Tobacco Products Control Amendment Bill is due for submission to Parliament; this will recommend partial or total restriction of tobacco advertising and sponsorship. The Economics of Tobacco Control Project (1996c; 1997a) findings suggest that the Bill will lead to a significant reduction in tobacco product consumption in South Africa.

(ii) Controls on tobacco use

Regulations based on the Tobacco Products Control Act of 1993 (which is aimed at discouraging the use of tobacco industry products) were imposed from May 1995. These and other regulations introduced from 1990 onwards include restrictions on smoking in public places and on public transport, prohibition of selling to minors, the use of health warnings on packaging and in all advertising, and the screening of anti-tobacco advertising in cinemas.

The findings of the Economics of Tobacco Control Project (1996c) did not support the hypothesis that the introduction of anti-smoking campaigns in 1990 reduced consumption, but the econometric analysis concerned was of course based on relatively few observations and was therefore inconclusive. Notwithstanding this data problem, there is some evidence that anti-tobacco advertising has some impact, including a significant decline in cigarette consumption from 1990 onward. Furthermore, studies in other countries have shown that anti-tobacco advertising reduces consumption (Hu, Sung and Keeler, 1995; Tremblay and Tremblay, 1995).

The output and employment effects of reduced tobacco consumption

If government were to pursue its public health objectives through more stringent tobacco control measures (including higher excise duty and restrictions on use and advertising), what would be the effect on the fiscus, on output in the economy, and on employment? In other words, what would happen if the 7.6 million smokers in South Africa in 1995 decided to give up their habit? The Economics of Tobacco Control Project (1997c) used input-output methodology and a Social Accounting Matrix (SAM) to examine different scenarios of output and employment effects resulting from this hypothetical change.

The SAM estimates private consumption expenditure on tobacco products to be R1 606 million and final demand to be R1 800 million. (These figures are drastic underestimates of consumption expenditure on tobacco, but the indicative directions of changes in consumption can still be determined from the model.) Consumers who stop smoking will reallocate their tobacco expenditure to other goods and services in the economy. South Africa typically has a low savings rate out of personal disposable income, 2 per cent in 1995; hence, little of the reallocated expenditure would be saved. Because most smokers in South Africa are in lower-income groups, and the import content of most goods and services consumed by such groups is comparatively low, such a switch in expenditure will probably be towards locally-produced goods and services.

The resources concerned will thus remain in the domestic economy to generate economic activity and employment opportunities. Falling employment in the tobacco industry will thus be offset by increases in employment in other industries, depending on how labour-intensive these other industries are relative to the tobacco industry. Government was assumed to respond to reduced tobacco tax revenue by reducing expenditure and public service employment and seeking alternative tax bases, in order to keep its budget deficit at more or less the same level. In addition, consumer expenditure switched to other sectors would increase company and income tax revenues originating in these sectors.

Table 6 shows the net employment effects of a reallocation of consumer spending from tobacco products to other goods and services in terms of four different scenarios. In Scenario 1 and 2 consumers who have given up smoking adopt spending patterns like those of the average (non-smoking) consumer in the economy. In Scenario 1, only final demand for tobacco products is reallocated; in Scenario 2, intermediate demand for tobacco products is also reallocated. This means that inter-industry reallocations also occur. Scenarios 3 and 4 show the employment outcomes when expenditure patterns are like those of the "recent stoppers" discussed in Buck *et al.* (1995), i.e. expenditure on non-essential items increases more than expenditure on essentials. A relatively larger share of the reallocated expenditure is thus spent on clothing, education, recreation, entertainment, communication, transport and other services, than on housing and durable goods. In Scenario 3 final demand for tobacco products is removed and reallocated according to this new expenditure pattern. In

Table 6. Net employment outcomes for 4 scenarios of reduced tobacco consumption and 21 sectors* of economic activity, 1995 (number of jobs gained)

Functional category	Money spent as average consumer		Money spent as recent stopper	
	Scenario 1: Remove final demand	Scenario 2: Remove final & intermediate demand	Scenario 3: Remove final demand	Scenario 4: Double current decline of tobacco consumption
Fishing, forestry, farming	6 438	5 261	2 245	-147
Field crops (incl. tobacco)	-2 992	123	-2 802	-931
Mining	2 252	2 707	-767	-922
Food, drinks	627	866	-406	-522
Tobacco manufacturing	-2 876	-2 924	-2 875	-650
Clothing	817	1 896	9 610	150
Furniture	384	958	407	-1 208
Paper, printing	-1 827	737	-1 630	-1 038
Chemicals	122	682	-327	-366
Petrol, rubber, plastic	243	538	-26	-209
Building materials	731	889	-326	-401
Machinery, equipment	1 159	1 830	-318	-464
Light manufacturing	90	96	-330	-334
Water, electricity, gas	635	964	-35	-247
Construction	1 232	1 387	-620	-806
Wholesale, retail	1 028	3 200	-437	-604
Accommodation	142	170	-284	-342
Transport	316	616	2 322	230
Communication	994	1 397	690	1 174
Business services	731	1 168	671	121
Govt. and other services	-1 030	11 814	45 474	11 054
Total	9 218	34 377	50 236	3 536

Note: * The SAM has a total of 104 economic activities, which have been grouped into the above 21 categories.

Scenario 4 the rate of decline in tobacco consumption (an average of 11 per cent per year during 1991-95) was increased to 20 per cent *per annum,* and the money not spent on tobacco products was reallocated in the expenditure pattern of "recent stoppers".

It can be seen that, in the scenarios as specified, South Africa as a whole would gain net increases in output and employment if smokers quit their habit completely or even partially during 1995. In Scenario 1 employment would be lost in those sectors immediately associated with cigarette production: tobacco farming, manufacturing, and paper and printing. Jobs would also be lost in government as a result of the loss in government revenue. However, there would be a net gain in employment in all other sectors. Scenario 2 shows an employment loss only in tobacco manufacturing, as inter-industry reallocation of expenditure takes place.

In Scenario 3 marginal employment losses occur across all sectors, as a large expenditure shift takes place towards more labour-intensive production. The major employment losses are again those most closely linked to the tobacco industry: tobacco farming, manufacturing, and paper and printing. However, these losses are again offset by very large increases in other industries, in particular the service industries, which are labour-intensive. In Scenario 4, which would most closely resemble the reality of a short-run decline in tobacco consumption in South Africa, losses occur across all sectors again, except for those receiving reallocated expenditure, such as clothing, transport, and communication, and business, recreational, educational and other services. The gains here again offset losses in all other sectors.

If expenditure reallocation occurs as per the average consumer, net gains in activity would be realised in every broad economic sector, which suggests that the required degree of structural re-adjustment would be limited. For example, it seems probable that most shops losing retail margin on cigarettes would enjoy net increases in income through greater sales of other goods and services. It is likely, however, that specialist tobacconists would lose income; one can therefore not assume that structural re-adjustment effects would be zero. There will be costs involved in making a transition to an economy less dependent on tobacco. Jobs will be lost, at least temporarily, in certain sectors, and the disruption for the newly unemployed would constitute a genuine cost. Because the transitional costs will in reality take place over a longer time and not instantaneously as represented here, the impact will be softer. If, however, expenditure occurs as per "recent stoppers" where people who quit smoking exhibit different expenditure patterns, there would be larger structural adjustments in the economy, but there would also be larger net gains.

Realisation of the net job gains requires that South Africa has sufficient spare capacity to satisfy the additional demands. Given that 50 000 jobs is less than 2 per cent of the (official) unemployment total for South Africa in 1995, this does not seem an unreasonable assumption.

The results presented indicate unequivocally that a cessation of cigarette purchasing would lead to significant net increases in South African output and employment. The inescapable conclusion is that stronger tobacco control policies do not jeopardise overall output and employment, as the industry argues. In addition to the obvious health benefits from stronger tobacco control policies and resulting decrease in smoking, there are also economic and employment benefits.

The political effects, however, of the employment redistribution from tobacco to non-tobacco-related jobs differ considerably from the economic effects. Many of the tobacco-sector job losses are identifiable; while the larger number of new non-tobacco jobs, spread throughout the economy, are not so readily associated with specific individuals. This explains the strong support for the preservation of tobacco industry jobs, and the absence of a constituency to lobby for the new employment that will result when tobacco spending declines. Diverse and powerful political interests constitute a significant barrier to increasing the stringency of tobacco control measures.

The Economics of Tobacco Control Project (1997c) showed that, contrary to the claims of these powerful lobbies, increases in excise taxes and other regulatory measures instituted by the South African government will have a positive net economic effect, in addition to the improvement which will occur in the country's public health. The South African government's intention to strengthen tobacco control policy therefore bodes well for public health, public finance and the economy as a whole.

The potential for cigarette smuggling in Southern Africa

A difficult issue confronting the South African government in implementing stronger tobacco control measures, is the potential effect this will have on other SADC countries and the potential for increased smuggling activity. Cigarettes can cross international borders into South Africa in small quantities in the form of "cross-border shopping", or in large quantities by airfreight and seafreight. Some South African ports are developing reputations for ineffectiveness in policing imports, apart from the logistical difficulties of checking vast quantities of cargo. A 6-metre shipping container can enter a port holding about 5 million contraband cigarettes, which might be distributed by many small operators, making detection, and determination of the origin of the cargo, very difficult. It has been estimated that 8-10 such containers enter South African ports each week. The containers are then broken down to smaller "bakkie" (pick-up truck) loads, with most of the cigarettes destined for convenience stores and the single cigarette market, and untraceable once stripped of South African tax stamps and packaging (*Cape Business News*, July 1996c).

The magnitude of this problem is very difficult to estimate; however, if the estimates regarding the rate of entry of such cargo are correct, approximately 2 billion cigarettes are being smuggled into South Africa *per annum*, suggesting a contraband market share of 5-7 per cent. It would appear that many of the following characteristics apply to cigarette smuggling in South Africa:
1. it is arranged through organised crime syndicates;
2. the cigarettes are passed through a wide range of owners;

3. they are distributed through non-official outlets (single-cigarette markets and small vendors);
4. cigarettes are sold without adequate (legally required) health warnings; and
5. they are sold without tax stamps.

The incentives for smuggling will naturally be influenced by the transaction costs involved in getting contraband cigarettes through South African ports. These would include costs of transportation to the South African ports, and then from there by small vans, "bakkies" or other means to the marketplace. Transaction costs will also include bribes and other disbursements that may have to be incurred in order to get the smuggled goods past Customs and Excise officials "unnoticed".

It is extremely difficult to estimate how much government revenue is lost through this activity, but if the estimate of 2 billion contraband cigarettes *per annum* is approximately correct, the associated lost excise receipts would have totalled roughly R100 million in 1995 (in 1995 rands). Some possible solutions to cigarette smuggling include enforcing the use of tax-stamps, increasing penalties for smuggling, restricting sales to official outlets (i.e. finding a way of regulating the single-cigarette market), and reducing supply. Reducing excise taxes is not an optimal solution, because it would only divert fraudsters from cigarettes to other goods, both consumables and durables — quite apart from the fact that public health would suffer, and government would suffer significant net resource loss.

(i) Tobacco companies accused of complicity

In a recent court case, rival tobacco companies Rembrandt and Philip Morris accused each other of promoting the smuggling of cigarettes into South Africa. In a UK court, the Rembrandt Group alleged that US-based Philip Morris, the world's largest cigarette manufacturer, allowed Marlboro cigarettes to be smuggled into South Africa from neighbouring countries, in violation of Rembrandt's exclusive license to make and sell Philip Morris products in South Africa. Rembrandt acquired this license in 1981 as part of a US$950 million payment by Philip Morris to Rembrandt for a 22 per cent interest in Rothmans. The substance of the accusation by Rembrandt was that cigarette smuggling helped Philip Morris get a foothold in the lucrative South African market. The trial ended in November 1997 with Rembrandt seeking an injunction against Philip Morris and unspecified damages (Bonner, 1997). Similar instances of the use of smuggling to establish cigarette brands in new markets have been noted elsewhere (see Chapters 12, 22 and 24).

An apparently significant proportion of cigarettes manufactured in South Africa are exported to neighbouring countries and then smuggled back, in order to avoid customs duties. Smuggling began in a noticeable way after the collapse of apartheid and the lifting of international sanctions against South Africa in the early 1990s. During 1997, customs officials at the border post between Mpumalanga province in South Africa and Mozambique confiscated cigarettes worth over R11 million. Border post officials regularly discover shipments of contraband cigarettes hidden in trucks, trains and cargo vehicles, and Customs officials believe that a transnational smuggling syndicate operates out of shunting yards in Johannesburg and Maputo. The syndicate allegedly recruits employees at Spoornet (the South African railway services) shunting yards and at the Mozambican railway service yards in Maputo. Again, all these cigarettes are manufactured locally and then smuggled back to avoid customs duty. However, because they are manufactured for export, none of the cartons carry the prescribed legal health warnings.

As with the international issue of smuggling, local cigarette manufacturers are suspected of complicity with the smugglers because they benefit from this illegal trade in several ways (see Chapter 12). First, they gain their normal profits by selling cigarettes legally on the export market. Second, contraband cigarettes that are intercepted by customs have to be replaced, therefore more sales. Third, the industry uses the smuggling issue to put pressure on the government to reduce excise taxes. Law enforcement officials have long argued that tobacco companies around the world are complicit with smugglers; not surprisingly, the tobacco companies have steadfastly denied it. Rarely has it happened, however, that rival tobacco companies have accused one another of dealing with smugglers, such as in the South African case described above.

(ii) The potential for smuggling between South Africa and Zimbabwe

The Economics of Tobacco Control Project (1997e) examined the potential for smuggling within the Southern African region, and in particular examined the trade relationship between South Africa and Zimbabwe, both countries being significant tobacco producers within the Southern African Development Council (SADC) region. If either South Africa or Zimbabwe were to increase excise tax rates on tobacco, resulting in substantially different cigarette prices, it could have implications for trade between the two countries, and more importantly, for smuggling activities. Price differences between neighbouring countries would lead to a diversion of tobacco trade, legally and illegally, to countries with cheaper cigarettes. Smuggling would generally take place from low-tax countries to high-tax countries where cigarettes are more expensive.

This argument has been used by the tobacco industry in South Africa to urge the government not to increase tax on tobacco products. Citing the presence of a major tobacco-producing country like Zimbabwe bordering South Africa, the industry has argued vociferously about the dire effects of cross-border shopping and smuggling and have asserted that tobacco taxes should be lowered.

Figures 3 and 4 compare the two countries in terms of their pricing and taxation policies during 1970-96. Figure 3 shows the retail price for a pack of 20 cigarettes in South Africa and Zimbabwe respectively, in US dollar terms. In particular, the figure highlights the growing disparity between the two countries in terms of their cigarette pricing when expressed in a common currency.

Figure 4 shows a comparison of real excise tax rates as a percentage of the real retail price of cigarettes in both countries. Even though there were large differences between the two countries in the 1980s, the gap has narrowed more

recently. In Zimbabwe the tax rate increased from 26 to 40 per cent from 1992
to 1996. Over the same period South Africa increased from 24 to 32 per cent.
There is now greater comparability in terms of the two countries' tobacco
taxation policies, which bodes well for the economic consequences of such
policies. The increased tobacco tax in South Africa in 1998 to 50 per cent, would
have brought the two countries even more in line with respect to their taxation

Figure 3. Retail price for a pack of 20 cigarettes in South Africa and Zimbabwe, 1970-96 (US$)

Sources: Central Statistical Services (South Africa) (annual); Tobacco Board (South Africa)
           (annual); Reserve Bank of Zimbabwe (quarterly); Tobacco and Commercial
           Agriculture Yearbook (Zimbabwe) (annual)

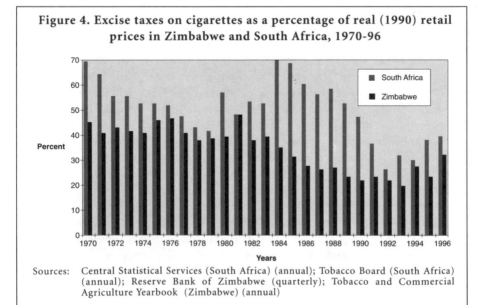

Figure 4. Excise taxes on cigarettes as a percentage of real (1990) retail prices in Zimbabwe and South Africa, 1970-96

Sources: Central Statistical Services (South Africa) (annual); Tobacco Board (South Africa)
           (annual); Reserve Bank of Zimbabwe (quarterly); Tobacco and Commercial
           Agriculture Yearbook (Zimbabwe) (annual)

policies. The taxation trends have therefore been significant in their shift to a greater policy alignment between the two countries. The increased tax in South Africa seen in this light, could therefore not have been harmful to trade policy between the two countries.

The figures suggest that although the two countries have become increasingly compatible in terms of taxation policies, the pricing structures have moved apart. There are two possible reasons for this: firstly, the Zimbabwe dollar depreciated against the US dollar faster than the South African rand, requiring higher nominal price increases for Zimbabwean cigarettes than South African cigarettes to maintain purchasing power parity of cigarette prices between the countries. Nominal price increases have, however, been very similar in the two countries, and Zimbabwe has also experienced greater fluctuation than South Africa in its US dollar exchange rate.

Secondly, the fact that the taxation policies have moved closer while the pricing structures have moved apart could suggest that the South African tobacco industry has a greater ability to pass on the increased excise tax to consumers. Because of the oligopolistic structure of the South African industry, manufacturers are able to increase the retail price of cigarettes by more than the size of the tax increase (Barzel, 1976; Sung, Hu and Keeler, 1994; Barnett, Keeler and Hu, 1995). It is not known by how much cigarette manufacturers in South Africa can increase the retail price and how much of the tax burden can be passed on to consumers, but it would appear that there is a greater capacity to do so in South Africa than in Zimbabwe.

The tobacco industry would clearly argue that this suggests a case for lowering tobacco taxes in South Africa, as higher prices in South Africa will induce contraband activity and the smuggling of cigarettes from Zimbabwe with the lower retail price, to South Africa. This is not however the full picture, as one still needs to consider demand specifications in the two countries, to gauge the actual incentives for smuggling and cross-border shopping. In addition, the taxation policies of the two countries will in the long-run reveal more about pricing structures than comparing two countries pricing trends in a single currency, as currency fluctuations and relative purchasing power will inevitably impair such comparisons.

One could argue that this does not automatically suggest a case for smuggling (and hence the lowering of tobacco taxes in South Africa); the demand side of the equation must also be examined. The Economics of Tobacco Control Project (1997e) calculated the short-run price elasticity of demand (at means) for both countries, which are very similar: -0.54 for South Africa, and -0.52 for Zimbabwe. In addition, excise tax as a proportion of real retail price, as seen in Figure 4, has moved closer over the last few years, suggesting that there is some comparability between the tax policies and the resultant demand specifications in the two countries. Hence, negative repercussions on trade, legal or illegal, resulting from an increase in excise taxes in either country are not such a severe threat as the industry would lead one to believe, and its recommendation to reduce excise taxes to avoid smuggling is not called for.

It is, however, imperative that uniformity develops between the two countries in terms of tobacco control policies and excise tax rates. A co-ordinated approach to tobacco control policies is imperative within SADC as a whole, and while South Africa and Zimbabwe are the major producers, inclusion of countries such as Mozambique, Namibia, Botswana, Swaziland and Zambia is needed.

Conclusion and policy implications

The policy implications of the analysis in this chapter are that a comprehensive tobacco control programme, including anti-tobacco advertising, increased excise taxation, and restriction of tobacco advertising, can significantly influence the South African consumer's decision to smoke. Due to tobacco control measures introduced since 1990, cigarette consumption has already declined by an average of 11 per cent *per annum* during 1991-95, and by nearly 20 per cent between the end of 1996 and the end of 1997. The findings of the Economics of Tobacco Control Project suggest that further reductions in consumption resulting from increased excise taxes and more stringent advertising restrictions will not jeopardise output, employment, the fiscus, or trade.

Tobacco in 1995 represented approximately 0.2 per cent of GDP and it sustained in all economic sectors, including the primary sector, around 15 000 people (Economics of Tobacco Control Project, 1997c). A fundamental reason why the loss of this output and these jobs do not represent formidable economic problems is because the tobacco industry is very small in terms of its output and employment contributions. Hence, even large declines in its activity are almost imperceptible from the perspective of the South African economy as a whole. The industry employs in total 0.1 per cent of South African workers. In other words, the elimination of all these jobs would raise the South African unemployment rate by less than one tenth of one per cent. Similarly, output in the economy would fall by 0.2 per cent.

This view does not, however, take into account the tendency of the economy to self-correct. Jobs and income are not irreplaceable. Without the tobacco industry, the expenditures on, and resources devoted to, the production of tobacco products would simply be shifted elsewhere in the economy. Although there will be transitional problems, costs of economic dislocation and differential industry levels of productivity, a hypothetical (and very unlikely) demise of the tobacco industry would not wreak havoc with the economy. Analysis by the Economics of Tobacco Control Project (1997c) suggests that a reduction in consumers' cigarette purchasing would lead to a net increase in economic activity in the following ways:

- between 9 000 and 34 000 jobs would have been created if cigarette purchasing had ceased completely in 1995, and consumers then spent their money as average consumers do;
- 50 000 jobs would have been created if cigarette purchasing had ceased completely in 1995, and consumers then spent their money in a way that resembles ex-smokers' expenditure patterns;

- 3 500 jobs would have been created if the current rate of decline in cigarette consumption had doubled in 1995.

While the Economics of Tobacco Control Project (1996b) argued that an optimal taxation on tobacco would be able to extract maximum revenue for government, it is not sure at what point an increased tax may result in a deterrent effect, which will result in a decline in consumption and hence revenues. In this chapter, it has been argued that because of the South African price inelasticity of approximately -0.6, the optimal taxation point is most probably above the current 50 per cent of retail price. It is a moot point as to exactly how high the excise tax should rise, but it is conceivable that revenue generation will increase up to a tax level well above 50 per cent.

The contribution of the tobacco industry to government revenue in 1997 was around R1.7 billion, or 1.2 per cent of total government revenue. The industry has argued that increased excise taxes and restrictions on advertising that reduce smoking, and hence cigarette sales, will lead to a loss in government income. Any loss of government income associated with a fall in tobacco use would require government to find alternative revenues. If government were to seek alternative sources of revenue, this might shift the tax burden to previous non-smokers. However, if the new revenues compensate for the loss of the former excise tax yield, then consumers as a whole would bear no additional tax burden. Thus a hypothetical demise of the tobacco industry would create a governmental revenue shortfall only if the excise tax revenue was not replaced with an equal-yield revenue source. The industry's argument of revenue loss is therefore misconceived.

In sum, more stringent tobacco control measures, by reducing tobacco consumption, would lead only to a healthier workforce, the avoidance of premature death, the preservation of skills and increased productivity, which cannot but improve economic performance.

References

Abedian, I. and R.E. Dorrington (1994), An evaluation of a recent attempt to assess the social benefits of cigarette smoking, *Journal of Studies in Economics and Econometrics*, 18:59-72.

Abedian, I., R. van der Merwe and N. Annett (1997), *Tobacco Control in South Africa: an Analysis of Contemporary Trends and Policy Issues*, working paper, Economics of Tobacco Control Project, Cape Town: University of Cape Town.

Allen, R.C. (1993), *The False Dilemma: the Impact of Tobacco Control Policies on Employment in Canada*, Ottawa: National Campaign for Action on Tobacco.

Baltagi, B.H. and D. Levin (1986), "Estimating dynamic demand for cigarettes using panel data: the effects of bootlegging, taxation and advertising reconsidered", *Review of Economic Statistics*, 68:148-155.

Barford, M.F. (1993), "New dimensions boost cigarette smuggling", *Tobacco Journal International*, 3:16-18.

Barnett, P.G., T.E. Keeler and T. Hu (1995), "Oligopoly structure and the incidence of cigarette excise taxes", *Journal of Public Economics*, 57:457-70.

Barnum, H. (1994), "The economic burden of tobacco — a World Bank analysis (summary of presentation in BASP newsletter)", *Smoking Prevention*, 26.

Barzel, Y. (1976), "An alternative approach to the analysis of taxation", *Journal of Political Economy*, 84:1177-97.

Becker, G.S., M. Grossman and K.M. Murphy (1994), "An empirical analysis of cigarette addiction", *The American Economic Review*, 84:396-418.

Bishop, J.A. and J.H. Yoo (1985), "'Health scare', excise taxes and advertising ban in the cigarette demand and supply", *Southern Economic Journal*, 2:402-11.

Bonner, R., (1997), "Rival asserts Philip Morris smuggles in South Africa: lawsuit by Rembrandt group on licensing", *New York Times*, 17 November.
Bonner, R. and C. Drew (1997), "Cigarette makers are seen as aiding rise in smuggling", *New York Times*, 25 August.
Buck, D., C. Godfrey, M. Raw and M. Sutton (1995), *Tobacco and Jobs: the Impact of Reducing Consumption on Employment in the UK*, Society for the Study of Addiction, Centre for Health Economics, York: University of York.
Cape Business News (July 1996a), "The main pushers".
Cape Business News (July 1996b), "Your typical addict".
Cape Business News (July 1996c), "Contraband and counterfeits".
Central Statistical Office (Zimbabwe) (1997), *Quarterly Digest of Statistics*, June, Harare: Government Printer.
Central Statistical Office (Zimbabwe) (1995), *Census of Industrial Production*, Harare: Government Printer.
Central Statistical Services (South Africa) (annual), *South African Statistics*, Pretoria: Government Printer.
Chapman, S. and J. Richardson (1990), "Tobacco excise and declining tobacco consumption: the case of Papua New Guinea", *American Journal of Public Health*, 80:537-40.
Department of Customs and Excise (Zimbabwe), Unpublished statistics, Harare: Dept. Customs and Excise.
Department of Finance (South Africa) (1997), *Republic of South Africa Budget Review*, Department of Finance, Pretoria: Government Printer.
Development Bank of Southern Africa (1995), *Social Accounting Matrix*, Midrand: DBSA.
Economics of Tobacco Control Project (1996a), *Cigarette Prices and Taxes in South Africa, 1970-1995: the Facts*, Update 1 (Annett, N.), Cape Town: University of Cape Town.
Economics of Tobacco Control Project (1996b), *An Econometric Estimation of Actual and Potential Government Revenue from Cigarette Taxation in South Africa: 1970-1995*, Update 2 (Annett, N.), Cape Town: University of Cape Town.
Economics of Tobacco Control Project (1996c), *An Econometric Analysis of the Effect of Advertising on Cigarette Consumption in South Africa: 1970-1995*, Update 3 (Annett, N.), Cape Town: University of Cape Town.
Economics of Tobacco Control Project (1997a), *An International Comparison of Tobacco Control Policies: Taxation, Pricing, and the Control of Advertising*, Update 4 (Van der Merwe, R.), Cape Town: University of Cape Town.
Economics of Tobacco Control Project (1997b), *Tobacco and Jobs: a Review of International Research*, Update 5 (Van der Merwe, R.), Cape Town: University of Cape Town.
Economics of Tobacco Control Project (1997c), *The Output and Employment Effects of Reducing Tobacco Consumption in South Africa*, Update 6 (Van der Merwe, R.), Cape Town: University of Cape Town.
Economics of Tobacco Control Project (1997d), *Cigarette Trade and Smuggling*, Update 7 (Joossens, L.), Cape Town: University of Cape Town.
Economics of Tobacco Control Project (1997e), *Cigarette Trade and the Potential for Smuggling in Southern Africa*, Update 8 (Van der Merwe, R.), Cape Town: University of Cape Town.
Fujii, E.T. (1980), The demand for cigarettes: further empirical evidence and its implications for public policy, *Applied Economics*, 12:479-89.
Godfrey, C. and A. Maynard (1988), "Economic aspects of tobacco use and taxation policy", *British Medical Journal*, 297:339-43.
Grossman, M. (1989), "Health benefits of increases in alcohol and cigarette taxes", *British Journal of Addiction*, 84:1193-204.
Hodgson, T.A. (1992), "Cigarette smoking and lifetime medical expenditures", *Milbank Memorial Fund Quarterly*, 70:81-125.
Hu, T., T.E. Keeler, H. Sung and P.G. Barnett (1995), "The impact of California anti-smoking legislation on cigarette sales, consumption, and prices", *Tobacco Control*, 4:S34-S38.
Hu, T., H. Sung and T.E. Keeler (1995), "The state anti-smoking campaign and the industry response: the effects of advertising on cigarette consumption in California", *The American Economic Review: Papers and Proceedings*, 85:85-90.
Joossens, L. and M. Raw (1995), "Smuggling and cross border shopping of tobacco in Europe", *British Medical Journal*, 310:1393-7.
Keeler, T.E., T. Hu, P.G. Barnett and W.G. Manning (1993), "Taxation, regulation, and addiction: a demand function for cigarettes based on time-series evidence", *Journal of Health Economics*, 12:1-18.
Leu, R. (1984), "Anti-smoking publicity, taxation and the demand for cigarettes", *Journal of Health Economics*, 3:101-16.
Lewit, E.M. and D. Coate (1982), "The potential for using excise taxes to reduce smoking", *Journal of Health Economics*, 1:121-45.
Martin, G., K. Steyn and D. Yach (1992), "Beliefs about smoking and health and attitudes toward tobacco control measures", *South African Medical Journal*, 82:241-5.
McNicoll, I.H. and S. Boyle (1992), "Regional economic impact of a reduction of resident expenditure on cigarettes: a case study of Glasgow", *Applied Economics*, 24:291-6.

Pieda PLC (1991), *The Economic Significance of the UK Tobacco Industry*, London: Pieda.
Radfar, M. (1985), "The effect of advertising on total consumption of cigarettes in the UK", *European Economic Review*, 85:225-31.
Reddy, P., A. Meyer-Weitz and D. Yach (1996), "Smoking status, knowledge of health effects and attitudes towards tobacco control in South Africa", *South African Medical Journal*, 86:1389-93.
Reekie, W.D. (1994), "Consumers' surplus and the demand for cigarettes", *Managerial and Decision Economics*, 15:223-234.
Reekie, W.D. and L.F.S. Wang (1992), "The benefits and costs of cigarette smoking — a state dependent approach", *Journal for Studies in Economics and Econometrics*, 16:1-12.
Rembrandt Controlling Investments, (1995), *Annual Report*.
Rembrandt Group Limited, (1996), *Annual Report*.
Reserve Bank of Zimbabwe, (quarterly), *Quarterly Economic and Statistical Review*, Harare: Government Printer.
South African Reserve Bank (quarterly), *Quarterly Bulletin*, Pretoria: Government Printer.
South African Institute of Race Relations (SAIRR) (1997), *South Africa Survey 1996/1997*, Johannesburg: SAIRR.
Stanley, K. (1993), *Control of Tobacco Production and Use*, in Jamison, D.T., H.W. Mosley, A.R Measham and J.L. Bobadilla (eds.), *Disease Control Priorities in Developing Countries*, New York: Oxford Medical Publications.
Sunday Times (Johannesburg) (1997), 15 March.
Sung, H., T. Hu and T.E. Keeler (1994), "Cigarette taxation and demand: an empirical model", *Contemporary Economic Policy*, 22:91-100.
Tobacco and Commercial Agricultural Yearbook (Zimbabwe) (annual).
Tobacco Board (South Africa) (annual), *Annual Report*, 1970-96.
Tremblay, C.H. and V.J. Tremblay (1995), "The impact of cigarette advertising on consumer surplus, profit, and social welfare", *Contemporary Economic Policy*, 13:113-24.
Van der Merwe, R. (1997), *An Empirical Analysis of the Output Effects of Cigarette Taxes in South Africa and the Regional Impact*, paper presented at the 10th World Health Conference on Tobacco or Health, Beijing, 24-28 August.
Van Walbeek, C.P. (1996), "Excise taxes on tobacco: how much scope does the government have?", *South African Journal of Economics*, 64:20-42.
Vernon, J.M., N.W. Rives and T.H. Naylor (1967), "An econometric model of the tobacco industry", *The Review of Economics and Statistics*, 1:149-58.
Warner, K.E. (1987), "Health and economic implications of a tobacco-free society", *Journal of the American Medical Association*, 258:2080-6.
Warner, K.E., F.J. Chaloupka, P.J. Cook, W.G. Manning, J.P. Newhouse, T.E. Novotny, T.G. Schelling and J. Townsend (1995), "Criteria for determining an optimal cigarette tax: the economist's perspective", *Tobacco Control*, 4:380-6.
Warner, K.E. and G.A. Fulton (1994), "The economic implications of tobacco product sales in a nontobacco state", *Journal of the American Medical Association*, 271:771-6.
Warner, K.E., G.A. Fulton, P. Nicolas and D.R. Grimes (1996), "Employment implications of declining tobacco product sales for the regional economies of the United States", *Journal of the American Medical Association*, 275:1241-6.
World Health Organisation (1996b), *Tobacco Alert: the Tobacco Epidemic: a Global Public Health Emergency*, Geneva: World Health Organisation.
Yach, D. (1982), "Economic aspects of smoking in South Africa", *South African Medical Journal*, 62:167-70.
Yach, D., D. McIntyre and Y. Saloojee (1992), "Smoking in South Africa: the health and economic impact", *Tobacco Control*, 1:272-80.
Yach, D. and Y. Saloojee (1994), "South African advertising agencies' involvement with tobacco products", *South African Medical Journal*, 84:871.
Yach, D. and G. Townshend (1988), *Smoking and health in South Africa: the need for action*, South African Medical Research Council, Centre for Epidemiological Research in Southern Africa, Technical Report No. 1, Cape Town: Medical Research Council.
Zimring, F.E. and W. Nelson (1995), "Cigarette taxes as cigarette policy", *Tobacco Control*, 4:S25-S33.

Chapter 21

Tobacco Production and the Search for Alternatives in Zimbabwe

Edward Maravanyika

A brief history of tobacco in Zimbabwe

Although Oriental tobacco was first grown commercially in Matebeleland in 1885, it was only in 1903 that a fully-fledged tobacco industry came into being in Zimbabwe. In 1920, nearly one million kilograms of flue-cured Virginia tobacco was produced, and by 1938 the yield had increased to 11.3 million kilograms. The high quality of the crop apparently caused a visiting British tobacco agent to say that Zimbabwe (then called Southern Rhodesia) had "found something as valuable as gold and diamonds, enough to make a country in itself" (*Tobacco and Commercial Agriculture Yearbook 1995*, p.11). By 1938, compulsory auctioning of all flue-cured Virginia tobacco under the auspices of the Tobacco Marketing Board had been legislated.

Tobacco farms in Zimbabwe are selected for their soil and climatic suitability. According to the Zimbabwe Tobacco Association (1993), flue-cured tobacco is grown in the Northern and North-Western areas of Mashonaland at altitudes of 1 050-1 650 metres, on light-textured soils in areas of 600-800 mm of annual rainfall. An advantage of tobacco is that it does not require rich soils to produce good results, and it is in areas of low-fertility medium sands and sandy loams that Zimbabwe's high-quality tobacco is produced. Only 3 per cent of the available arable land in the country is under tobacco cultivation.

The tobacco industry's contribution to Zimbabwe

Agriculture is the spine of the Zimbabwean economy, and (unlike most other developing countries) tobacco production is a very significant component of total agrarian output. In this regard, Zimbabwe and Malawi are exceptions among developing countries in terms of dependence on tobacco exports.

(i) Tobacco as a share of total agricultural output

Agricultural output represented 15 per cent of Zimbabwe's gross domestic product (GDP) in 1996 (Central Statistical Office (Zimbabwe), 1997). Tobacco's own contribution to GDP was estimated as 8.6 per cent, and the sub-sector's share of total agricultural output has averaged approximately 35 per cent since 1990. The area planted with tobacco rose from 41 197 hectares in 1970 to a peak

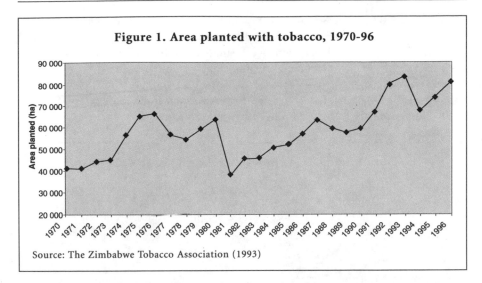

Figure 1. Area planted with tobacco, 1970-96

Source: The Zimbabwe Tobacco Association (1993)

of 66 209 ha in 1976 before falling sharply to 38 899 ha in 1981. It recovered steadily to 59 425 ha in 1990, and had increased to 81 348 ha by 1996 (Figure 1).

(ii) Tobacco's contribution to other crops

The economic impact of Zimbabwe's tobacco farmers is, however, felt beyond the sphere of tobacco: they also produce some 35 per cent of the country's maize, 30 per cent of the beef, 30 per cent of total wheat output and 20 per cent of the Soya beans (Zimbabwe Tobacco Association, 1993). It has been argued that tobacco income was used for many years to develop farms, including both cattle production and irrigation. The *Tobacco and Commercial Agriculture Yearbook, 1995* asserts that "tobacco financed the spectacular improvement in farming methods which have led to Zimbabwe's achieving self-sufficiency and exportable surpluses in food and cash crops" (p.8).

(iii) Tobacco farming and employment

Tobacco's impact on the Zimbabwean economy is perhaps most profound in terms of employment creation. The industry accounts for one tenth of the national work force (Central Statistical Office, (Zimbabwe) 1995), and is the largest single employer in the country. This includes labour involved in primary production on farms, through tobacco leaf processing, to cigarette manufacturing. Approximately 70 per cent of the total population resides in rural areas or on commercial farms, and tobacco farming accounts for 33 per cent of total agricultural employment due to its labour-intensive nature.

Primary production relates to all the activities that take place from the planting of the tobacco seed, to the drying of the leaf on the farm. According to the Zimbabwe Tobacco Association, the number of registered tobacco growers was 1 602 in 1970, fluctuated around 1 600 during the 1970s with a sharp decrease and slow recovery after 1980, and rose rapidly after 1990 (Figure 2). There were 2 917 tobacco growers registered with the association in 1996, and approximately two-thirds of them were small-scale black farmers. This figure does not include an estimated 10 000 small-scale communal growers not registered with the growers' association. The Central and Southern African chapter of the International Tobacco Growers Association estimates that a total of 98 000 people are in turn employed by tobacco growers.

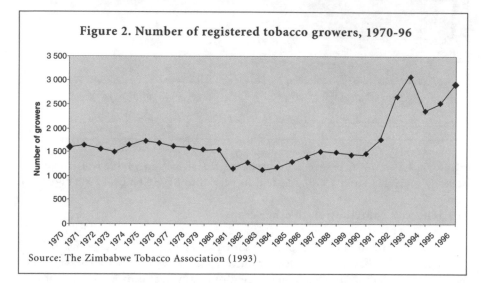

Figure 2. Number of registered tobacco growers, 1970-96

Source: The Zimbabwe Tobacco Association (1993)

The process of tobacco manufacturing includes post-auction grading, packing and processing. These functions are performed respectively by eight licensed buying companies, six packing houses and many co-operatives and processors.

The manufacturing process also includes the activities of Zimbabwe's only two cigarette manufacturers, BAT and Rothmans. These two firms combine cigarette production with the production of relatively smaller quantities of pipe tobacco and snuff. Nearly 6 000 people were employed in the tobacco manufacturing sector in 1996 (Central Statistical Office (Zimbabwe), 1997).

The industry's ancillary services comprise research work and training provided by the Tobacco Research Board and the Tobacco Training Institute respectively. In addition, there are service companies and associations such as the Tobacco Trade Association (which represents manufacturers) and the Zimbabwe Tobacco Association (representing growers), the Tobacco Sales Floor and Tobacco Marketing Board.

(iv) Exports

Tobacco and gold are two of Zimbabwe's largest sources of foreign currency; in 1995, tobacco contributed 24 per cent of Zimbabwe's total export earnings, while gold contributed 13 per cent. Zimbabwe is the sixth largest producer of tobacco in the world, and has become one of the world's major tobacco exporters. In 1996 Zimbabwe exported 99 per cent of its total domestic yield, earning Z$6.5 billion (US$660 million) after adding value through processing, packaging, storage and transport. Of the total export shipment, 41 per cent went to the European Union market, and 21 per cent to the Far East (*The Herald*, 1997).

In recent years tobacco's status as a major export commodity was to some extent boosted by the country's adoption of economic structural adjustment policies. An escalating government deficit and high unemployment rates led the World Bank and the International Monetary Fund to prescribe a strategy of export-led growth for Zimbabwe, highlighting the contribution of tobacco production as a foreign exchange earner. However, while the World Bank's policy on tobacco makes exceptions for the few countries like Zimbabwe that are heavily dependent on the tobacco industry, it is of course keen to encourage client countries to move away from tobacco production (see Chapter 5).

(v) Other socio-economic benefits

The Zimbabwe tobacco industry is virtually a self-sustaining industry, and has never received a government subsidy. Instead, excise revenue from cigarette taxation constitutes 1 per cent of total government revenue; in 1993, 36 per cent of the cost of a pack of cigarettes went to the government in the form of taxation. In addition, the government collects 10 per cent of tobacco farmers' sales proceeds in the form of a "growers' levy"; this amounted to Z$650 million (US$66 million) in 1996. The Zimbabwe Tobacco Association finances the Tobacco Research Board, apparently the major source of improvements in quality and yield of the crop, and runs a training institute where farmers receive training in tobacco growing.

Policy options for tobacco control in Zimbabwe

(i) Domestic consumption and cigarette taxation

The extent to which cigarette taxation is effective as a tobacco control measure depends largely on the price elasticity of cigarette demand. For this purpose a model of cigarette demand in Zimbabwe was estimated. Some cigarette demand models, such as that of Sung, Hu and Keeler (1994), include the supply-side since this allows for the inter-relationship between demand and supply. Such a methodology could not be implemented in this study, however, due to the unwillingness of the two cigarette manufacturers in Zimbabwe to reveal vital cost (supply-side) data and information, hence the model presented below considers only the demand side. There is a precedent for this expediency: Chapman and Richardson (1990) were also forced by cost information constraints to omit the supply-side in their cigarette price elasticity analysis of Papua New Guinea. The cigarette demand model for Zimbabwe thus takes the form:

$$LPCCON_t = \propto + \beta_1 LPCCON_{t-1} + \beta_2 LRRETP_{t-1} + \beta_3 LRPCYD_{t-1} + \varepsilon_t$$

where $LRRETP_{t-1}$ and $LRPCYD_{t-1}$ represent the logarithms of Zimbabwe's real retail cigarette price and *per capita* disposable income during the previous year. The ordinary least squares regression results of this model, using data for 1970-96, are presented in Table 1.

Table 1. Regression results on cigarette demand variables in Zimbabwe

Variable	Coefficient	Std. Error	t-stat	2-tail sig.	Adjusted-R^2
$LPCCON_{t-1}$	0.3353	0.1764	1.9012	0.0705	
$LRRETP_{t-1}$	-0.8551	0.3909	-2.1875	0.0396	0.5996
$LRPCYD_{t-1}$	1.6707	0.4918	3.3970	0.0026	

The coefficient on $LRRETP_{t-1}$ indicates that the estimated price elasticity of demand (at means) is -0.85 (i.e. a 10 per cent increase (or decrease) in the real price of cigarettes will cause an 8.5 per cent decrease (or increase) in cigarette consumption), a high price-sensitivity consistent with those of other developing nations. It would appear that cigarette price increases (via cigarette excise tax increases) should be effective in lowering cigarette consumption in Zimbabwe, which is already low: in 1996 Zimbabwe's annual cigarette consumption *per capita* was 150 sticks, compared with 850 for neighbouring South Africa.

(ii) Tobacco exports and alternative crops

It is argued that switching resources (especially labour and land) from tobacco growing to alternative crop growing would assist in the elimination of smoking. Zimbabwe, as one of the largest producers of tobacco for export, would naturally present a challenge to such a policy: as discussed above, tobacco farming is an important source of employment, foreign exchange and government excise revenue. A switch to the production of other crops, such as food or fibre crops, would be seriously considered only if the alternatives are as economically beneficial as tobacco. In addition, of course, the feasibility of switching from tobacco to other crops depends on whether the latter are suited to cultivation in the areas of low-fertility medium sands and sandy loams currently planted with tobacco. The following section briefly investigates the feasibility of other crops as potential substitutes for tobacco.

Gross margin analysis

Coffee, wheat, cotton, groundnuts, maize and soya beans are Zimbabwe's principal food crops. Table 2 below compares the economic yield per hectare of these food crops to that of flue-cured tobacco during the mid-1980s. Gross margin is calculated as the sales value of output less variable costs (including seeds, fertilisers, insecticide and labour), on a per-hectare basis.

Table 2. Gross margins for tobacco and selected crops (Z$ per hectare)

Crop	Gross income	Variable cost	Gross margin
Flue-cured tobacco	25 740	8 431	17 309
Coffee	10 716	8 023	2 689
Wheat	2 857	1 769	1 088
Cotton	2 498	1 702	795
Groundnuts	3 190	2 516	674
Maize	1 500	1 196	304
Soya beans	1 344	1 051	293

Source: Agricultural Marketing Authority (1986)

Coffee, the most profitable alternative crop, had a gross margin per hectare only one-sixth that of tobacco. Hence, even when tobacco prices are low, it is not economically prudent for farmers to reduce tobacco production in favour of such alternatives. As Robey (1994, p.14) notes, "even in 1984, when farmers received some of the lowest prices for tobacco in the 1980s, the return on production was still almost twice that for coffee, the next most profitable alternative".

Fixed costs

Fixed costs are a highly significant factor in the decision to diversify into other crops. Fixed costs for the tobacco farmer would include the equipment and utensils for cultivation and the barns used for curing tobacco. While no generic figures for fixed costs are available, the infrastructure required for the cultivation and curing of tobacco is specialised enough to suggest that these fixed costs are high. Thus, in light of the figures in Table 2, it appears economically prudent for farmers to maximise their tobacco profits in order to ameliorate their fixed cost burden. Furthermore, it may not be sound economic judgement for a tobacco farmer to grow more of another alternative crop while leaving idle costly infrastructure and equipment specific to tobacco production.

A significant overhead confronting farmers is that of interest charges and debt repayments. With the implementation of Zimbabwe's Economic Structural Adjustment Programme (ESAP) in 1990, interest rates were increased significantly in an attempt to constrain a high rate of inflation. According to figures released by the International Monetary Fund (1994), interest rates in Zimbabwe moved from 9 per cent in 1989 to just over 30 per cent by 1992. Currently, basic interest rates in Zimbabwe are approximately 40 per cent, and could indeed climb further if the Zimbabwean dollar continues to depreciate. While the interest rate increases were intended to curb high and rising inflation, in effect they "led to growers' profits halving and the banks' profits doubling between 1991 and 1993" (Robey, 1994, p.15). Rising interest rates increase farmers' debt service burden and thus undermine their ability to diversify into alternative crops, since it becomes prohibitively expensive to raise the necessary capital. Thus, spiralling interest payments may actually 'trap' some farmers into continued tobacco production.

Trade

As previously highlighted in this paper, tobacco in Zimbabwe is grown primarily for export. As tobacco export revenues are crucial to Zimbabwe's economic and social stability, from a national economic viewpoint any alternative crop would need to at least match tobacco's generation of foreign currency. Table 3 presents a historical comparison between tobacco and a few principal alternatives in this regard.

Table 3. Zimbabwe's principal agricultural exports, 1990-96 (US$ million, current prices)

	Tobacco	Cotton	Sugar	Coffee
1990	406.0	82.0	19.0	31.0
1991	313.0	43.0	21.0	16.0
1992	406.0	25.0	0.0	11.0
1993	351.0	23.0	0.2	5.0
1994	433.0	60.0	90.0	13.0
1995	481.0	46.0	63.0	27.0
1996	697.0	80.0	96.0	2.0

Source: Central Statistical Office (Zimbabwe) (1997)

From Table 3 it is apparent that no alternative food crop has been as effective as tobacco in generating foreign currency for Zimbabwe. It has been suggested, however, that since Zimbabwe imports 20 per cent of its wheat requirements and all of its rice supplies, potential still exists for import substitution at the expense of some tobacco production. However, the absence of adequate irrigation facilities impedes any attempt at growing more rice or wheat instead of tobacco. In fact only 12-15 per cent of existing tobacco farms possess irrigation facilities (personal communication, Barry Wright, 1997).

Horticultural alternatives

While the principal alternative crops discussed above do not appear to be economically viable options, the "crop substitution which has been economically successful is characterised by the specialised production of horticultural crops specifically for export to the developed world" (Robey, 1994, p.15). The International Tobacco Growers Association (1992, p.11) concur that "(t)he potential for diversification in Zimbabwe appears to be limited to horticultural crops: fruit, vegetables and cut flowers". Zimbabwe's varied climate, from the hot and dry Southern lowveld to the cool, damp Eastern Highlands, can accommodate a wide range of options. The country already produces and exports sizeable quantities of fruit such as peaches, nectarines, melons, strawberries, passion fruits and kiwis. The Agricultural Marketing Board estimates that in 1990 just over 1 000 tons of deciduous, tropical and citrus fruits at a value of US$1.75 million were shipped overseas. Coupled to this, exports of vegetables such as sweet corn, asparagus and French beans earned US$5.5 million in the same year.

As promising as the figures above pertaining to fruit and vegetables may be, the real possibility for crop substitution in Zimbabwe lies in rose blooms. Zimbabwe has already become a significant exporter of roses, and by 1990 was ranked the sixth largest rose exporter in the world. According to the Horticultural Promotion Council the area under rose production has doubled to just over 200 hectares since 1990. Cash flow projections compiled in 1991 by the Agricultural Marketing Division of Standard Chartered Bank suggest that the high potential market revenue from rose blooms is more than sufficient to offset the substantial initial investment involved and the high costs of production (Table 4).

Table 4. Cash flow projections for rose blooms (Z$/ha)

Crop	Gross income	Variable costs	Gross margin
Flue-cured tobacco	25 740	8 431	17 309
Rose blooms	919 170	162 163	757 007

Source: Standard Chartered Bank (1991)

As Table 4 reveals, the projected gross margin per hectare for rose blooms is approximately 44 times that of flue-cured tobacco. Thus, while it is true that rose blooms are expensive to cultivate, transport and market, and that they require a large initial investment, the financial returns they offer are nevertheless well in excess of those offered by tobacco. If roses are to be considered as an alternative to tobacco growing, this is just as well, as judging by the relatively very small land area in Zimbabwe already successfully supplying the rose market, it would not be possible for tobacco farmers to switch more than a fraction of the 81 000 hectares planted with tobacco in 1996 to rose production without very quickly saturating the rose market. Indeed, the Horticultural Promotion Council contend that the wide variety of climates and soils could mean that production may be broadly diversified into other horticultural crops and still result in minimal market disruption. A further factor in favour of horticultural alternatives is that most of the crops are labour-intensive by nature and would thus be able to absorb some of the labour shed in the reduction of tobacco production.

However, there are significant obstacles to horticultural substitution. Firstly, the initial capital investment in cultivation and irrigation equipment may prove a deterrent. Roses require at least two years before the grower realises any profit. In the case of deciduous tree fruit or citrus, no income will be generated until the trees have attained bearing age, which is likely to be several years after the (significant) initial investment.

Secondly, there is difficulty in transporting such perishable goods to market. Roses must be brought to market within 48 hours of harvesting, and while air transport is an obvious solution, this option is undermined in Zimbabwe's case by high airfreight charges, low capacity and a meagre selection of destinations. The availability of northbound air cargo space has so far been directly related to the demand for southbound capacity; i.e. the size and frequency of air shipments northwards has been constrained by the potential of Sub-Saharan Africans to purchase northern goods. Transportation by sea could provide a suitable alternative. Zimbabwe is a landlocked country, but the port of Beira in neighbouring Mozambique is within relatively close proximity by road and rail. However, while less perishable produce such as avocados and citrus could be ferried by rail and sea, rose blooms and other flowers must be airfreighted to market, and until Zimbabwe implements drastic improvements in this regard rose bloom production cannot expand to the extent required for roses to constitute a feasible substitute for tobacco.

Thirdly, tobacco growing has been carried on in Zimbabwe for almost a century now and is deeply embedded in the psyche of many tobacco farmers in the country. Indeed, tobacco's influence in all spheres of activity in Zimbabwe is pervasive. Fourthly, Zimbabwe is a country very prone to drought, and tobacco has consistently managed to produce substantial yields where other crops have failed; it is uncertain whether roses would be able to yield consistent financial benefits in the face of frequent droughts.

Conclusion

Since Zimbabwe exports 99 per cent of the tobacco it produces, health issues pertaining to tobacco are a low national priority. Further, because of tobacco's economic importance to Zimbabwe, one cannot divorce commercial interests from the global health agenda. It would be pointless to tell Zimbabwean tobacco farmers to decrease tobacco production without providing an equally lucrative alternative, or ensuring that other suppliers do not replace Zimbabwean tobacco. This chapter has demonstrated that there are no financially viable alternatives among food crops. Only horticultural alternatives were seen to be potential substitutes, rose blooms having a far superior gross margin per hectare than tobacco. However, roses are unlikely to prove an immediate solution for the reasons advanced above — unless the government intervenes and implements measures such as improving the capacity and efficiency of the national air freight carrier, Affretair, and taking other steps to facilitate horticultural exports.

References

Agricultural Marketing Authority (1986), *Economic Review of the Agricultural Industry in Zimbabwe*.

Central Statistical Office (Zimbabwe) (1995), *Census of Industrial Production*, Harare: Government Printer.

Central Statistical Office (Zimbabwe) (1997), *Quarterly Digest of Statistics*, June.

Chapman, S. and J. Richardson (1990), "Tobacco excise and declining tobacco consumption: the case of Papua New Guinea", *American Journal of Public Health*, 80(5):537-540.

The Herald (1997), "Tobacco to earn Z$6 billion", 25 March.

International Monetary Fund (1994), *International Financial Statistics*, Washington, DC: International Monetary Fund.

International Tobacco Growers' Association (ITGA) (1992), *The Economic Significance of Tobacco Growing in Central and Southern Africa*.

Personal communication, Barry Wright (1997), Commercial Farmers Union, Zimbabwe.

Robey, J.K. (1994), *An Examination of the Factors Affecting the Supply of and Demand for Zimbabwean Tobacco Leaf*, Southampton: University of Southampton.

Sung, H., T. Hu and T.E. Keeler (1994), "Cigarette taxation and demand: an empirical model", *Contemporary Economic Policy*, 22:91-100.

Zimbabwe Tobacco Association (1993), *Zimbabwe Tobacco Industry Profile*.

Tobacco and Commercial Agricultural Yearbook (Zimbabwe) (1995).

Chapter 22

The Need for Tobacco Control in Poland

Witold Zatonski, Sergiusz Matusiak and Krzysztof Przewozniak

Between 1965 and 1991, a strange phenomenon was observed in Poland: decreasing life expectancy in men above 45 years of age, in sharp contrast to a steadily decreasing incidence of infant and child mortality during the same period. This unexpected decline in male life expectancy resulted from increasing premature (i.e. before age 65) mortality among men in middle age (35-64 years). In women, a similar but weaker trend in life expectancy appeared during the mid-1970s. The main cause of these phenomena was an increase in morbidity and mortality from degenerative, so-called 'lifestyle' diseases, mainly cancer and cardiovascular disease. As a result of increasing middle-aged male mortality during 1965-91, in the early 1990s overall male mortality was higher than it had been during the immediate post-war period.

These changes took a more adverse course than trends in more developed countries. Premature mortality in Poland during the early 1990s was among the highest in Europe, equivalent to levels in Finland or West Germany during the mid-1960s. Moreover, at that time the probability of a 15-year-old Polish boy reaching the age of 60 was not only much lower than that of Western European teenagers, but lower than those of teenagers in Latin America, China or even India (Murray and Lopez, 1996; Feachem 1994). Clearly, Poland entered the 1990s in a catastrophic state of adult health (Zatonski 1995; Zatonski, Didkowska *et al.*, 1996).

Reports of the World Bank have warned that the loss of productive ability resulting from high mortality of people in their productive years, and the high costs of treating chronic 'lifestyle' diseases in the productive age groups, can be serious barriers to the social-economic development of Poland (Feachem *et al.*, 1992; Murray *et al.*, 1993). Therefore, the phenomenon of incredibly high premature mortality, especially in men, is undoubtedly one of the most important social-economic challenges currently facing Poland. Intervention to rapidly decrease premature mortality is not only one of the main tasks of public health policy, but a necessary condition of social-economic transformation in Poland.

Epidemiological studies prove that one of the main causes of increasing premature death in the Polish population is lifestyle factors (Zatonski, 1995; Zatonski, Didkowska *et al.*, 1996). Along with alcohol consumption and some characteristics of the traditional diet (high intake of animal fat and low intake of fruit and vegetables), tobacco smoking is a major lifestyle health hazard in

Poland. There are more than 10 million smokers in Poland, with an annual cigarette consumption of 95-100 billion cigarettes, and Poles have been the world's greatest consumers of cigarettes for more than 20 years (Zatonski and Przewozniak, 1992; 1996) (see Chapter 3, Table 5 for international comparisons).

Until the mid-1980s there were no tobacco control programmes in Poland, and until the early 1990s no comprehensive tobacco control policy was in place; both have the potential to dramatically change attitudes towards smoking. The initiation of local and nation-wide tobacco control campaigns during the mid-1980s, and tobacco control programmes during the early 1990s, resulted in a decrease in smoking prevalence rates, especially among the youth, and mortality due to lung cancer started to decrease.

However, some of these positive changes were temporarily halted with the onset of the social-economic transformation of Poland in the 1990s. Billions of attractively packaged and aromatised foreign cigarettes were imported and sold in the newly liberalised domestic market. Cigarette consumers were confronted with aggressive cigarette advertising and other tobacco marketing techniques. Despite enactment of the Tobacco Control Law in 1995, there was no comprehensive taxation and pricing policy on tobacco products. Real prices of cigarettes are still relatively low in Poland, and taxation policy on tobacco products differs considerably from European Union or World Bank standards. If the positive changes in smoking behaviour and declining trend in tobacco-related mortality previously experienced are to be consolidated and continued, it is important to implement long-term economic policy on tobacco products in accordance with EU and World Bank recommendations.

Tobacco smoking in Poland and its health consequences

Prior to World War II, annual *per capita* cigarette consumption did not exceed 500-600 cigarettes. A dramatic increase in smoking was observed in the post-war period: from 893 cigarettes *per capita* per year in 1949 to 2 741 in 1979. Averaged among adults (people aged 15 and over) only, consumption was naturally even higher, rising from 2 475 cigarettes per adult in 1963 to 3 611 cigarettes per adult in 1979 (Figure 1). In the early 1980s, consumption reached a very high level (one of the highest in the world), fluctuating between 2 300 and 2 700 cigarettes *per capita* in the general population, and between 3 000 and 3 600 per adult. Since then cigarette consumption in both populations has remained within this range (Zatonski and Przewozniak, 1996; Przewozniak and Zatonski, 1996).

Clearly, smoking is a very common phenomenon in Poland. Smoking prevalence rates were especially high at the beginning of the 1980s, when only 18 per cent of men had never smoked tobacco (Figure 2). A nation-wide survey based on a randomised sample of Polish adults (16 years and over) carried out in 1997 showed that 68 per cent of men and 37 per cent of women have ever smoked. The prevalence of current smoking is 47 per cent for men and 29 per cent for women, while 42 per cent of men and 23 per cent of women smoke daily (Figure 3).

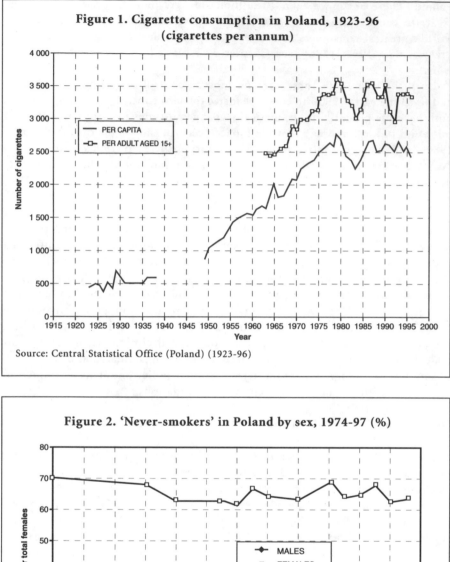

Figure 1. Cigarette consumption in Poland, 1923-96 (cigarettes per annum)

Source: Central Statistical Office (Poland) (1923-96)

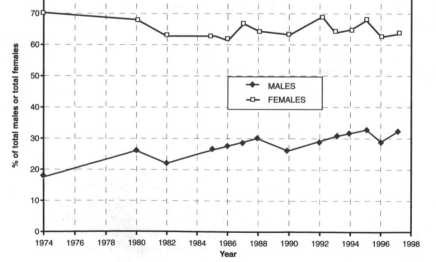

Figure 2. 'Never-smokers' in Poland by sex, 1974-97 (%)

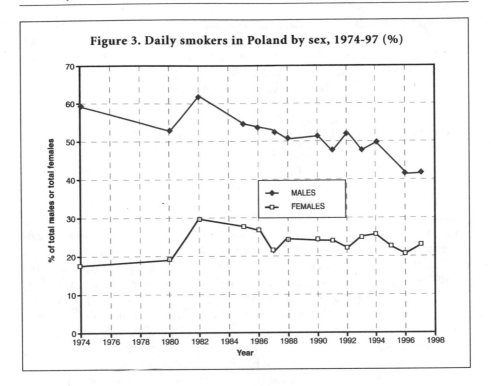

Figure 3. Daily smokers in Poland by sex, 1974-97 (%)

The highest degree of risk associated with daily smoking is seen in the middle-aged groups (50-59 per cent of men aged 20-59 are daily smokers, while 36-48 per cent of women aged 20-49 are daily smokers). The data also demonstrate that regular smokers smoke a lot (an average of 19 cigarettes a day for men, and 14 cigarettes a day for women), and in the long-term (an average of 20 years for men, and 18 years for women). In addition, chemical studies show that cigarettes sold in Poland tend to contain higher levels of tar and other carcinogenic agents than cigarettes sold in the European Union market (Zatonski and Przewozniak, 1992; 1996; Zatonski, Brzezinski et al., 1996). The government standard for permissible level of tar (a Class A carcinogen) in cigarettes sold on the Polish market was introduced only in 1991, and was 20 mg of tar per cigarette. In July 1998 this standard was reduced to 15 mg of tar per cigarette. However, these limits are still much higher than those in the European Union, where the permissible tar content has been 12 mg per cigarette from 1 January 1998.

An additional health hazard is exposure to environmental tobacco smoke (ETS). On average, 47 per cent of non-smoking men and 52 per cent of non-smoking women are involuntarily inhaling tobacco smoke at home, whereas 55 per cent of non-smoking men and 27 per cent of non-smoking women are exposed to ETS in the workplace.

Trends in tobacco consumption over the past four decades are reflected in the pattern of mortality from tobacco-attributable diseases (Zatonski and Przewozniak, 1992; 1996). During 1960-90, a steady rise in the risk of tobacco-attributable diseases in Poland was observed, mainly lung cancer and cardiovascular diseases (Zatonski, Becker *et al.*, 1988; Zatonski, Smans *et al.*, 1995). As with tobacco smoking, the risk of cardiovascular disease was particularly high in the middle-aged population. Epidemiological studies (Peto *et al.*, 1994; Doll *et al.*, 1993) suggest that about 42 per cent of deaths in middle-aged men and 10 per cent of deaths in middle-aged women during the late 1980s were due to tobacco smoking. This means that approximately 50 000 middle-aged Polish men and 6 000 middle-aged Polish women died prematurely every year. Since the early 1980s, smoking-attributable cancers are the main cause of cancer deaths among middle-aged men in Poland. In 1990, among middle-aged men, 58 per cent of cancers and 42 per cent of cardiovascular diseases were tobacco-related (Zatonski and Przewozniak, 1992; 1996).

As noted above, in recent years several positive changes have been noted in cigarette consumption and smoking attitudes of adult Poles. The steady increase in tobacco consumption following the end of World War II stopped at the end of the 1970s (Figure 1), and tobacco consumption has since stabilised at about 95 billion cigarettes per year. During 1974-97 the proportion of men who have never smoked rose from 18 to 32 per cent (Figure 2). Since smoking prevalence rates peaked in 1982, the prevalence of daily smoking has also dropped considerably among men, from 62 to 42 per cent (Figure 3), most noticeably in the youngest age groups. As a result of the Great Polish Smoke-out campaign, the percentage of ex-smokers grew substantially in both sexes, from 12 per cent of men in 1986 to 21 per cent in 1997, and from 3 per cent of women in 1985 to 7 per cent in 1997 (Figure 4).

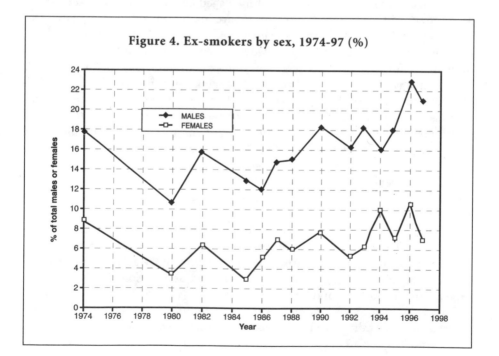

Figure 4. Ex-smokers by sex, 1974-97 (%)

The decreases in smoking prevalence among men have now been followed by a slight decrease in lung cancer mortality in the 20-44-year age group since the early 1980s. Lung cancer rates in this age group should be the earliest indicators of changes in the population's exposure to the cancer-causing effects of tobacco. These findings in Poland are even more significant when compared with the continuing increase in mortality rates from lung cancer among men aged 20-44 in Hungary, where the consumption of tobacco has not slowed (Kubik et al., 1995; Zatonski, Didkowska et al., 1996). Hungary can therefore be used as a control for appraising changes in tobacco-attributable disease risk in the Polish population. Comparisons show a divergence of the trends for mortality from cancer among men in Hungary and Poland from about 1980. Mortality from lung cancer in Hungarian men aged 20-64 years has now reached a level never previously seen in any country (Zatonski, Didkowska et al., 1996).

Negative trends in tobacco smoking are, however, being observed in the female population of Poland. Although the proportion of women who have never smoked remains above 60 per cent (Figure 2), the percentage of women daily smokers rose from 18 per cent in 1974 to 30 per cent in 1982 (Figure 3), and this increase was particularly marked among younger women. Since the early 1980s, the level of smoking among Polish women has stabilised rather than declined. The increase in smoking among women during the 1970s is currently reflected in increasing female mortality from lung cancer, the rates having doubled in the 20-44 age group between 1974 and 1996 (Zatonski, Brzezinski et al., 1996).

Economics and tobacco control in Poland

(i) The tobacco market before and after transition

Before 1990, a few state-owned cigarette producers together enjoyed a monopoly of the domestic market in Poland, and consequently had no shortage of customers or sales. As discussed above, after World War II cigarette production and sales in Poland increased steadily to a very high level; production was limited only by technological inefficiency. Polish cigarette manufacturers produced relatively few cigarette brands, so consumers had very little choice; five or six brands accounted for almost all market share during that era. Smoking cigarettes was in effect a privilege, as a result of restrictions on cigarette supplies. Yet, just as in any other economy of scarcity, money made a difference: cigarette consumption was higher in the richer voivodships (districts) of Poland.

After the onset of its political and economic transformation, Poland became a very attractive market to multinational cigarette producers. Due to increasingly restrictive tobacco policies and declining consumption in the West, they have had to start looking for new customers for their products. Poland was clearly a very good place to invest and to expand cigarette production, being a market of 40 million people with one of the world's highest rates of tobacco consumption. Multinationals entered the market via joint venture agreements with Poland's biggest producers, and now have controlling stakes in those companies and a dominant share of the domestic cigarette market (Table 1).

Table 1. Market shares of, and multinational interests in, major cigarette producers in Poland, 1997

Producer	Multinational shareholder	Market share (%)
Kraków	Philip Morris (USA)	33
Poznan	Reemstma (Germany)	28
Radom	Seita (France)	12
BAT Group Poland	BAT (UK/USA)	13
Others	n/a	14

Note: n/a: not available

Most of the recent changes in smoking trends, and the resulting changes in health, began before 1989. Unfortunately, the economic reforms implemented since 1989 have left tobacco products with relatively very low prices; a packet of the most popular cigarettes is still cheaper than a loaf of bread. Foreign cigarettes were introduced into the market immediately after the country's borders were opened, mostly through smuggling, and are also relatively cheap. At the beginning of the socio-economic transition, in 1992, almost 90 per cent of all imported cigarettes were contraband. Introduction of special customs regulations and the use of excise stamps caused this proportion to fall to 20-30 per cent. At present, it is estimated that smuggling accounts for roughly 10 per cent of all cigarettes legally sold in Poland. Notwithstanding excise tax, cigarette prices in Poland are still three or four times lower than in the EU, with the result that smuggling of cigarettes between Poland and its neighbours is still a major problem.

Imported cigarettes sold in Poland's newly-liberalised market have attractive, colourful packaging and aromatised tobacco; they were also promoted as being "healthier" than local brands. Contrary to popular opinion, however, the cigarettes produced by foreign companies do not necessarily have lower levels of carcinogenic substances — indeed, they sometimes deliver more tar and nicotine than those produced locally (Zatonski, Brzezinski et al., 1996). Since 1989, stylish cigarette advertisements have been introduced on Polish streets and in the press on a huge scale, creating a positive image for tobacco. Most advertising agencies and newspaper publishers (and some politicians) soon became strongly 'dependent' on the tobacco industry, which also began organising rock concerts and other activities targeted at the young. Cigarette producers admit that they had to reduce production by roughly 10 per cent during 1997, and have redoubled their efforts to increase demand; their budgets for advertising and promotional campaigns are clearly not declining.

(ii) Current taxation and pricing policy

Nowadays, Poles have a large choice of cigarettes, and product 'quality' is improving. For example, almost 90 per cent of all cigarettes consumed now have a filter. However, the most popular cigarettes are the cheapest ones, which still maintain a substantial market share (Table 2). International brands lag behind in sales, but are increasingly popular.

Table 2. Popularity and price of selected cigarette brands sold in Poland at the end of 1997

Cigarette brand	Smoking frequency (%)	Price (US$)
Marlboro	4.5	1.17
Golden American	2.0	1.17
Sobieskie	3.5	0.85
Sobieskie Light	3.0	0.85
Mars	1.5	0.80
Mocne	11.0	0.62
Klubowe	10.0	0.62
Popularne	10.0	0.57
Radomskie	2.5	0.62
Valet	2.0	0.62
Extra Mocne	1.5	0.62

Cigarette prices are very low by Western standards. One reason for this may be the government's cigarette pricing policy — or rather the lack thereof for many years. Cigarette prices increased at the same rate as general consumer price inflation until 1994, when the situation changed. Since then cigarette prices began to increase faster than the rate of consumer price inflation, a possible sign that policy-makers had begun to pay special attention to the problem. Apparently they realised that higher cigarette prices enhance both tax revenues and public health.

The data also show that the number of cigarettes available for an average salary was decreasing from 1992 to 1996 (Table 3). This positive trend ended in 1996, when cigarette prices rose more slowly than inflation, and there was an increase in the number of cigarette packs an average salary could purchase.

Table 3. Purchasing power of an average salary in Poland in terms of cigarettes and selected food products, 1991-97

	1991	92	93	94	95	96	97
Average salary (Polish Zloty)	200	300	400	610	750	919	1166
Inflation (1990 = 100)	803	143	135	132	128	120	113
Bread (kg)	509	476	468	497	536	418	530
Cigarettes (packs of "Popularne")	909	857	833	824	619	540	583
Apples (kg)	323	563	745	488	500	707	777
Oranges (kg)	200	258	216	265	300	287	364

Prices, production and consumption of cigarettes are, of course, determined to a large extent by the level and structure of taxes imposed on them. Unfortunately, Poland does not tax all tobacco products uniformly, as recommended by the EU or World Bank. Instead, excise duty is levied on four different categories of cigarette (Table 4). Value-added tax is imposed on tobacco products at a rate of 22 per cent.

Tables 5 and 6 present cigarette prices and tax burdens as a percentage of retail price for Poland and other countries, showing that Poland still has relatively low prices and a lower tax burden than many other countries. This is

Table 4. Cigarette excise taxes, 1997 and 1998

Cigarette taxation group	Excise duty (US$ per 20)	
	1997	*1998*
1. Imported cigarettes; foreign brands produced in Poland	1.28	1.53
2. Cigarettes with filter, longer than 70 mm	1.05	1.31
3. Cigarettes with filter, shorter than 70 mm	0.92	1.03
4. Cigarettes without filter	0.89	1.00

Table 5. Comparative cigarette tax burdens in 20 countries world-wide

	Tax amount (US$ per 20)	Tax (% of retail price)	Retail price (US$ per 20)
Norway (max.)	5.69	71	8.00
Canada (max.)	2.92	72	4.04
(min.)	1.18	54	2.18
Iceland	2.80	72	3.86
New Zealand	2.66	68	3.92
Australia	2.65	64	4.11
Hong Kong	1.87	52	3.62
Switzerland	1.56	56	2.76
Singapore	1.53	48	3.16
Japan	1.20	62	1.94
Malta	1.16	66	1.75
Barbados	1.14	55	2.09
Argentina	1.09	68	1.60
Sri Lanka	1.07	79	1.36
Uruguay	0.99	67	1.49
Croatia	0.95	66	1.44
Chile	0.93	71	1.32
Fiji	0.79	45	1.76
Jamaica	0.77	35	2.21
South Korea	0.75	65	1.15
Poland (Marlboro)	0.58	47	1.17
(Popularne)	0.36	62	0.62

Table 6. Cigarette taxes and prices in selected European countries						
	Belgium	*Greece*	*Spain*	*Sweden*	*Poland*	*Hungary*
Proportional taxes (% of retail price):						
Ad valorem	50.0	53.9	54.0	17.8	–	18.7
VAT	17.4	15.3	13.8	20.0	18.0	20.0
Combined	67.4	69.1	67.8	37.8	18.0	38.7
Specific tax (US$ per 20)	0.20	0.07	0.07	2.20	0.26	0.18
Retail price (US$ per 20)	2.92	2.18	1.15	5.76	0.70	0.74
Total tax burden (US$ per 20)	2.16	1.58	0.84	4.38	0.40	0.47
Excise tax (% of retail price)	56.8	57.2	59.9	56.0	37.6	47.2
Total tax (% of retail price)	74.1	72.5	73.7	76.0	min. 47.0 max. 62.0	63.0

especially important with regard to the possibility of Poland joining the European Union, where cigarette prices are significantly higher, and the tax burden as a percentage of retail price is higher. Clearly, much needs to be done to harmonise Poland's cigarette tax system with those of other countries.

(iii) Positive change in economic policy toward tobacco?

The situation in the Polish cigarette market changed a little at the beginning of 1998, when the Ministry of Finance announced sizeable increases in the excise duty on cigarettes (see Table 4), and increased the duty on international brands more than that on domestic brands. The Ministry has also been considering varying the excise duty on cigarettes according to their level of tar. The Minister of Finance is attempting to rectify past imbalances in the taxation of tobacco products, subject every cigarette category to equal treatment, and collect as much tax revenue as possible. It will be interesting to evaluate the results of this stronger tobacco policy.

Appropriate tax and pricing policies (as well as labelling of cigarettes that are to be sold in Poland in ways that discourage smuggling), effective legislation against tobacco promotion, and clearer health warnings in cigarette advertisements and on packs could lead to a significant decrease in the risk of death from tobacco-attributable diseases among the Polish population. This is especially true for young people and children, who are the subject of the tobacco industry's special attention, and who more and more often become physiologically addicted to nicotine before they reach their majority.

References

Central Statistical Office (Poland) (annual), *Statistical Yearbook*, 1923-96, Warsaw: CSO.

Doll R., R. Peto, K. Bjartveit, L. Chazova, G. Cholmogorova, A. Hirsch, V. Levshin, D. Simpson and W. Zatonski (1993), "Tobacco and death in Eastern Europe", in Bodmer, W. and D. Zaridze (eds), *Cancer Prevention in Europe*, London: Organisation of European Cancer Institutes.

Feachem, R. (1994), "Health decline in Eastern Europe", *Nature*, 367:313-314.

Feachem, R., T. Kjellstrom, C. Murray, M. Over and M. Phillips (eds) (1992), *The Health of Adults in the Developing World*, World Bank and Oxford University Press.

Kubik, A.K., D.M. Parkin, I. Plesko, W. Zatonski, E. Kramarowa, M. Möhner, H.P. Friedl, L. Juhasz, C.H.G. Tzvetansky and J. Reissigova (1995), "Patterns of cigarette sales and lung cancer mortality in some Central and Eastern European countries, 1960-1989", *Cancer*, 75:2452-2460.

McMichael, A.J. and W. Zatonski (1996), "Environmental, behavioral, and socioeconomic influences: tackling the historical jigsaw puzzle of health in Central and Eastern Europe", *International Journal of Occupational and Environmental Health*; 2:161-163

Murray, C.J.L. and A.D. Lopez (1996), *The Global Burden of Disease*, Cambridge, Mass.: Harvard University Press.

Murray, C.J.L., G. Yang and X. Qiao (1993), "Adult mortality: levels, patterns and causes", in World Bank (eds.), *World Development Report 1993: Investing in Health*, New York: Oxford University Press.

Peto, R., A.D. Lopez, J. Boreham, M. Thun and C. Heath Jr (1994), *Mortality from Smoking in Developed Countries 1950-2000: Indirect Estimates from National Vital Statistics*, New York: Oxford University Press.

Przewozniak, K. and W. Zatonski (1996), "Trendy, geografia i spoeczno-behawioralna charakterystyka palenia tytoniu w Polsce" ["Trends, geography, and social-behavioural characteristics of tobacco smoking in Poland"], in Zatonski, W., B. Hulanicka and J. Tyczynski (eds.), *Stan zdrowia Polaków* [*The health status of the Poles*], Wrocaw: Monografie Zakadu Antropologii Polskiej Akademii Nauk.

Zatonski, W. (1995), "The health of the Polish population", *Public Health Review of Israel*, 23:139-156.

Zatonski, W., N. Becker, K. Gottesman, A. Mykowiecka and J. Tyczynski (1988), *Atlas of Cancer Mortality in Poland 1975-1979*, Berlin: Springer-Verlag.

Zatonski, W., Z. Brzezinski, J. Didkowska, J. Engel, E. Florek, J.M. Jaworski, J. Lissowska, Z. Mielecka-Kubien, T. Parchimowicz, M. Przetakiewicz-Koziej, K. Przewozniak, H. Szczecinska, J. Szymborski, W. Tarkowski, J. Tyczynski and U. Wojciechowska (1996), "Ekspozycja populacji polskiej na tyto: palenie tytoniu, substancje toksyczne, nastêpstwa zdrowotne" ["Exposure of the Polish population to tobacco: tobacco smoking, toxic substances, health effects"], *Magazyn Med.*; 7:1-12.

Zatonski, W., J. Didkowska, K. Przewozniak, W. Tarkowski, J. Tyczynski and U. Wojciechowska (1996), *Stan zdrowia Polaków* [*The health status of the Poles*] Expert Appraisal, Warsaw: Cancer Center.

Zatonski, W. and K. Przewozniak (1992), *Zdrowotne nastêpstwa palenia tytoniu w Polsce* [*The health effects of smoking in Poland*], Warsaw: Ariel.

Zatonski, W. and K. Przewozniak (1996), *Palenie tytoniu w Polsce: postawy, nastepstwa zdrowotne i profilaktyka* [*Tobacco smoking in Poland: attitudes, health consequences and prevention*], Warsaw: Cancer Center.

Zatonski, W., M. Smans, J. Tyczynski and P. Boyle (eds.) (1995), *Atlas of Cancer Mortality in Central Europe*, IARC Scientific Publications No. 134, Lyon: International Agency for Research on Cancer.

Chapter 23

The Economic Regulation of Tobacco Consumption in New Zealand

Brian Easton

A brief history of tobacco in New Zealand[1]

Tobacco was introduced in New Zealand by the Europeans about 200 years ago. Smoking became very popular with the Maori: surgeon Henry Weekes wrote in the early 1840s that it was "universal among New Zealanders [the Maori] of both sexes" (Rutherford and Skinner, 1940). It was also used as a currency and a commodity of exchange in the middle of the nineteenth century. By 1860 attempts were made to grow tobacco leaf, although this was not a successful industry until the 1930s. Cigars were being manufactured by 1884. About 80 per cent of adult males and 35 per cent of adult females born at the turn of the century were regular smokers at some stage in their lives. The Maori rates were about the same for males and 65 per cent or more for females (Easton, 1995).

Initially, opposition to smoking encompassed a purity argument and a health argument. The understanding of the health effects of tobacco was primitive: the first *New Zealand Medical Journal* reported in 1887-8 that tobacco was associated with insanity. An Anti Nicotine Society formed in Christchurch in 1883, and in 1889 the Women's Christian Temperance Union (also influential in the women's electoral franchise of 1893) denounced tobacco.

Almost all the discussion was about male smoking, with few references to women. A special concern was juvenile smoking, it being believed that smoking was damaging to growing youth (but not to adults, as a number of smokers in the parliamentary debates at the turn of the century were wont to mention). Three factors reinforced concerns in the late 19th century: the introduction of cigarettes which made secret smoking harder to monitor, a general concern about juvenile misbehaviour, and similar concerns overseas (the most influential countries being Australia, Britain, and the United States). Moreover, *per capita* tobacco consumption levels rose from 1.9 lbs. a year in 1887-94 to 2.6 lbs. a year in 1904.

In 1882 legislation was introduced into the New Zealand parliament to ban juvenile smoking, although by the time the Juvenile Smoking Suppression Act

---

1. This section is based mainly on Thomson (1992a) and Thomson (1992b), which is the source for all facts unless otherwise stated. Broughton (1996) contains much useful historical information on the Maori and tobacco.

was passed in 1903, a number of other legislatures had passed similar provisions. Its seven clauses prohibited supplying tobacco products to those under the age of 15 and smoking in a public place.[2] The Act has long since been repealed, but the prohibition of selling to youth (currently defined as under the age of 18) remains in New Zealand law. Although there were some prosecutions, the Act proved little deterrent to the rise of tobacco consumption.

Table 1. Annual consumption, 1887-1995			
Year(s)	Kg per person over 15	Year(s)	Kg per person over 15
1887-94	1.48	1956	3.14
1904	1.73	1961	3.30
1910-14	1.79	1966	3.32
1921	1.86	1971	3.11
1926	2.04	1976	3.15
1931	1.91	1981	2.91
1936	2.09	1986	2.30
1941	2.50	1991	1.79
1946	2.81	1995	1.40
1951	3.29		

Note: 1 000 cigarettes = 1 kg
Source: Various official sources

Table 1 shows *per capita* consumption rising sharply after the mid 1930s, to a peak during the 1950s and 1960s of about 3.3 kgs per adult or double the 1904 level, and declining thereafter. By 1995 consumption levels were back at those of the late 19th century. While 80 per cent of men born before 1925 had ever-smoked (regularly), the proportion fell to below 45 per cent of men born in 1970. The crucial factor may have been the ending from 1945 of widespread military service, where tobacco was cheap and social pressures favourable. About half of women from the cohort born about 1910 have been ever-smokers, a ratio which remained through to 1970.

Table 2 shows current and ever (regular) smoking rates by ethnicity, as self-categorised in the 1996 Population Census.[3] Today average smoking prevalence is at similar levels for men and women, at just over one-fifth of the adult population. Many previous smokers have given up, with a quit rate of near 50 per cent for the adult population as a whole.[4]

The ethnic data needs to be interpreted with care, since different groups have different age structures and educational levels, which also affect smoking behaviour.[5] Because the data has just been published there is no systematic

---

2. There was a caveat that a youth could so smoke if they had a medical certificate that it would be beneficial.
3. Some respondents give two or more categories — e.g. Maori and Pakeha — so the total of ethnic groups exceeds the total population.
4. The quit rate equals 1 −(prevalence/ever smoking).
5. Another factor to be investigated is whether the respondent is locally or overseas born, which may explain the divergence in Asian rates.

Table 2. Adult[a] smoking rates by ethnicity, 1996

Ethnic group	Adult pop.	Male Prevalence	Male Ever smoking	Female Prevalence	Female Ever smoking
	%	%	%	%	%
NZ European-Pakeha	69.2	22.9	48.4	21.2	41.7
NZ Maori	11.7	39.7	57.4[c]	47.4	65.0[c]
English	8.7	21.2	61.6[b]	18.5	42.8[b]
Scottish	3.2	25.5	55.3[b]	23.7	46.6
Samoan	2.2	33.3	42.6[c]	23.4	31.1[c]
Chinese	2.2	16.8	26.8[c]	5.9	9.7[c]
Irish	2.1	26.5	54.7	25.7	48.2
Australian	1.5	27.4	53.7	22.3	45.7
Dutch	1.3	22.6	58.1[b]	18.5	43.5[b]
Cook Island Maori	1.0	37.1	48.7[c]	37.9	49.2[c]
Indian	1.1	9.6	15.1[c]	5.9	9.4[c]
Tongan	0.7	39.5	50.0[c]	19.3	26.9[c]
Niuean	0.4	34.4	46.2[c]	30.9	40.8[c]
German	0.4	25.0	51.8	22.3	44.8
Korean	0.3	35.6	52.8[c]	6.3	9.5[c]
Welsh	0.3	23.1	55.4[b]	20.0	43.6
Filipino	0.2	20.0	32.8[c]	5.5	9.2[c]
American (US)	0.2	17.9	43.4[b]	15.5	38.2[b]
South Slav	0.2	24.4	49.1	22.6	39.4[c]
Fijian[d]	0.3	25.7	41.1[c]	22.1	35.7[c]
Japanese	0.2	37.4	54.1[c]	14.3	25.8[c]
South African	0.2	13.1	38.8[b]	12.9	32.9[b]
ALL	100.0	24.8	49.7	22.8	42.1

Notes: a: over 15 years
b: quit rate above 55%
c: quit rate below 45%
d: excludes Fijian Indians
Source: Statistics New Zealand (1997)

commentary on it, but it confirms that the (New Zealand) Maori smoking prevalence rates are substantially higher than average and their quit rates lower.[6] Pacific Island smoking rates also tend to be higher than average.

Smoking is thought to reduce the average life expectancy of New Zealand smokers by about 7 years (Peto *et al.*, 1994) Some tentative calculations suggest Maori non-smokers live as long as non-Maori non-smokers, Maori shorter life expectation being almost entirely attributable to the higher incidence of smoking (Easton, 1995). This may exaggerate the mortality impact of smoking, but it may well be the right order of magnitude.

6. Easton (1995) shows the true ever-smoking rates are higher, especially for Maori relative to the total, because the differential mortality of smokers lowers (relatively) the numbers alive who report having ever been regular smokers.

Following the growing evidence linking tobacco consumption to various medical conditions (convincingly from the 1950s) a handful of New Zealand physicians led by Dr David Hay, medical director of the National Heart Foundation, campaigned actively against smoking. Initially this was individual medical advice rather than national policy, but a plethora of anti-smoking organisations developed. A Ministerial Advisory Committee on Smoking and Health was instituted in 1977.[7] Another official initiative which had considerable influence, was questions about ever-smoking and now-smoking in the 1976, 1981 and 1996 Population Censuses.

Among other influences on public policy on top of the growing awareness of smoking's health effects, was that the removal of import controls led to the elimination of tobacco growing and a substantial reduction in cigarette manufacture with increasing offshore supply. Thus the size of the production lobby was significantly reduced. Tobacco products are generally sold in general outlets, rather than tobacconist shops, again blunting the supplier lobby. Another key change was the identification of passive smoking, which created a far larger reaction than the statistics warranted, compared to deaths from smoking. But it gave anti-smokers a political lever to repress smoking in public, since it was no longer a matter of tobacco-induced diseases affecting only smokers.

Table 3. The social costs of tobacco consumption, 1990	
Intangible:	NZ$m
Effect of population mortality	14 000
Effect of population morbidity	7 250
Tangible:	
Reduced production from mortality	400
Reduced production from morbidity	145
Additional resources from not consuming tobacco	580
Additional resources from not treating tobacco induced diseases	205
Additional resources because of fewer fires	15
Less	
Benefits from tobacco consumption	-125
TOTAL COSTS FROM TOBACCO USE	22 470
Intangible costs:	
Total	21 250
Percentage of total human capital	3.2%
Tangible costs:	
Total	1 220
Percentage of GDP	1.7%
Population decrease:	2.0%
Source: Easton (1997)	

7. Maori anti-smoking organisations became active in the 1990s reflecting a growing commitment by the Maori to deal with their own problems.

A previous study by this author calculated the social costs of tobacco use, arriving at a 1.7 per cent loss of material GDP with a 3.2 per cent loss of the total value of life (covering mortality and morbidity costs) in 1990 (Easton, 1997). A summary of the conclusions appears in Table 3.

Fiscal policy and tobacco[8]

Excise duties on tobacco were initially for fiscal purposes. In 1839, the British colonial Secretary, Lord Normanby, confidently advised putative governor Hobson that "[d]uties on the import of tobacco, spirits, wine and sugar will probably supersede the necessity for other taxation . . ." (McClintock, 1958, p.90). There was a brief period in 1844 and 1845 when the duties imposed in 1841 were repealed, but since then excise duties on imports on tobacco, and later on domestic manufactures, have been an integral part of New Zealand's fiscal revenue.

Normanby's forecasts of excise duties being sufficient to fund government proved wrong, and in the 1997 fiscal year excise duty on tobacco products amounted to NZ$658 million, or 2.0 per cent of total taxation and 0.7 per cent of GDP. In addition tobacco, like almost all other products, has the uniform 12.5 per cent GST (Goods and Services Tax, a VAT) levied on it.

A 1994 study divided the price of a pack of 20 (Rothmans) cigarettes into manufacturing costs of 22.4 per cent, excise tax of 55.1 per cent, wholesale margin of 2.8 per cent, retail margin of 8.5 per cent, and GST of 11.1 per cent (see Figure 1). However, since the GST (a uniform comprehensive sales tax) is imposed upon the excise duty, the totality of excise duty plus the resulting GST

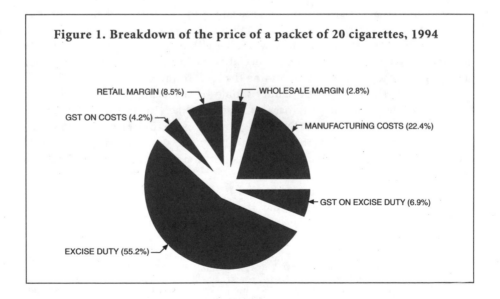

Figure 1. Breakdown of the price of a packet of 20 cigarettes, 1994

RETAIL MARGIN (8.5%)

WHOLESALE MARGIN (2.8%)

GST ON COSTS (4.2%)

MANUFACTURING COSTS (22.4%)

GST ON EXCISE DUTY (6.9%)

EXCISE DUTY (55.2%)

---

8. This section is based on Easton (1991), which also covers alcohol duties, and James (1995).

made up 62 per cent of the price.[9] James (1995) estimated that the average smoker paid NZ$763 in 1993 in excise duty, which might be compared with the average weekly wage of about NZ$556.

Historically, the justification for excise duty on tobacco has been a combination of fiscal pragmatism with the view that consumption of tobacco was indulgent, if not downright sinful. Because the demand for tobacco is price-inelastic, it is a good substance to tax without efficiency losses (whatever the health and equity considerations), while the fact that the consumption activity is considered problematic by a significant and vocal proportion of the population makes the technical recommendation politically feasible. For instance, during the debate following the excise duty hike on tobacco of the infamous 1958 "Black" Budget, there is no mention of health effects. The 1967 Taxation Review Committee does not discuss health aspects of any tobacco excise duty, either.[10]

But the 1970 budget stated that "it is clear that cigarettes and tobacco can be subjected to additional tax without harming in any way the general welfare of the community. In fact it is increasingly argued that discouraging the consumption of these commodities is likely to make a positive contribution to our general health" (Muldoon, 1970). By the 1977 budget the view had moved to "the adverse effects on health of smoking and drinking have been well publicised" (Muldoon, 1977). A specific sales tax was imposed, the proceeds of which were used for community health services. The levy did not last long, but was consolidated into the overall excise duty. The New Zealand Treasury is strongly opposed to tagged or earmarked taxes. Another complication was that excise duties were not then inflation-proof. Today they are indexed to the consumer price index.

The notion that excise duty on tobacco consumption serves a health purpose is now an integral part of the justification for that duty. It might be that were there no such case, the excise duty would be eliminated, since fiscal policy in general has attempted to eliminate special taxes in favour of a uniform GST. However, this factor does not determine the level of the duty.

The narrowest view is that the duty should be sufficient to cover the cost to the state of tobacco-induced diseases and the like. In 1990 public health treatment costs came to about NZ$180m, while excise duties were NZ$560m. Even if the reduction of taxation from mortality and morbidity were included, the revenue would still include direct costs to the state of tobacco consumption of NZ$160m (Easton, 1997).

But even ignoring the matters covered in the next paragraph, the rule that special tobacco duties should equal the costs to the government is clearly wrong. Optimal decisions involve marginal conditions, but this is an average

---

9. Sometimes the entire GST is included in the calculation of the tax on tobacco products (which would take the total up to 66 per cent). This is misleading since GST is imposed upon (almost) all goods and services. Insofar as analysis is concerned with the relative price between tobacco and other products, the effect of the GST is neutral. Note that excise duty makes up 62 per cent of the pre-GST price, just as it (with the GST levied on it) makes up 62 per cent of the post-GST price.
10. It hardly discussed excise duties at all, except to note that they tend to be regressive.

rule, although it could be argued that the marginal social cost of the consumption of tobacco is the average cost (which is obviously not true for the consumption of alcohol). Even so, social costs induced by tobacco use mainly occur a considerable time (even decades) after the act of smoking.

However, the costs to the state are not the entirety of social costs. For comparison, and using the official value of a quality life year prolonged of NZ$200 000, the total social costs came to NZ$22.4 billion against the NZ$560 million revenue in 1990 (see Table 2). Again, for the reasons mentioned in the previous paragraph, there is no logical necessity that revenue from excise duty on tobacco should cover all the social costs of tobacco consumption.

Moreover, some of these social costs are incurred by the smoker (although there is some allowance for this in the calculations). Except for the addictive element of tobacco consumption, the treatment of such costs would be straightforward. If there was no addiction the social costs incurred by the smoker would offset their private costs by the gains to them of smoking.[11] However, where there is addiction the rationality assumption is harder to apply. Moreover, the way in which the New Zealand official value of life is calculated implies that part of the value of the individual's life accrues to other people, so a rational person smoking her or himself to death (or trying to commit suicide) still generates social costs to others.

Whether through health and social costs arguments, or through modern variations of the purity argument (presenting tobacco as a demerit good), the anti-smoking pressure groups have lobbied vigorously for higher taxation on tobacco, with marked success in the late 1980s and early 1990s. A government under fiscal stress found it convenient to respond positively to the lobbyists' demand.

The 1991 tax hike resulted in little extra excise revenue. This might suggest that the excise duty rate had reached the level of no additional revenue, but it is generally thought that other (income-reducing) measures taken at the same time, which were particularly harsh on the poor (who are the heaviest smokers), resulted in smokers cutting back consumption to save expenditure. However, there has been no real increase in tobacco excise duties since 1991. In any case, one can see here the potential of a conflict between the fiscal purpose of raising revenue and the health purpose of reducing consumption.

In evaluating the impact of excise duty in New Zealand, at least three groups of smokers with differing behaviour need to be considered, although little is known about their proportions, other than anecdotally:
1. The addicted, typically older, smoker who has already resisted a range of economic and non-economic incentives to give up smoking. For many, a hike in excise duty reduces their real income rather than their tobacco consumption, while others are less insensitive to price and information.
2. Occasional, light, and non-addictive (adult) smokers whose consumption may be price-elastic or sensitive to price increases (although occasional smokers may not be). However, this group may not be a high policy priority

---

11. The study uses the convention that private costs are included in social costs.

except to discourage their joining the first group.

3. New and potential smokers, who in New Zealand are almost entirely teenagers, since few begin smoking after the age of 18, typically having highly price-elastic demands. One estimate put the youth price elasticity at 1.1, although the sample population includes youth aged 20 years and over, so the true elasticity for teenagers is likely to be even higher (Laugesen and Meads, 1990). Excise duty hikes may not appear to reduce their consumption in the short-run, because it is already low. In the long-run, because they don't join the first group, their potential consumption may be cut drastically.

A tax hike will impact on these different groups in different ways. In particular it may not be particularly effective on the first group, but may be effective on the long-term smoking behaviour of the third.

A complication is that the magnitude of the price (and hence excise duty) change may affect the behavioural response (in contrast to standard economic analysis which assumes that the aggregate elasticity from a number of small changes will be the same as the elasticity for a one-off increase of the same aggregate magnitude). The addicted may be inured to small changes, and it may be only when there is a large price hike that they take the short-term pain to reduce their consumption and save revenue. Fiscally, then, optimal revenue is to be gained by regular small increments, whereas reductions of consumption require occasional large hikes. The strategy of the 1990s of indexing excise duty to the consumer price index belongs to the first strategy, while the occasional major hikes in the 1970s and 1980s belong to the second.

Note that there is a leakage in the existence of duty-free entitlements for travellers (all the more ironically on no-smoking flights). New Zealanders are major international travellers, averaging one overseas trip roughly every three years. The elimination of duty-free goods between European Union countries in the near future is likely to lead to pressures for a similar elimination between Australia and New Zealand, where there is also high economic integration. (There may also be pressure for elimination between the latter two countries and the independent South Pacific states.) Whatever the economic case for duty-free goods generally, the case for duty-free tobacco imports is thin.

There have been a number of New Zealand econometric estimates of the price and income elasticities of demand for tobacco products, and some for advertising (and even news items). These are summarised in Table 4. Not all the estimates are significant, consistent with one another, or consistent with *a priori* theory. Sometimes the data period is far too short to provide quality long-run estimates. For instance, if it is believed that higher prices discourage teenagers taking up smoking, the full effect of an excise duty hike will not be for decades.

Non-fiscal regulation

As reported in the historical section, legal prohibitions was imposed in 1903 on juveniles from being supplied with tobacco products, or smoking in public places. In principle such restrictions can be converted to fiscal measures (a prohibitively high tax rate on the activities), although practically the fiscal

Table 4. Elasticity estimates for New Zealand

Article	Period	Elasticity			
		Price	Income	Adverts	News
Salter (1981)	1961-1979[A]	-0.15[SR]	·0.37[SR]		
Salter (1985)	1961-1983[Q]	-0.52[LR]	0.09[LR]		
Chetwynd *et al.*, (1988)	1973-1985[Q]	-0.11[SR]	0.50[SR]	0.07[SR]	
Harrison *et al.*, (1989)	1973-1985[Q]	-0.08[SR]	0.50[SR]	0.08[SR]	
Harrison & Chetwynd (1990)	1973-1989[Q]	-0.32[LR]	0.81[LR]	0.07[LR]	-0.04[LR]
Simester & Brodie (1990)	Meta-analysis	-0.54[PD]	0.27[PD]	0.05[PD] 0.22[SD]	
Laugesen & Meads (1990)	1988-1989[W]	-0.41[LR]	0.59[LR]	0.04[DM] -0.03[RE] -0.02[UM]	-0.04[LR]
Meads (1991)	1973-1986[M]	(rise) -0.07[LR] (fall) -0.02[LR]	(rise) 0.04 (fall) 0.03	-0.03[AD] 0.03[SP]	
Evans & Meads (1991)	1973-1989[M]	(rise) -0.13[SR] -0.07[LR] (fall) 0.08[SR] 0.05[LR]		newspaper 0.01[SR] magazine 0.02[SR]	

Notes: A = annual; M = monthly; Q = quarterly; W = weekly.
         SR = short-run; LR = long-run; PD = primary demand; SD = selective demand.
         AD = advertising; DM = downmarket; RE = regular; SP = sponsorship; UM = upmarket.
Source: James (1995)

alternative may not be very operational. Other prohibitions began to be imposed in the late 1980s. The main ones can be summarised as follows:

1. Restrictions on commercial access to tobacco by the young (currently under 18).
2. Prohibitions on advertising, sponsorship, (with a few exceptions, typically concerned with international events), display, and compulsory labelling including health warnings. (Ten-packs have just been removed from circulation, with the hope that this will reduce purchases by the young and poor. Plain packs are a major item on the reformer's agenda.)
3. Creation and extension of smoke-free environments. (The rules have been supported by many businesses — most evidently airlines — happy to comply in their own interests while attributing the restrictions to the government.)

It is not the task of this chapter to detail these measures. In economic terms the first two might be primarily thought as being concerned with limiting access and improving understanding of adolescents who are judged unable to make quality rational decisions. There is a complementary anti-smoking education campaign.

Non-smoking areas reflect another economic principle — the allocation of property rights. It was not so long ago that smokers had an informal social right to pollute other people's air with their smoke (even if the polite smoker asked for permission, the expectation was that it would be given). Today that position is reversed, and it is the non-smoker who usually has the (legal) right in public places to determine the quality of the air (in regard to tobacco smoke).[12]

For completeness it is mentioned that there are also private restrictions on smoking. For instance the Maori, having taken over responsibility for their (typically government-funded) own anti-smoking campaigns, have applied smoking prohibitions to their *marae* (meeting areas and halls). (On the other hand the Maori derive no direct benefit from an excise duty hike,[13] while they have a particularly high proportion of addicted smokers, so their lobbyists have shown some resistance to using tax for tobacco control.)

Generally very little is known about the effectiveness of these various measures on overall tobacco consumption.

Some issues

Epidemiologists will note that as in the case of many other epidemics, smoking prevalence peaked before public policy took conscious action. Indeed it might be argued that it was only possible to take public initiatives when smoking was in retreat, and the anti-smoking lobby sufficiently augmented by ex-smokers to have the required political weight. But if the smoking epidemic has peaked, the health consequences of smoking have not, for there is often a long lead time between smoking and the resulting disease. While the health consequences for men smoking have probably peaked (or troughed), the damage for women smoking is still rising.

Figure 2 shows *per capita* tobacco consumption between 1921 and 1991. It may be a little misleading in the 1940s, since considerable numbers of New Zealand smokers were in the armed services overseas. Indeed the experience probably encouraged smoking, given the social circumstances, and the cheap tobacco provided to soldiers.

Allowing for this, the main trends are the switch from loose tobacco to cigarettes, the rising consumption in the period until immediately after the war, the plateau from then till the early 1970s, and the decline thereafter (steep from the 1980s).

There is not enough historical data to provide a confident account of the changes, but a best conjecture might be as follows. Before 1940, tobacco consumption (especially cigarettes) became increasingly fashionable as the tobacco companies sought market expansion, in women's markets as well. This probably continued during the war, although the numbers overseas obscure the data. On returning, smokers faced much higher tobacco prices because of excise duties which had been imposed during the war for fiscal reasons. This discouraged increasing consumption levels, and discouraged young men from taking up smoking regularly. The momentum of past addiction plus rising

---

12. It is interesting to construct a formal model of individual property rights to replace the law *a la* Coase, although it soon becomes evident that the transaction costs of such an arrangement make it impractical.
13. They could be indirect beneficiaries, depending how the additional revenue was spent.

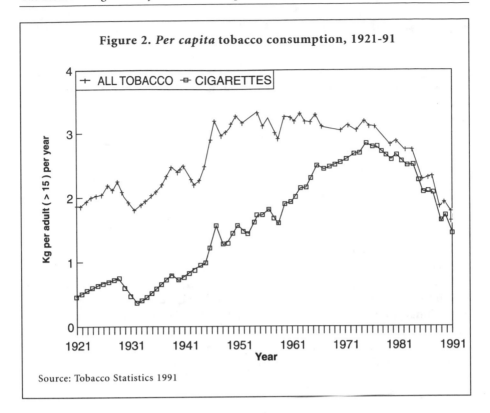

Figure 2. *Per capita* tobacco consumption, 1921-91

Source: Tobacco Statistics 1991

prosperity continued the high levels of tobacco consumption, but the underlying long-term consumption was fragile.

The tax hike of 1958 probably led to further quitting, and discouraged the young taking up the habit (Easton, 1967). Health and fitness concerns probably affected social judgements, especially among the better-educated (and higher-income). It seems possible that higher socio-economic classes took up smoking and smoked more before the 1930s, and they quit earlier, so that generally smoking in New Zealand is a lower socio-economic phenomenon (and hence tobacco taxation would now *prima facie* be regressive — see Chapter 8). The reduced consumption of those in the highest socio-economic classes made smoking less fashionable, and facilitated the anti-smoking policies, which collectively have led to the rapid decline in recent years.

If this account has any veracity, it may have an important implication for developing countries with low tobacco consumption. Their situation is more like New Zealand's in the early part of the twentieth century. This is not a gloomy prediction of the inevitably of tobacco consumption levels accelerating, but draws attention to the fact that an earlier use of economic instruments than occurred in New Zealand may prevent consumption levels and disease rising to Western peaks.

But New Zealand cannot be complacent about the reduction in its smoking levels. The latest data suggests there may have been a small rise during 1997, although this may be a statistical artefact, so further data is necessary to make an assessment.[14]

The historical account given here is sketchy. International comparisons may enable gaps to be filled by the pooling of scarce data. However, it lacks one component, characteristic of much economic analysis. Differences in social behaviour are taken as given, rather than explained. But why do men and women have different smoking behaviour? Why do the Maori behave differently from the non-Maori (and why are Pacific Island smoking rates more similar to Maori than non-Maori)? Perhaps some progress can be made with the enormous data base of the 1996 Population Census, but ultimately the economist faces a reality of important phenomena being explained by other disciplines. A similar problem applies to the phenomenon of addiction. It may be too much to expect economics to explain addictive behaviour, but until there is an explanation economic policy must tread warily about how its policy recommendations may work.

Whatever the technical economic recommendations, there is a political problem in obtaining enough public support for them. Crucial in the New Zealand political experience has been the staunchness of the medical professionals on the health effects of smoking, the desperation of the Treasury for raising fiscal revenue, the significance of passive smoking to the non-smoker, and the decline of the tobacco growing and manufacturing industry as a part of industry (rather than health) policy.

References

Broughton. J. (1996), *Puffing up a Storm: 'Kapai te Torori!'*, Department of Preventive and social Medicine, Otago: University of Otago.

Chetwynd, J., R. Brodie and R. Harrison (1988). "Impact of cigarette advertising on aggregate demand for cigarettes in New Zealand", *British Journal of Addiction*, 83:409-14.

Easton, B.H. (1967), *Consumption in New Zealand 1954/5 to 1964/5*, NZIER Research Paper No. 10.

Easton, B.H. (1991), *Economic Instruments for the Regulation of Licit Drugs*, paper presented to Perspective for Change conference, November.

Easton, B.H. (1995), "Smoking in New Zealand: a census investigation", *Australian Journal of Public Health*, 19:125-8.

Easton, B.H. (1997), *The Social Costs of Tobacco Use and Alcohol Misuse*, Public Health Monograph, Department of Public Health, Wellington, NZ: Wellington School of Medicine.

Evans, L. and C. Meads (1991), *An Empirical Study of the Effects of Advertising, Prices and Incomes on Cigarette Consumption in New Zealand*, Wellington, NZ: Victoria University of Wellington.

Harrison, R. and J. Chetwynd (1990), *Determinants of Aggregate Demand for Cigarettes in New Zealand*, Discussion Paper 9002, Department of Economics, Canterbury, NZ: University of Canterbury.

Harrison, R., J. Chetwynd and R. Brodie (1989), "The influence of advertising on tobacco consumption: a reply to Jackson and Ekelund", *British Journal of Addiction*, 84:1251-4.

James, D. (1995), *A Review of Tobacco Taxation*, NZIER Contract 723, Wellington.

Laugesen, M. and C. Meads (1990), "Tobacco advertising restrictions and consumption in OECD Countries, 1960-86", in Durston, B. and K. Jamrosik (eds.), *Proceedings of the Seventh World Conference on Tobacco and Health*, Perth: Health Department of Western Australia.

McClintock, A.H. (1958), *Crown Colony Government in New Zealand*, Wellington: Government Printer.

Meads, C. (1991), *An Empirical Study of the Effects of Advertising, Prices, and Incomes on Cigarette Consumption in New Zealand: 1973-1986*, Masters Dissertation, Wellington: Victoria University of Wellington.

---

14. The data covers supplies from bonded warehouses, and hence does not allow for changes in commercial inventory levels. Another confounding effect may be purchases by tourists from Asia.

Muldoon, R.D. (1970; 1977) *Economic Statement*, Wellington: Government Printer.

Peto, R., A.D. Lopez, J. Boreham, M. Thun and C. Heath Jr. (1994), *Mortality from Smoking in Developed Countries 1950-2000*, New York: Oxford University Press.

Public Health Commission (1995), *Tobacco Taxation as a Health Issue*, Wellington.

Rutherford, J. and W.H. Skinner (1940), *The Establishment of the New Plymouth Settlement*, New Plymouth.

Salter, D. (1981), "The demand for cigarettes in New Zealand — an econometric analysis of the effects of increased taxation", in *Economics and Health: Proceedings of the Second Australian Conference of Health Economists*, Canberra: Australian National University.

Salter, D. (1985), *Paying Lip Service to Health: an Evaluation of the National Government's Policy on Cigarette Taxation, 1975-1983*, Department of Community Health, Wellington: Wellington Clinical School of Medicine.

Simester, D. and R. Brodie (1990), *The Effects of Advertising on Brand and Industry Demand for Tobacco: a Meta-analysis of Economic Studies*, working paper, Department of Marketing and International Business, Auckland: University of Auckland.

Statistics New Zealand (1997), "1996 Census of Population and Dwellings: Population Characteristics", *Hot off the Press*, 7 May.

Taxation Review Committee (1967) *Taxation in New Zealand* (the Ross Committee report), Wellington: Government Printer.

Thomson, S. (1992a), *Evils of 'The Fragrant Weed': A History of the 1903 Juvenile Smoking Suppression Act*, essay in partial fulfilment of MA degree, Auckland: University of Auckland.

Thomson, S. (1992b) *Stubbing out the Social Cigarette*, essay in partial fulfilment of MA degree, Auckland: University of Auckland.

Tobacco Statistics 1991, Wellington: Department of Statistics and Department of Health.

Chapter 24

The Economics of Tobacco Control in Taiwan

Chee-Ruey Hsieh and Yan-Shu Lin

In recent years, the opening-up of national cigarette markets has become a world-wide phenomenon under the global trend of trade liberalisation. For example, under the threat of retaliatory trade sanctions, four Asian nations have agreed to open their markets to US cigarette producers: Japan in 1986, Taiwan in 1987, South Korea in 1988, and Thailand in 1990 (Chaloupka and Laixuthai, 1996). The immediate effect of opening a cigarette market is to change the market structure of the importing countries. In the Asian countries mentioned above, prior to market opening cigarettes were typically produced and sold by a state-run monopoly firm. After each country's cigarette market was opened to imports, its structure became oligopolistic competition: a state-run monopoly firm *versus* multi-national cigarette manufacturers.

The change of market structure, in turn, has led to a fundamental change of tobacco control policies in such countries. Before the domestic market was opened to imports, government policy mainly focused on collecting revenue for government spending through the direct control of cigarette production. Because trade liberalisation introduced competition into the cigarette market, the increase in cigarette consumption resulting from price-cutting and other marketing strategies has raised serious policy concerns. Consequently, the focus of cigarette policy has shifted from the production side to the consumption side, and government agencies have begun to use a variety of policy options to control cigarette consumption.

The purpose of this chapter is to analyse the effects of the opening-up of a cigarette market on cigarette production and consumption and on tobacco control policies, focusing specifically on Taiwan. The focal points of the chapter are the following:

- to what extent do market opening and other economic factors influence the evolution of tobacco control policies?;
- what are the effects of various tobacco control policies on the production and consumption of cigarettes?;
- what are the policy implications of the Taiwanese experience for other developing countries?

The following sections review the institutional history of the tobacco industry in Taiwan, and investigate the contribution of the tobacco industry to the Taiwanese economy. Thereafter, the chapter summarises the historical pattern of cigarette consumption, and discusses the evolution of tobacco control policies and their impact. The future perspective on the formulation of an optimal policy mix for tobacco control in Taiwan, and the implications of this for other developing countries, are discussed in the concluding section of the chapter.

Historic review of the tobacco industry in Taiwan

The most distinctive feature of the tobacco industry in Taiwan was the monopolistic system, which was established by the Japanese colonial government. When Japan acquired Taiwan in 1895, one of the immediate concerns of the colonial government was to achieve financial self-sufficiency. In the early years of colonialism, Japan had to provide large cash subsides for the colonial government in Taiwan; these subsidies ceased in 1904 (Ho, 1971). Due to the lack of tax revenue from domestic sources, the administration speedily established monopoly bureaux for many consumption goods to generate steady streams of revenue. As suggested by Chang and Myers (1963), monopoly profits played an important role in making Taiwan fiscally independent of Japan, accounting for about 30-60 per cent of the government's total current receipts during the colonial period.

Table 1. The share and distribution of monopoly profits, selected years 1897-1944

Year	Monopoly profits		Source of monopoly profits (%)				
	Amount ('000 Yen)	% of govt's total current receipts	Opium	Salt	Camphor	Tobacco	Wine
1897	1 640	30	100	-	-	-	-
1900	8 346	64	50	4	45	-	-
1905	10 605	49	40	6	40	14	-
1910	15 034	36	31	5	36	28	-
1915	16 588	43	35	5	31	29	-
1920	32 141	40	20	4	37	39	-
1925	42 368	46	10	6	28	27	29
1930	43 373	44	10	6	14	37	33
1935	51 005	41	5	6	15	35	39
1940	90 294	37	3	4	11	39	43
1944	200 881	41	1	3	1	43	51

Sources: Zhou (1980)

As shown in Table 1, the monopoly profits came mainly from opium and camphor in the early years of Japanese colonialism, but their importance declined sharply later in the colonial period. In contrast, the revenue share generated from tobacco and wine increased steadily since these goods were incorporated into the monopolistic system. By 1944, tobacco accounted for 43 per cent of the government's total monopoly profits.

After World War II, the monopoly business was continued by the Taiwanese government. The monopoly bureau was re-organised under its present name, the Taiwan Tobacco and Wine Monopoly Bureau (TTWMB). Opium was banned, and certain other monopoly goods consigned to the jurisdiction of relevant organisations, while the TTWMB continued to control the production, manufacturing and sale of tobacco, wine and camphor (Taiwan Provincial Government, 1971). With regard to production and manufacturing, TTWMB has monopsony (i.e. sole buyer) power over tobacco growers in Taiwan. Inputs into tobacco production such as the land area cultivated and the number of farmers, are regulated by TTWMB through contracts. Only farmers who have contracts with TTWMB can plant tobacco, and all the tobacco output has to be sold to TTWMB at a contracted price. TTWMB is the only firm permitted to manufacture cigarettes in Taiwan, and currently owns and operates four cigarette factories and four tobacco leaf re-drying plants (TTWMB, 1997a).

With regard to cigarette distribution, the monopolistic system imposed two regulations upon Taiwan's cigarette market. First, TTWMB controlled the number of retailers (by licence) and the retail cigarette price. Second, prior to 1987, TTWMB was protected by high tariffs and quotas on imported cigarettes (Chen and Winder, 1990; Chaloupka and Laixuthai, 1996). As a result of this protection, imports comprised less than 2 per cent of total cigarette consumption prior to the opening-up of the market (see Figure 1).

The tobacco industry in Taiwan could therefore be characterised as a domestic-demand industry which was highly protected by the government. The major functions of this industry were to satisfy the domestic demand for cigarettes and to provide a stable source of government revenue. Therefore, in contrast to other export-oriented industries in Taiwan, TTWMB was passive about expanding its oversees markets. Over the past half-century, exported cigarettes have accounted for less than one per cent of TTWMB's total cigarette production, the major export market being airport tax-free shops; of the 19 million cigarettes exported by the TTWMB in 1996, 97 per cent were sold at these stores (TTWMB, 1997a). Monopoly profits continued to play a very important role in government finances, especially in the early post-war years. For example, prior to market liberalisation, monopoly profits accounted for more than 10 per cent of the government's total tax revenue, and about 40-60 per cent of these monopoly profits came from the sale of tobacco (TTWMB, 1997a).

In other major industries in Taiwan, such as textiles, electrical and electronic equipment, however, expansion of the exported market is the engine of growth for firms and ultimately for the whole economy. Under the global trend of free trade, the difference in industrial policy between the tobacco industry and other major exporting industries led to international pressure to change the government's protectionist policy toward the cigarette market. In particular, the limited market access to imported cigarettes resulting from high tariffs and quotas, in combination with the unfavourable balance of trade between the

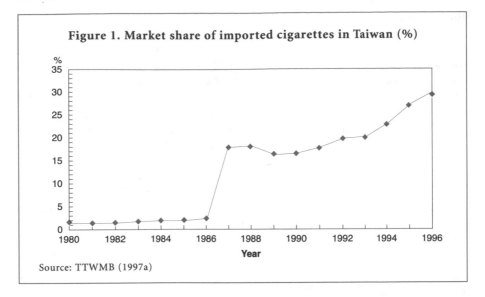

Figure 1. Market share of imported cigarettes in Taiwan (%)

Source: TTWMB (1997a)

United States and Taiwan, caused the US Trade Representative to initiate a Section 301 case against Taiwan in late 1986 (Chaloupka and Laixuthai, 1996). Under the threat of trade sanctions, and in conformity with the international policy trend towards trade liberalisation, Taiwan agreed to open its cigarette market (and its beer and wine markets) to US producers in 1987.

After the cigarette market was opened to imports, the monopolistic system remained unchanged for domestic cigarettes. However, the open policy led to three major changes in the Taiwanese cigarette market:
1. the government now uses an excise tax, set at NT$16.6 per pack since 1987, to replace the monopolistic profit for imported cigarettes;
2. the market share of imported cigarettes has increased rapidly since the cigarette market was opened to imports, from 1.94 per cent in 1986 to 17.71 per cent in 1987, and to about 30 per cent in 1996 (Figure 1);
3. competition was introduced into Taiwan's cigarette market, necessitating advertising for new entrants, and resulting in cigarette advertising and other promotional activities becoming a pervasive phenomenon in Taiwan. The potential impact thereof on cigarette consumption led to widespread public and professional concern, and helped motivate tobacco control measures, as will be discussed below.

The contribution of the tobacco industry to the Taiwanese economy

(i) Government revenue

As mentioned above, the most important contribution of the tobacco industry to the Taiwanese economy has historically been to provide a reliable source of government revenue. Under the monopolistic system, the retail price of cigarettes consists of production costs and monopoly profits (forwarded to the government), the latter comprising normal profit and excess profit. Clearly, the excess profit is an implicit form of indirect tax. However, it is difficult to distinguish normal profit and excess profit from the financial report of the monopoly firm. Using the average return of the Japanese stock market as the normal profit, Chang (1955) estimated that the excess profit rate of the monopoly bureau during the colonial period was in the range of 23-48 per cent. Following a similar method, which uses the average return on total assets for the top 1 000 firms as the normal profit, it is calculated that the excess profit rate of the TTWMB (including tobacco and wine) during 1985-96 was 28-51 per cent (Figure 2). This suggests that the monopoly has been a very effective and reliable source of government revenue.

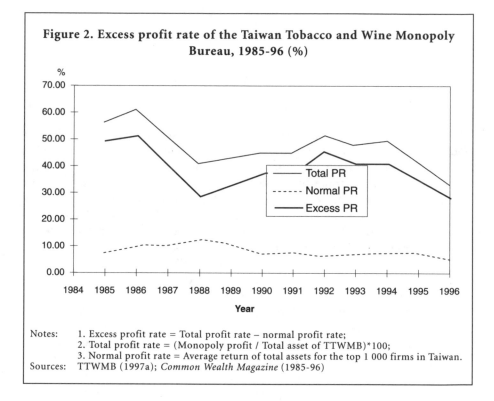

Figure 2. Excess profit rate of the Taiwan Tobacco and Wine Monopoly Bureau, 1985-96 (%)

Notes: 1. Excess profit rate = Total profit rate − normal profit rate;
           2. Total profit rate = (Monopoly profit / Total asset of TTWMB)*100;
           3. Normal profit rate = Average return of total assets for the top 1 000 firms in Taiwan.
Sources: TTWMB (1997a); *Common Wealth Magazine* (1985-96)

Figure 3 shows the historical pattern of monopoly profit from tobacco products as a percentage of total government tax revenue. After World War II, this share declined temporarily and reached a peak percentage of 17.3 per cent again in 1962. Since then, the importance of cigarette monopoly profits has fallen steadily as revenues from other taxes (such as income taxes) have increased as a result of economic growth. While tobacco monopoly profit generally contributed over 10 per cent of total government tax revenues before 1970, in recent years its contribution has been only about 2 per cent of total government tax revenue. For example, total government tax revenue in 1996 was NT$1197 (US$42.75) billion, while the monopoly profit of tobacco the same year was NT$21 (US$0.75) billion (TTWMB, 1997a).

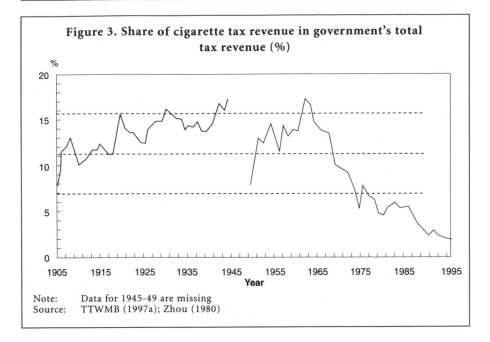

Figure 3. Share of cigarette tax revenue in government's total tax revenue (%)

Note: Data for 1945-49 are missing
Source: TTWMB (1997a); Zhou (1980)

(ii) Employment effects

The second contribution of the tobacco industry to the economy is job creation in both the agricultural and manufacturing sectors. As shown in Figure 4, the number of tobacco farmers grew rapidly in the 1950s and reached a peak in 1969 of 8 954 farm households. Since then, there has been a considerable decrease in the number of tobacco farmers: during 1969-96, the total number of tobacco farmers decreased by 72 per cent, until only 2 543 farm households were growing tobacco in Taiwan. There are two plausible explanations for the decline. First, tobacco growing has become more capital-intensive due to increasing labour costs in Taiwan. This trend in turn has led to an increase in the tobacco-growing area per farmer of about 60 per cent between the early 1950s and 1996. Second, the shrinkage of market share for domestic cigarettes due to trade liberalisation has reduced the demand for tobacco leaves, and hence forced TTWMB to reduce the number of growing contracts with farmers. Consequently, the output of tobacco leaves has decreased by 54 per cent over the past decade (TTWMB, 1997a).

The land area used to grow tobacco shows a similar historical pattern to the number of tobacco farmers (Figure 5). Only about 4 000 hectares of land were used for tobacco production in 1996, representing a 65 per cent decrease since 1969. In addition, the tobacco-growing area as well as the number of tobacco farmers accounts for only a tiny share of total agriculture inputs in Taiwan. The percentage of farmers growing tobacco reached a peak in 1957 of 1.14 per cent, and then declined gradually to 0.33 per cent in 1996. The percentage of agricultural land used to grow tobacco revealed a similar pattern.

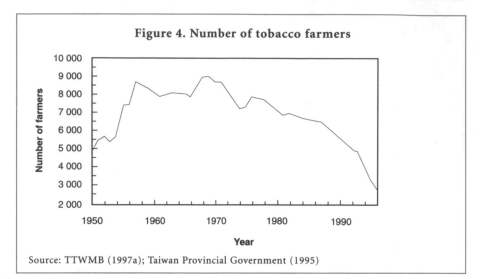

Figure 4. Number of tobacco farmers

Source: TTWMB (1997a); Taiwan Provincial Government (1995)

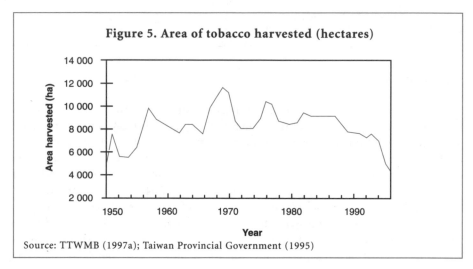

Figure 5. Area of tobacco harvested (hectares)

Source: TTWMB (1997a); Taiwan Provincial Government (1995)

As in agriculture, the number of jobs associated with the manufacturing, distribution and sale of tobacco products is also small, and shows a steadily declining trend. In the 1970s, there were about 4 000 jobs in the tobacco manufacturing sector, representing only about 0.3 per cent of total employment in all manufacturing sectors in Taiwan (TTWMB, 1997a; Directorate-General of Budget, 1996). In recent years, due to the shrinkage of the domestic cigarette market, employment in the tobacco manufacturing industry has declined further to about 2 500, constituting only 0.1 per cent of total manufacturing employment in Taiwan. Hence, compared to its contribution to government revenue, the contribution of the tobacco industry to agricultural and manufacturing employment is small: a total of about 5 000 jobs in 1996, less than 1 per cent of total employment in these two sectors.

(iii) Output effects

The third contribution of the tobacco industry to the economy is its share of output or gross domestic product (GDP). Production of tobacco grew rapidly in the 1950s and reached a peak in 1984 of 26 491 tons, decreasing steadily since then mainly due to the opening-up of the domestic cigarette market (Figure 6). In addition, TTWMB imports foreign tobacco, mainly from the US, to increase the quality of domestic cigarettes: during 1979-96, the average quantity of tobacco imported annually was about 13 000 metric tons (TTWMB, 1997a). (TTWMB also exports small quantities of tobacco leaves to overseas markets.) Consequently, the total amount of tobacco produced in Taiwan decreased to 11 230 metric tons in 1996, about 42 per cent of the production level in 1984.

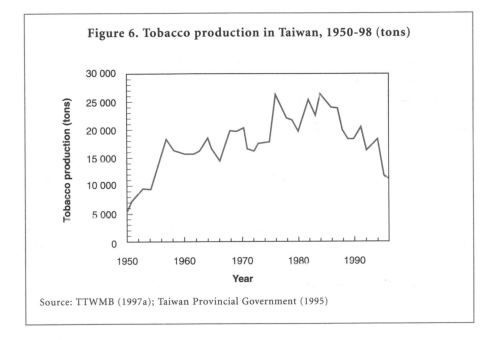

Figure 6. Tobacco production in Taiwan, 1950-98 (tons)

Source: TTWMB (1997a); Taiwan Provincial Government (1995)

A similar trend can be observed for cigarette production, which increased from 1 million cases (500 million packs) during the 1950s to a peak of 3.2 million cases in 1985 (Figure 7). After the market was opened to imports, the production of domestic cigarettes decreased by 13 per cent, from 3.1 million cases in 1986 to 2.7 million cases in 1996.

Since 1950, tobacco production has contributed only about 1.2-2.4 per cent by value of output produced in the agricultural sector. Similarly, the manufacture of cigarettes has contributed about 2 per cent of manufacturing sector GDP during the period 1981-96, while the manufacturing sector as a whole contributed 28 per cent of national GDP in 1996 (Directorate-General of Budget, 1997). Hence, the contribution of the tobacco industry to national output is minor.

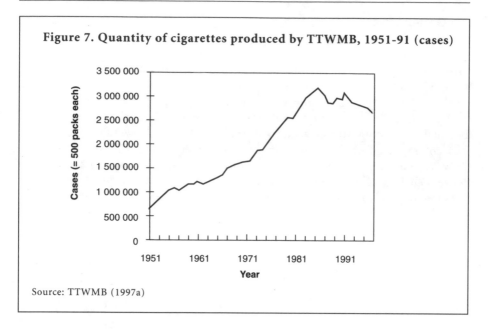

Figure 7. Quantity of cigarettes produced by TTWMB, 1951-91 (cases)

Source: TTWMB (1997a)

Cigarette consumption in Taiwan

This section analyses historical trends in cigarette consumption in Taiwan by examining the following three trends: (1) expenditure on tobacco; (2) cigarette consumption *per capita*; and (3) smoking rates.

The share of tobacco expenditure in total consumption has decreased, from over 3 per cent in 1966 to less than 1 per cent in 1996 (Figure 8). The share of tobacco expenditure in household disposable income reveals a similar pattern.

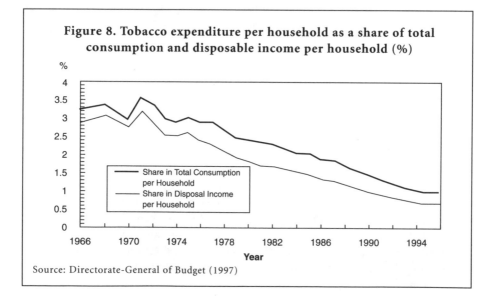

Figure 8. Tobacco expenditure per household as a share of total consumption and disposable income per household (%)

Source: Directorate-General of Budget (1997)

In recent years, annual nominal expenditure on tobacco per household remained almost constant at NT$5 000 (US$178) and was the smallest item of consumption expenditure, except for expenditure on family management (Directorate-General of Budget, 1997). After adjustment for price inflation, however, real expenditure on tobacco has begun to decline in recent years.

Annual cigarette consumption per adult (aged 15 and older) in Taiwan was about 70 packs in 1951, rising rapidly to a peak of 104.5 packs in 1955 before declining slightly to 94 packs in 1962 (Figure 9). Consumption continued to grow thereafter, levelling-off at about 120 packs in 1985, subject to short-term fluctuations. The increase from the mid-1960s to the mid-1980s suggests that the 1964 US Surgeon General's Report on smoking and health did not have any significant influence on Taiwanese consumers. Figure 9 reflects a significant reduction in cigarette consumption in 1986, which was due to an anti-smoking protest against the trade negotiation between the USA and Taiwan. However, this fall vanished immediately upon the opening of the domestic market to imports.

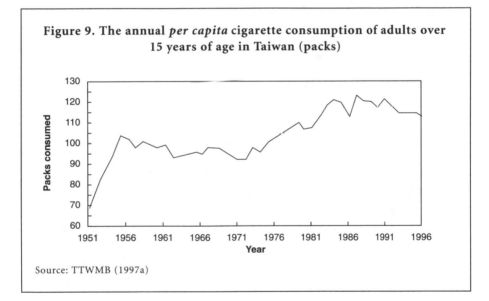

Figure 9. The annual *per capita* cigarette consumption of adults over 15 years of age in Taiwan (packs)

Source: TTWMB (1997a)

In the first year after market liberalisation, adult cigarette consumption increased by nearly 9 per cent, from 114 packs in 1986 to 124 packs in 1987. This significant rise induced the Taiwanese government and many private organisations to introduce measures to discourage cigarette consumption, as is discussed below. Consequently, since 1988 there has been a declining trend in per-adult cigarette consumption in Taiwan, and in 1996 cigarette consumption per adult was 113.2 packs, the lowest since 1986.

Historical trends in smoking prevalence by gender are illustrated in Figure 10. In comparison with other developed countries, there are two distinctive features of smoking in Taiwan. Firstly, there is a very wide gender gap: during the past three decades, smoking prevalence has been estimated at 55-64 per cent of men and only 2-6 per cent of women. This gender gap is very similar in size to that in other Asian nations (Hu, 1997; Mackay, 1995). For the population as a whole, the average smoking rate has been estimated at 28-34 per cent, which is very similar to most developed countries (Townsend, 1987; Viscusi, 1992). Secondly, the smoking participation rate among male adults (age 16 and older) was relatively high during the period 1968-84, and remained almost constant at 60 per cent. Since 1986, the smoking rate of males has declined to about 55 per cent.

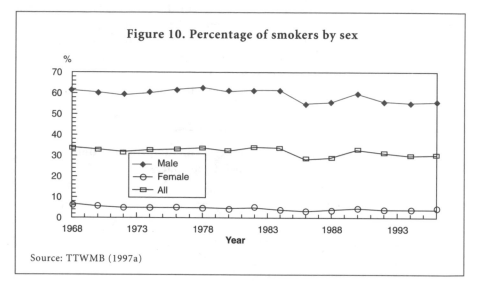

Figure 10. Percentage of smokers by sex

Source: TTWMB (1997a)

The prevalence of smoking is analysed by demographic characteristics in Table 2, using the most recent survey reported by the TTWMB (1997b). Males show an inverse U-shaped relationship between smoking participation and age, with peak rates of smoking (65.1 per cent) observed in the 31-35 age group. For females, the smoking rate increases with age, with a few exceptions. There is also an inverse relationship between education level and smoking rate. The smoking rate of college graduates is about 34 per cent for males and less than 1 per cent for females, which is significantly lower than the smoking rates of individuals with other education levels. This pattern is similar to that observed in other developed countries (Townsend, 1987; Kenkel, 1991). There is also a wide variation of smoking rates between different regions: smoking rates are higher in rural areas than in urban areas for males, but lower for females.

Tobacco control policies in Taiwan

(i) The origins of tobacco control policies

As mentioned above, the cigarette market in Taiwan was controlled by a national monopoly prior to the opening-up of the market in 1987. During the period of monopoly control, competition and advertising were naturally almost

Table 2. Percentage of smokers, by sex, age, educational level and region, 1996			
	Male	*Female*	*Total*
Total	55.11	3.28	29.71
Age:			
18-20	22.81	1.13	12.14
21-25	52.34	2.05	25.55
26-30	62.87	3.43	33.17
31-35	66.50	3.44	37.29
36-40	62.46	4.48	34.10
41-45	57.88	3.37	31.63
46-50	56.01	2.73	29.28
51-55	55.70	3.96	29.17
56-60	56.25	2.53	29.78
61-65	55.85	3.64	30.85
66-70	49.31	3.79	30.04
71+	43.39	5.12	24.75
Education:			
College	33.93	0.73	19.86
Middle School	62.49	3.65	35.52
Primary	58.99	4.08	30.96
Illiterate	52.98	3.66	15.00
Region:			
Urban	49.45	4.39	26.69
Town	57.87	2.46	31.41
Rural	60.49	2.22	32.64

Note: * The smoker is defined as the respondent whose average number of cigarettes smoked per day was greater than three.

Source: TTWMB (1997a)

non-existent, and monopoly profits from tobacco products provided a reliable and significant contribution to government revenue. Consequently, prior to 1987 the Taiwanese government did not take any action to discourage cigarette smoking. The liberalisation of the cigarette market fundamentally changed the government's attitude toward tobacco control policies, for three main reasons.

Firstly, the liberalisation of cigarette imports introduced competition into the market, prompting an increase in cigarette advertising by new entrants and a fall in prices resulting from competitive marketing (and also tariff reduction), which in turn resulted in increased cigarette consumption. Given the adverse consequences of cigarette consumption on health, this naturally led to widespread concern, and in response the government began to implement tobacco control polices.

Secondly, the Taiwanese government lifted martial law in 1987 and instituted other political reforms which democratised the legislative process (Chiang, 1997). As a result, a more active role in government decision-making was played by public interest groups such as the Tung's Foundation, active since 1984 in promoting a smoke-free society. The Tung's Foundation and other public interest groups organised many street protests to oppose the opening of the cigarette market during the trade negotiation between Taiwan and the US, and also lobbied the government to implement anti-smoking measures.

Thirdly, as discussed above and illustrated in Figure 3, the contributions of monopoly profit from tobacco products to government revenue had significantly declined. Thus, the fiscal benefit that the government would have to sacrifice if tobacco control policies were introduced was no longer very high.

There is other evidence that liberalisation of the cigarette market transformed the government's policy stance towards smoking. Firstly, no government agency in Taiwan had previously enjoyed any specific budget allocation to finance an anti-smoking programme. In 1987, however, the Department of Health received its first annual budget allocation for this purpose; the amount was initially only NT$1 million (about US$35 000), but has increased to more than NT$10 million since 1991 (Figure 11). Secondly, Taiwan began requiring warning messages in all cigarette advertising and on every cigarette pack in 1987. This requirement was one of the conditions reached in the agreement with the US on the opening-up of its cigarette market (Chaloupka and Laixuthai, 1996).

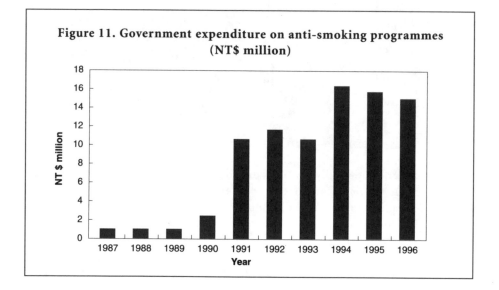

Figure 11. Government expenditure on anti-smoking programmes (NT$ million)

(ii) The evolution of tobacco control policies

Information provision

During the past decade, information about the health hazards of smoking has been communicated to individuals in Taiwan through three main channels: (1) warning labels placed on cigarette packages and advertising; (2) anti-smoking media campaigns; and (3) school education.

As mentioned above, Taiwan has required warning messages in all cigarette advertising and on every pack of cigarettes since 1987. During 1987-91, the message on the health warning label was that "excessive smoking is dangerous to health". The government further strengthened the messages on warning labels in 1992. The current warning messages include six categories that communicate more certain information about the smoking hazards to the public than the message of the early period (see Table 3).

With regard to anti-smoking media campaigns, the efforts of the Department of Health can be measured by the annual expenditure on its anti-smoking programme. Up to the end of 1996, the Department of Health in Taiwan spent a total of NT$86.3 million on anti-smoking campaigns. This includes the net costs of buying television and radio time, printing anti-smoking brochures, providing educational programmes in schools, and sponsoring anti-smoking activities. Many private organisations in Taiwan have also made significant contributions to anti-smoking information campaigns. A leading example is the Tung's Foundation, which during the past decade has sponsored many activities to educate the public about the hazards of smoking, and to promote anti-smoking legislation to restrict smoking in public places.

Regulation

In addition to information provision, since 1987 the government has used regulation to control cigarette smoking. Initially, the major regulation was restriction of cigarette advertising, which was one of the clauses of the trade agreement between Taiwan and the United States. The government banned all cigarette advertising on the radio, television and in newspaper media, but each cigarette manufacturer was allowed 120 magazine advertisements annually. Since then, however, no legislation has been passed that restricts smoking in public places and reduces the access of youth to tobacco. In response to the lack of a comprehensive anti-smoking law, the Tung's Foundation and many other public interest groups have intensively promoted the concept of restricting cigarette smoking in public places. They have also lobbied the Department of Health to enact an anti-smoking law. Through the efforts of such groups, many public places have begun to impose a no-smoking policy, for example in hospitals, theatres, and department stores, and on aeroplane flights, buses, and trains. In addition, the government agreed to enact the Smoking-Hazards Prevention Act (SHPA) and sent the clauses of the draft SHPA to the Legislative Yuan in 1991.

The major clauses of SHPA focus on three areas: (1) restriction of smoking in public places; (2) a ban on all forms of cigarette advertising; (3) reduction of youth access to tobacco. After the passage of SHPA through the executive, interest groups took many actions to lobby the legislators to pass the bill. At the same time, the Tobacco Institute of the Republic of China (TIROC), representing multinational cigarette manufacturers, opposed SHPA through political and media lobbying. TIROC was particularly opposed to the clause banning all forms of cigarette advertising. After a six-year period of lobbying

Table 3. Major components of anti-smoking legislation in Taiwan

Items	Description
Information Provision:	
Warning label (7)	The outside of the cigarette package should list a warning label in Chinese (*The current contents of this label include the following six categories:* (1) *Smoking is harmful to health;* (2) *Smoking is causally related to cancers;* (3) *Smoking is causally related to lung cancer, cardiovascular disease and emphysema;* (4) *Smoking by pregnant women may result in premature births and low birth weight;* (5) *Smoking is harmful to you and to others;* (6) *Quitting smoking now greatly reduces serious risk to your health.*)
Tar and nicotine (8)	The amount of tar and nicotine in each cigarette should be listed in each cigarette package. The amount of tar and nicotine should not exceed the maximum amount permitted by the government.
Education (17-19)	Each school and institute should provide educational programmes to prevent smoking hazards. It should not emphasise the image of smokers in TV programmes, shows, concerts, and sports events.
Regulation:	
Selling channels (5)	Cigarettes should not be sold through the vending machine, mail order, electronic purchasing, and other channels that cannot identify the buyer's age.
Minimum smoking age (11-12)	Smoking is prohibited for individuals below age 18. The owner of a cigarette store or clerk should not sell cigarettes to individuals below age 18.
Restriction on cigarette advertising (9)	The following ways are prohibited for cigarette promotion or cigarette advertising: (1) broadcasting, T.V., movies, video, newspaper, billboard, post, brochures, sample, exhibition; (2) price discount; (3) free gift whose value is greater than 25% of the cigarette price; (4) using cigarettes as a gift to promote other goods; (5) packing cigarettes and other goods together for sale; (6) free cigarette sample; (7) sponsoring sports events, art, and other activities using the name of cigarette brands. Cigarette advertising in magazines is limited to 120 advertisements per cigarette manufacture per year. The magazine advertising should not target a magazine whose major readers are youths below age 18. Cigarette manufacturers, importers or sellers could use the company name to sponsor activities, but the promotion and sale of cigarettes are not permitted in these activities.

Note: Values in parentheses are the clause numbers in the Smoking-Hazards Prevention Act.

and debate, the Legislative Yuan finally passed the SHPA, the first anti-smoking law in Taiwan, on March 4, 1997; it became effective on September 19, 1997. Although compromise clauses still permit cigarette advertising in magazines, the SHPA is the greatest achievement of the anti-smoking campaign in Taiwan since 1987.

The SHPA offers comprehensive legislation to control cigarette smoking and to provide the public with information and education on the harmful effects of smoking. In addition to the mandatory warning label mentioned above, the SHPA requires that all tobacco packages should disclose the tar and nicotine content. Furthermore, the SHPA requires that each school and institution provide educational programmes on smoking. With regard to reducing youth access to tobacco, the SHPA has two regulations: (1) a prohibition on cigarette selling by vending machine, mail order, electronic purchasing, and other ways that cannot identify the buyer's age; (2) the minimum smoking age is set at 18, and stores are not allowed to sell cigarettes to individuals below this age.

With regard to restriction of smoking in public places, the SHPA lists over 30 places in which smoking is completely prohibited, such as on aeroplanes, buses, and trains, and another 23 places where smoking is permitted only in designated smoking areas, such as airports, theatres, and department stores. However, the SHPA does not restrict smoking in private worksites. Finally, the plan to ban all forms of cigarette advertising did not survive the legislation process completely intact. Cigarette advertising and promotion are permitted in three ways: (1) magazine advertisements; (2) a free gift with purchase; and (3) using the cigarette manufacturer's name instead of the brand's name to sponsor activities. Magazine advertising is a compromise within the current status of cigarette advertising, as is the allowance of indirect advertising via sponsorship in the names of cigarette manufacturers rather than cigarette brands. In the case of free gift promotions, the value of the gift is limited to less than one quarter of the cigarette price.

Cigarette taxes

While the SHPA represents major progress in anti-smoking legislation, government has not attempted to use cigarette tax to discourage consumption. The excise tax on imported cigarettes has remained constant at NT$16.6 (US$0.63) per pack since 1987 (Table 4). The monopoly profit from selling domestic cigarettes can be treated as an implicit form of tax: dividing this by total cigarette sales indicates the implicit tax on domestic cigarettes. This was NT$11.2 (US$0.43) per pack in 1994, while the average price of domestic cigarettes was NT$23.4 (US$0.89) per pack, significantly lower than imported cigarettes.

Using data on the amount of tax imposed on cigarettes and their average retail price, the tax rate on cigarettes in Taiwan can be calculated. As shown in Table 4, the tax rate on imported cigarettes was 38 per cent and the average tax rate of all cigarettes was 45 per cent in 1994, which is significantly lower than those imposed by developed countries, except the US. For example, in 1994 tax

Table 4. Average retail cigarette price and total taxes per pack in Taiwan and other countries, 1994

Country	Total taxes (US$)	Average retail price (US$)	Tax as % retail price
Taiwan:[1,2]			
Imported	0.63	1.65	38
Domestic	0.43	0.89	48
Average	0.48	1.06	45
Other Countries:[3]			
Denmark	3.63	4.33	84
Norway	3.20	4.68	68
United Kingdom	2.88	3.77	76
Ireland	2.78	3.67	76
Sweden	2.63	3.59	73
Finland	2.39	3.23	74
Germany	2.13	3.00	71
France	2.04	2.71	75
Belgium	2.00	2.67	75
New Zealand	2.00	2.95	68
Canada	1.96	3.05	64
Netherlands	1.69	2.34	72
Australia	1.55	2.59	60
Hong Kong	1.50	2.78	54
Greece	1.42	1.97	72
Luxembourg	1.36	1.97	69
Italy	1.28	1.75	73
Japan	1.25	2.09	60
Portugal	1.22	1.51	81
Switzerland	1.09	2.19	50
Argentina	0.96	1.37	70
United States	0.56	1.89	30
Spain	0.56	0.80	70
Korea	0.45	0.74	60

Sources: 1: TTWMB (1997a); 2: TIROC, unpublished data; 3: Non-Smokers' Rights Association (1996).

rates were 84 per cent for Denmark, 76 per cent for the United Kingdom, 64 per cent for Canada, and 60 per cent for Japan.

There are three major reasons why the Taiwanese government has not increased cigarette taxes during the past decade in order to decrease tobacco consumption. Firstly, the current tax rate on imported cigarettes was determined by the trade agreement between Taiwan and the United States in 1987. Thus, changing the tax rate on imported cigarettes is not a simple issue of domestic policy, but also an issue of bilateral trade negotiation. Secondly, during the past decade, Taiwan undertook drastic political reform and holds frequent democratic elections; raising cigarette taxes is not (yet) helpful in winning elections. Finally, the government of Taiwan faces an internal conflict between different sectors. Although the Department of Health has supported the increasing of cigarette taxes, the Department of Public Finance has often opposed this, because it was concerned about losing further government revenue obtained from the monopoly profits on tobacco products. As a result, increasing cigarette taxes has become a sensitive political and economic issue in Taiwan, and many difficulties need to be overcome before cigarette tax can be used as a tool of tobacco control policies.

(iii) The impact of tobacco control policies

Effects of information provision

The purpose of the information provision policy is to educate the public about the potential hazards of cigarette smoking. The effect of this policy can therefore be evaluated by examining its effect on consumers' awareness of the hazards of smoking. A recent study by Hsieh *et al.* (1996) showed that many anti-smoking activities in Taiwan have helped people to learn more about smoking hazards. (The surveyed variable 'health knowledge' was measured as the sum of respondents' answers to ten multiple-choice questions about the health hazards of smoking, assigning a value of one if the answer was correct and a value of zero if the answer was incorrect or unknown.) For example, after controlling for the effects of other variables, the average health awareness of respondents who had seen anti smoking advertising in the mass media during the previous three months was about 20 per cent higher than those who had not. Similarly, the average health awareness was 14 per cent higher for people who had received anti-smoking messages as a result of legislation campaigns.

Although the above results suggest that the recent anti-smoking campaigns in Taiwan have had a significant positive effect on the public's health knowledge on average, health awareness is not uniform among individuals. Hsieh *et al.* (1996) found that the youth (ages 18 to 22) have more health awareness than other age groups. Health knowledge also correlates positively with level of education. These distribution patterns of health knowledge are consistent with consumer perception of smoking risks in Taiwan (Liu and Hsieh, 1995), suggesting that youth and educated people are more likely to absorb information from anti-smoking campaigns.

Effects of regulation

In recent years, the effectiveness of anti-smoking regulations, such as restricting smoking in public places and the limits on youth access to tobacco, has been widely recognised in the empirical literature. For example, Wasserman *et al.* (1991) found that regulations restricting smoking in public places have a significantly negative effect on cigarette consumption among both adults and teenagers. Chaloupka and Wechsler (1997) also found that relatively strong restrictions on smoking in public places significantly reduce the smoking rates of college students. The existing empirical evidence on limiting youth access to tobacco suggests that the effectiveness of this policy depends on whether the legislation is actively enforced (Chaloupka *et al.*, 1998).

In the case of Taiwan, legislation (in the form of the SHPA) to restrict smoking in public places and reduce youth access to tobacco became effective only in September 1997. Thus, empirical evidence on its effectiveness is still not available. However, a national survey conducted in early 1993 (Hsieh *et al.*, 1996) suggested that 89 per cent of respondents agreed with the government's effort to restrict smoking in public places. Respondents who supported restrictions on smoking in public places tended to have above-average health knowledge. In addition, it was found that restrictions on smoking in the workplace discouraged respondents from smoking, but the effect was not statistically significant.

Impact on smoking rate

Hsieh *et al.* (1996) found that the increase in health knowledge in turn significantly decreased the smoking rate. It was estimated that a 10 per cent increase in health knowledge will reduce the smoking rate by 4.8 per cent for all adults and 5.6 per cent for males. Similarly, Liu and Hsieh (1995) found that risk perceptions of cigarette smoking have a significantly negative effect on smoking probability. These results suggest that providing the public with information and education on the harmful effects of cigarette smoking have been effective in decreasing the smoking rate in Taiwan over the past decade.

The magnitude of the decline in the overall smoking rate is nevertheless small. As shown in Figure 10, the smoking rate for males has decreased from 60 per cent to 55 per cent over the past decade. For the whole population, the average smoking rate has decreased only about 3 percentage points (from 32 per cent to 29 per cent). This result, in combination with the finding that health knowledge is not uniform among individuals, implies that the effects of tobacco control policies on smoking rates are not uniform for different population groups. Since individuals with a higher education have more knowledge about smoking hazards, it can be expected that tobacco control policies will be more effective among more educated people (Liu and Hsieh, 1995; Hsieh, *et al.* 1996). Figure 12 provides preliminary evidence to support this argument. Firstly, a declining trend in smoking among individuals with college degrees is observable since 1990. However, the smoking rate has increased in recent years for individuals with high school diplomas. Secondly, for both male and females, differences in smoking rates between different education groups have enlarged during the past decade. This suggests that tobacco control initiatives in Taiwan have led to only a moderate reduction in the smoking rate, the bulk of this impact being felt among higher-educated people, with limited impact on the less well-educated.

The impact on cigarette consumption

As shown in Figure 9, there has been a declining trend in *per capita* cigarette consumption in Taiwan since 1988. Two items of evidences support the

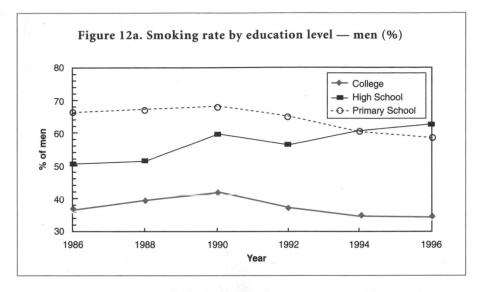

Figure 12a. Smoking rate by education level — men (%)

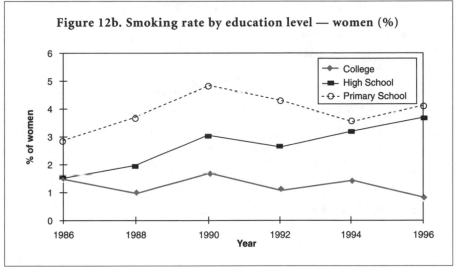

Figure 12b. Smoking rate by education level — women (%)

argument that this decline can be attributed to the anti-smoking efforts of the government and many public interest groups in Taiwan.

Firstly, the impact of cigarette imports on cigarette consumption is disaggregated into two effects: a switching effect and a market expansion effect. The former indicates that cigarette imports induce smokers to switch to imported cigarettes. The latter one indicates the effect of cigarette imports on overall cigarette consumption. As shown in Table 5, *per capita* cigarette consumption was 114 packs in 1986. Of these, 2.2 packs were imported cigarettes and 111.8 packs were domestic cigarettes. In 1987, the first year of trade liberalisation for tobacco, the *per capita* consumption of imported cigarettes increased to 21.91 packs. The increment of 19.69 packs came from two sources: a switch of 10 packs from domestic to imported cigarettes, and a 9.66-pack increase in total cigarette consumption. This suggests that the opening of the cigarette market in Taiwan not only induced smokers to switch to imported cigarettes, but also increased overall cigarette consumption. Although *per capita* consumption of imported cigarettes has continued to grow since 1987, the source of growth has gradually shifted to the switching effect (see Table 5). In 1996, the market expansion effect became negative, i.e. *per capita* cigarette consumption in 1996 was less than in 1986. This result suggests that Taiwan has completely offset the impact of market opening on overall cigarette consumption through tobacco control policies.

Table 5. The annual *per capita* cigarette consumption of adults over 15 years of age in Taiwan (number of packs)

Year				Impact of Opening Market		
	Imported cigs (q_I)	Domestic cigs (q_D)	All cigs[1] (Q)	Total effect[4] (Δq_I)	Switching effect[2] (Δq_D)	Expansion effect[3] (ΔQ)
Pre Opening:						
1986	2.22	111.80	114.02	—	—	—
Post Opening:						
1987	21.91	101.77	123.68	19.69	10.03	9.66
1992	22.83	95.31	118.14	20.61	16.49	4.12
1996	33.29	79.87	113.16	31.07	31.93	-0.86

Notes: 1. $Q = q_D + q_I$.
        2. Switching effect $= \Delta q_D = q_D|_{postopening} - q_D|_{preopening}$.
        3. Expansion effect $= \Delta Q = Q|_{postopening} - Q|_{preopening}$.
        4. Total effect $= \Delta q_I = q_I|_{postopening} - q_I|_{preopening}$.
Sources: TTWMB (1997a)

Secondly, an empirical study by Hsieh, Hu and Lin (1997) also provides indirect evidence that anti-smoking campaigns have a significant and negative effect on total *per capita* cigarette consumption in Taiwan. Following the approach used in Schneider, Klein and Murphy (1981), Hsieh, Hu and Lin (1997) used the market share of low-tar brands for domestic cigarettes to measure the spread of anti-smoking information in Taiwan and then estimate the demand for cigarettes in Taiwan based on annual time-series data from 1966 to 1995. After accounting for the prices of cigarettes and income, the empirical result indicated that a 10 per cent increase in the market share of low-tar cigarettes would lead to a 0.5 per cent reduction in total cigarette consumption. Schneider, Klein and Murphy (1981) point out that the switch to low-tar cigarettes is a market response to the spread of anti-smoking information. Therefore, the above empirical results provide further evidence to support the effectiveness of tobacco control policies in discouraging cigarette consumption.

Simulation effects of cigarette taxes

Although the government in Taiwan has not increased cigarette taxes over the past decade, the effects of such an increase can be simulated using existing estimates of price elasticities. Hsieh, Hu and Lin (1997) found that cigarette smoking in Taiwan is responsive to price, with short-term price elasticity ranging from -0.6 to -0.7. According to this estimate, a 10 per cent increase in the price of cigarettes would lead to a 6-7 per cent reduction in cigarette consumption. This suggests that cigarette taxes can be used as a policy tool to decrease cigarette consumption.

Table 6. Simulation effects of increasing cigarette excise taxes

	Before increase (1995)	After increase $\varepsilon = -0.6$	After increase $\varepsilon = -0.7$
Average taxes per pack (NT$)	12.30	15.18	15.18
Average retail price (NT$)	28.80	31.68	31.68
Total cigarette consumption (million packs)	1 881	1 768	1 749
Per-adult cigarette consumption (packs)	115.81	108.86	107.70
Decrement in total consumption (millions packs)	-	113	132
Decrement in per-adult consumption (packs)	-	6.95	8.11
Cigarette tax revenue (NT$ million)	23 136	26 839	26 553
Increment in tax revenue (NT$ million)	-	3 703	3 417
Increment in tax revenue (%)	-	16.00	14.77

Notes: ε =price elasticity; US$ 1 = NT$ 27.27 in December 1995.
Sources: TTWMB (1997a)

Using the 1995 data as a comparison base, Table 6 reports the simulation effects of increasing cigarette excise taxes in Taiwan. The average cigarette tax per pack was NT$12.30 in 1995; if this is increased by NT$2.88 per pack, and it is assumed that the tax increment will be completely born by the consumers, there will be a ten per cent increase in cigarette price from NT$28.80 per pack to NT$31.68 per pack. In this case, annual sales of cigarettes in Taiwan would be reduced by 113-132 million packs (or 6.95-8.11 packs per adult), depending on the specification of price elasticities, while government revenue would increase by NT$3.4-3.7 billion. These results suggest that raising cigarette taxes could be an effective policy to reduce cigarette consumption in Taiwan, while still being financially beneficial to the government.

Conclusion: policy implications

Over the past decade, Taiwan has made major progress in tobacco control through regulation and providing the public with information on the harmful effects of cigarette smoking. Anti-smoking information campaigns in Taiwan by government and public interest groups have significantly decreased smoking rates, but this impact has occurred largely among more well-educated people. The overall decline in cigarette smoking has therefore been small over the past decade, but tobacco control measures have nevertheless completely offset the impact of the opening of the domestic cigarette market to imports in 1987.

Nonetheless, it is clear that tobacco control is still in a critical phase in Taiwan. In addition, the positive impact achieved by tobacco control measures in Taiwan came mainly from information provision. The potential effectiveness of other measures, such as imposing regulation and raising cigarette taxes, should be taken into account in the decision of tobacco control strategies.

As mentioned, the passage of anti-smoking legislation (the SHPA) in 1997 is regarded as the greatest achievement of tobacco control efforts in Taiwan since 1987. It is still too early to examine the effectiveness of SHPA. However, the international experience suggests that the effectiveness of the regulatory measures adopted in the SHPA (such as limiting youth access to tobacco) depends on enforcement: poor enforcement of the law will render the legislation ineffective. Thus, an important challenge of future tobacco control work in Taiwan is to ensure better enforcement of the SHPA.

In addition, the government in Taiwan can consider increasing cigarette taxes, which would reduce cigarette consumption while increasing government revenue. The major barrier to this move is political concern instead of economic consideration, but a possible strategy to gain political support for this would to impose a supplemental tax on cigarettes to finance health care expenditure and other health promotion programmes, including anti-smoking information campaigns. The earmarking of cigarette taxes has become popular in many countries and states in recent years (Hu, 1997), as is discussed in Chapter 9.

An important implication of this analysis is that a policy on tobacco control should be adopted in conjunction with policy on trade liberalisation. The empirical evidence in Taiwan shows that opening a cigarette market will lead to an increase in overall cigarette consumption (see also Chapter 22 for comparison with the liberalisation of the Polish cigarette market). Cigarette imports are, however, not simply an issue of trade liberalisation, but also an issue of health. In order to offset the market expansion effect resulting from trade liberalisation, the government of the home country should be active in adopting tobacco control policies. The experience of Taiwan, as described in this paper, provides a good example to other Asian countries of the offsetting of the impact of cigarette imports, especially for those countries who are currently under pressure to open their cigarette markets.

References

Chaloupka, F.J. and A. Laixuthai (1996), *US Trade Policy and Cigarette Smoking in Asia*, NBER Working Paper No. 5543, Cambridge, Mass: National Bureau of Economic Research.

Chaloupka, F.J. and H. Wechsler (1997), "Price, tobacco control policies and smoking among young adults", *Journal of Health Economics*, 16:359-373.

Chaloupka, F.J., R.L. Pacula, M. Grossman and J.A. Gardiner (1998), "Limiting youth access to tobacco: the early impact of the Synar Amendment on youth smoking", paper presented to the *Third Biennial Pacific Rim Allied Economic Organization Conference*, 14 January, Bangkok.

Chang, H. (1955), "The transition of the Taiwanese economy in the colonial period", in Bank of Taiwan (eds.), *Economic History of Taiwan*, Vol. 2, (in Chinese), Taipei: Bank of Taiwan.

Chang, H. and R.H. Myers (1963), "Japanese colonial development policy in Taiwan, 1985-1906: a case of bureaucratic entrepreneurship", *Journal of Asian Studies*, 22(4):433-449.

Chen, T.T.L. and A.E. Winder (1990), "The opium wars revisited as US forces tobacco exports on Asia", *American Journal of Public Health*, 80:659-662.

Chiang, T. (1997), "Taiwan's 1995 health care reform", *Health Policy*, 39:225-239.

Directorate-General of Budget, Accounting and Statistics (1996), *Yearbook of Manpower Survey Statistics in Taiwan Area*, (in Chinese), Taipei: DGBAS.

Directorate-General of Budget, Accounting and Statistics (1997), *National Income in Taiwan*, (in Chinese), Taipei: DGBAS.

Ho, S.P.S. (1971), "The development policy of the Japanese colonial government in Taiwan, 1895-1945", in Rains, G. (ed.), *Government and Economic Development*, New Haven: Yale University Press.

Hsieh, C., L. Yen, J. Liu and C.J. Lin (1996), "Smoking, health knowledge, and anti-smoking campaigns: an empirical study in Taiwan", *Journal of Health Economics*, 15:87-104.

Hsieh, C., T. Hu and C.J. Lin (1997), "The demand for cigarettes in Taiwan: domestic versus imported cigarettes", paper presented at the *72nd Annual Conference of the Western Economic Association*, 9-13 July, Seattle.

Hu, T. (1997), "Cigarette taxation in China: lessons from international experiences", *Tobacco Control*, 6:136-140.

Kenkel, D.S. (1991), "Health behavior, health knowledge, and schooling", *Journal of Political Economy*, 99:287-305.

Liu, J. and C. Hsieh (1995), "Risk perception and smoking behavior: empirical evidence from Taiwan", *Journal of Risk and Uncertainty*, 11:139-157.

Mackay, J. (1995), "Transitional tobacco companies vs. state monopolies in Asia", in Slama, K. (ed.), *Tobacco and Health: Proceedings of the Ninth World Conference on Tobacco and Health*, New York: Plenum Press.

Schneider, L., B. Klein and K.M. Murphy (1981), "Governmental regulation of cigarette health information", *Journal of Law and Economics*, 24:575-612.

Taiwan Provincial Government (1971), *Taiwan Province Statistical Summary* (in Chinese), Taichung: Taiwan Provincial Government.

Taiwan Tobacco and Wine Monopoly Bureau (TTWMB) (1997a), *Taiwan Tobacco and Wine Statistical Yearbook* (in Chinese), Taipei: TTWMB.

Taiwan Tobacco and Wine Monopoly Bureau (TTWMB) (1997b), *The General Survey on the Consumption of Tobacco and Wine in Taiwan* (in Chinese), Taipei: TTWMB.

Townsend, J.L. (1987), "Cigarette tax, economic welfare and social class patterns of smoking", *Applied Economics*, 19(3):355-365.

Viscusi, W.K. (1992), *Smoking: Making the Risky Decision*, New York: Oxford University Press.

Wasserman, J., W.G. Manning, J.P. Newhouse and J.D. Winkler (1991), "The effects of excise taxes and regulations on cigarette smoking", *Journal of Health Economics*, 10:43-64.

Zhou, X. (1980), *Economic History of Taiwan* (in Chinese), Taipei: Kai-Ming Publishing.

Chapter 25

The Economics of Tobacco Control in Japan

Toshitaka Nakahara and Yumiko Mochizuki

The economic impact of tobacco and tobacco-related diseases is one of the most important issues of tobacco control. This chapter estimates social costs of smoking in Japan from a medico-economic viewpoint, and tries to assess the magnitude of economic burden derived from smoking as a step for promotion of anti-smoking activities.

Methods and results

(i) Presupposition

Firstly, it is necessary to define the composition of social costs, and then to try to calculate economic costs for each item. In these calculations, items for which statistical data were not available have been excluded. As regards the effects of passive smoking, the method reported by the US Environmental Protection Agency (1992) was used, because the necessary epidemiological data relating to passive smoking in Japan are not available. This analysis deals with lung cancer only. For these reasons, this study should be regarded as an attempt to estimate the "minimum" social costs of smoking; the actual magnitude of the social costs incurred is greater than this calculation.

The estimation was made for the year 1993. Costs due to tobacco-related diseases were calculated by assuming that the time lag from the beginning of smoking to the onset of the diseases is 25 years. Smoking was started in 1968 at the age of 20 years or more. The mortality and morbidity of smokers were evaluated in those aged 45 years or above in 1993. The smoking rate in 1968 was assumed to be about 50 per cent, being the mean prevalence of males and females combined, on the basis of the data of Japan Tobacco Incorporated (Ministry of Health and Welfare (Japan), 1993).

(ii) Social costs

Table 1 details the composition of the social costs of smoking. Due to lack of data, only the social costs marked in this table could be calculated.

(iii) Calculation of social costs

Increased medical expenditure from tobacco-related diseases

In Japan, data are available from Dr Hirayama's epidemiological study of the

Table 1. Composition of social costs of smoking

Items			Calcu-lated?
Health:	Excess morbidity:	Increased medical expenditure	Yes
		Economic losses: Hospitalisation	Yes
		Hospital visits	
		Unemployment	
		Care by the family	
		Others	
	Excess mortality:	Economic losses	Yes
	Others:	Purchases of OTC drugs, etc.	
		Screening and examinations	
		Research and education	
Environment:		Loss of property due to fire	Yes
	Deaths (burned)		Yes
	Injuries (burns)		Yes
	Others		
	Cleaning		
Others:	Loss of labour time spent smoking		
	Premium*		
	Cost for purchases of tobacco*		

Note: * These are not social costs

health hazards of smoking (Hirayama, 1990). It was a population-based cohort study on the relationship between life-style and cancer during the period 1966-82. A "disease" is regarded as tobacco-related if the 90 per cent confidence interval of the sex- and age-adjusted relative risk of death due to the disease in relation to smoking was 1 or greater. Tobacco-related diseases were classified into those listed in Table 2, in compliance with Japanese Vital Statistics classifications. As mentioned above, in the case of passive smoking only lung cancer was considered.

Data on medical expenditure in Japan is available from the *National Medical Expenditure* reports issued by the Ministry of Health and Welfare (Japan) (1994c). The increase in medical expenditure associated with tobacco use was calculated by multiplying the expenditure on treatment of each tobacco-related disease by the contributory risk involved. The contributory risk of death calculated by Dr Hirayama was used instead of the excess morbidity rate of each tobacco-related disease because of the unavailability of the required data. The results are ¥1 151 billion for active smoking, and ¥11 billion for passive smoking.

Costs due to hospitalisation from tobacco-related diseases

Since the objective of this study was to estimate social costs, costs due to hospitalisation were calculated by multiplying the *per capita* national income

Table 2. Calculation Procedure

1. *Increased medical expenditure from tobacco-related diseases:*
   Calculation: (medical expenditure for each tobacco-related disease × excess morbidity rate of each tobacco-related disease)
   - Tobacco-related diseases: malignant neoplasms, hypertensive diseases, ischemic heart diseases, cerebrovascular diseases, respiratory diseases, gastric and duodenal ulcers, liver diseases (based on Hirayama, 1990)
   - Excess morbidity rate: substituted by contributory risk of death calculated by Hirayama (1990) (because of data limitations)

2. *Costs due to hospitalisation from tobacco-related diseases:*
   Calculation: (per capita national income per day × number of days of hospitalisation from each tobacco-related disease × excess morbidity rate)
   - Number of days of hospitalisation: based on Patients Survey (Ministry of Health and Welfare (Japan), 1994a)

3. *Costs due to excess deaths from tobacco-related diseases:*
   Calculation: (per capita national income per year × "mean number of years lost from the life span" × excess number of deaths)
   - Excess number of deaths: (number of deaths from each tobacco-related disease × contributory risk of each disease)
   - Number of deaths from each tobacco-related disease: based on vital statistics (Ministry of Health and Welfare (Japan), 1994b)
   - "Mean number of years lost from the life span": 12 years (theoretically calculated by Peto *et al.*, 1994)

4. *Costs due to fire caused by smoking:*
   - Based on the data in the *White Paper on Fire Fighting* (Ministry of Home Affairs (Japan), 1995)

per day by the number of days of hospitalisation due to each tobacco-related disease. The total number of days of hospitalisation for each tobacco-related disease was calculated by multiplying the mean number of days of hospitalisation in the Patients Survey of the Ministry of Health and Welfare (1994a) by the contributory risk. The results are ¥27 billion for active smoking, and ¥0.3 billion for passive smoking.

Costs due to excess deaths from tobacco-related diseases

The excess number of deaths due to smoking can be calculated by multiplying the number of deaths due to each tobacco-related disease by the contributory risk of each disease. As there are various theories for calculation of the economic costs associated with these deaths, national *per capita* income was used. The economic value of the social loss of excess deaths due to tobacco-related diseases per person was represented as the *per capita* national income multiplied by the mean number of lifespan years lost. The mean number of years of lifespan lost was estimated for developed countries by Peto *et al.*

(1998), and is 12 years for Japan. The results are ¥2 590 billion for active smoking, and ¥60 billion for passive smoking.

Costs due to fire caused by smoking

The social costs of deaths, injuries and property loss due to fire caused by smoking was calculated from data presented in the Japanese White Paper on Fire Fighting (Ministry of Home Affairs (Japan), 1995). The results are ¥23 billion in total.

The total sum of social costs

Table 3 aggregates the estimated costs of the items listed above. The estimated total social cost of active smoking is at least ¥3 791 billion, and the total social cost of passive smoking is at least ¥71 billion.

Table 3. Estimated social costs of active and passive smoking in Japan, 1993 (¥ billion)

Area	Items	Active	Passive
Health:	Increase in medical expenditure	1 151.2	10.5
	Loss due to excess hospitalisation	26.5	0.3
	Loss due to excess deaths	2 590.4	60.3
Environment:	Loss of properties from fire*	15.1	-
	Loss due to deaths from fire*	7.8	-
	Loss due to injuries from fire*	0.2	-
Total:		3 791.2	71.1
National medical expenditure (1993)		24 363.1	24 363.1
Social costs of smoking as % of medical expenditure		15.6%	0.03%

Note: *Fire caused from smoking

For purposes of comparison, total medical expenditure in Japan in 1993 was about ¥24 trillion, and the social cost of smoking was about 5 per cent of national medical expenditure. Total revenue from taxes on tobacco was ¥374 billion in the same year, or at most about 10 per cent of the social costs of smoking. These figures are naturally most noteworthy from the point of view of the Japanese macro-economy, and its public finances.

Tobacco control policy in Japan

In recent years a declining trend in smoking prevalence among Japanese men has been observed, but this prevalence nevertheless remains quite high. In the case of Japanese women, especially young women, an increasing trend in the prevalence of smoking has been noted. Tobacco control is thus one of the most important public health issues in Japan. However, most people in Japan perceive that the Japanese government is reluctant to take effective counter-measures against smoking, because the tobacco consumption tax is very important for local governments and there are many farmers growing tobacco.

However, from the mid-1980s the Japanese government gradually assumed greater responsibility for tobacco control activities, especially after the privatisation of the state tobacco monopoly in 1985. It was also guided by the pressure of the international movement against smoking, especially the trend induced by the WHO, and increasingly strong Japanese public feeling against the selfish attitudes of smokers, the irritating smell of tobacco smoke and the litter problem caused by discarded cigarette ends. Consequently, there is increasing public support for restrictions on smoking, which must be actively promoted in order to reduce the environmental and public health impact of passive smoking in public places.

The Ministry of Health and Welfare launched a Committee on Tobacco in 1994 to discuss a concrete Action Plan intended to become the basis of comprehensive tobacco-control measures in the future. In 1995 the Ministry of Health and Welfare formally announced the "Action Plan against Smoking", which promoted tobacco control in Japan around three strategies:

1. prevention of smoking, which consists mainly of measures to prevent minors from taking up and developing the smoking habit;
2. separation of smoking areas from smoke-free areas, in order to eliminate or reduce the adverse effects of passive smoking;
3. assistance for smoking cessation and the encouragement of "good manners" among smokers.

The Japanese Ministry of Labour issued guidelines on restriction of smoking in the workplace in 1995. In 1996 the Personnel Affairs Agency, which deals with the health management of the public service, announced smoking policy guidelines for public sector workplaces. These guidelines indicate that the main policy of the Japanese government on tobacco control at present is the separation of smoking areas from smoke-free areas. This policy is very suited to the present social climate in Japan, as it means that health effects related to passive smoking should be minimised as far as possible. Interestingly, Japanese private sector firms are now also gradually expanding the coverage of smoke-free areas in the workplace.

In response, the above-mentioned Committee conducted a study on Guidelines for Smoking Restriction in Public Places. The Committee selected the public places as locations where smoking should be restricted. In case of indoors, the first category is the places where measures based on smoke free are desirable such as health facilities, educational institutions, and governmental offices. The second category is the places where the strong promotion of smoking restriction measures is desirable such as public transport, financial institutions, museums, sport facilities and so on. The third category is the places where the promotion of appropriate smoking restriction measures is desirable based on the initiative of the manager, such as restaurants, stores, lodging facilities, entertainment and recreational facilities and so on. The Committee selected the outdoor locations, such as sport facilities, parks, roads, and so on, too.

Nowadays, the Ministry of Health in Japan has been more active than ever in the implementation of tobacco control measures:

1. The Ministry of Health and Welfare proposed the concept of "life-style related diseases" in 1996. The Ministry announced that one of the most important causes of "life-style-related diseases" is smoking, and stresses the importance of counter-measures against smoking as a main part of health education by public health centres and municipalities nation-wide.
2. As mentioned before, the "Action Plan against Smoking" was established by the Ministry of Health and Welfare in 1995, and further progressions of anti-smoking measures were achieved by the Ministries of Labour and Education and the National Personnel Agency.
3. For the first time in its history, the Ministry of Health and Welfare described the situation of smoking and anti-smoking measures in the White Paper of Health and Welfare in 1997 under the approval of Ministry of Finance.

Conclusion

It is clear that the actual magnitude of social costs due to smoking in Japan is so great that the Japanese government must implement effective tobacco control measures. It should be borne in mind that since there is a time lag between smoking and the onset of tobacco-related diseases, the effects of anti-smoking measures, even if immediately enforced, will not become apparent for more than 20 years. Nevertheless, anti-smoking measures must be taken quickly and efficiently, and continuous evaluation of their impact is also important.

References

Hirayama, T. (1990), *Life-style and Mortality: a Large-scale Census-based Cohort Study in Japan*, Karger.

Ministry of Health and Welfare (Japan) (1993), *Smoking and Health*, 2nd edition (in Japanese), Ministry of Health and Welfare.

Ministry of Health and Welfare (Japan) (1994a), *Patients Survey 1993*, (in Japanese), Ministry of Health and Welfare.

Ministry of Health and Welfare (Japan) (1994b), *Vital Statistics 1993*, (in Japanese), Ministry of Health and Welfare.

Ministry of Health and Welfare (Japan), (1994c), *National Medical Expenditure 1993*, (in Japanese), Ministry of Health and Welfare.

Ministry of Health and Welfare (Japan) (1995), *Action Plan against Smoking*, (in Japanese), Ministry of Health and Welfare.

Ministry of Home Affairs (Japan), (1995), *White Paper on Fire Fighting 1993*, (in Japanese), Ministry of Home Affairs.

Peto, R., A.D. Lopez and B. Liu (1998), "Global tobacco mortality: monitoring the growing epidemic", in Lu, R., J. Mackay, S. Niu and R. Peto (eds.), *The Growing Epidemic: Proceedings of the Tenth World Conference on Tobacco or Health*, Beijing, 24-28 August 1997, Singapore: Springer-Verlag, in press.

Peto, R., A.D. Lopez, J. Boreham, M. Thun and C. Heath Jr (1994), *Mortality from Smoking in Developed Countries 1950-2000: Indirect Estimates from National Vital Statistics*, New York: Oxford University Press.

US Environmental Protection Agency (1992), "Population Risk of Lung Cancer From Passive Smoking", in *Smoking and Tobacco Control Monograph No.4*, Environmental Protection Agency.

Chapter 26

The Brazilian Cigarette Industry: Prospects for Consumption Reduction

Vera Luiza da Costa e Silva

This chapter is based partly on a study commissioned by the National Cancer Institute (INCA) of Brazil from the Getúlio Vargas Foundation, a Brazilian economic research institute. It uses economic data to assess the importance of tobacco to Brazil's economy and to build an economic model of tobacco consumption, with the objective of formulating new policies and strategies in tobacco control.

Tobacco production

Brazil is a major tobacco producer, ranked fourth largest in the world behind China, USA and India with 13 per cent of world tobacco leaf production during 1990-95, and total annual production of 535 000 tons in 1996 (Almeida, 1997). Tobacco growing is concentrated mainly in the Southern states of Brazil: 296 100 hectares of land was used for tobacco in Brazil during 1973-94, 71 per cent of which lies in the Southern part of the country and represents 82 per cent of the national crop (Instituto Brasileiro de Geografia Estatística (IBGE), 1994). Tobacco is also cultivated in the North-East of Brazil, particularly in the states of Alagoas and Bahia. The primary difference between cultivation in the South and the North-East is that the former area produces mainly tobacco leaf destined for cigarette manufacture, while the latter specialises in black tobacco and tobacco leaf for cigar wrapping.

Tobacco leaf production in Brazil is controlled by large multinational companies. Estimates by the Ministry of Agriculture show that it is financially advantageous for many farmers to continue growing tobacco, a situation reinforced by a relationship of interdependence between the industry and the farmer. Frequently the tobacco companies provide farmers with technical guidance and support, seeds, and chemical fertilisers, and in turn, despite the lack of a formal contract, farmers are able to sell at least part of their production to the industry.

On the other hand, there is no action by the federal government of Brazil to ensure that tobacco profits are translated into greater socio-economic benefit to the country, either by increasing income and employment in the agricultural sector, or by assuring all farmers (many of whom are smallholders) of a return higher than mere subsistence (Economist Intelligence Unit, 1976). Thus, a comprehensive tobacco control policy involving curtailment of tobacco growing must include compensatory measures for tobacco farmers. The suggestion of alternative crops, on its own, would be insufficient: measures are necessary to ensure that alternative crops are at least as profitable as tobacco.

Employment generation

Brazilian tobacco farming is mainly a family enterprise. A survey of more than 1 000 growers found that 80.6 per cent were landowners, 11 per cent were tenant farmers, and 8.4 per cent were partners (Federação dos Trabalhadores da Agricultura (FETAG), 1993). This type of crop fits perfectly into the model of family run farming that the federal government has nurtured, especially through the National Programme of Family Agriculture. Tobacco farmers are essentially small rural businesspeople, so closely linked to the industry that they can be seen as tobacco industry workers, but without the legal rights of such workers.

The economic structural adjustment process recently experienced in Brazil led to a reduction in both the number of tobacco farmers and in the industry's labour force during 1992-94. In 1992/93 there were 157 520 landowners growing tobacco, but by 1994/95 this had decreased to 132 680, mostly due to a decline in formerly stable tobacco industry demand (Associação dos Fumicultores Brasileiros (AFUBRA), 1995). However, tobacco industry registers show an increase in the number of tobacco-growing landowners to 206 000 in the 1995/96 period (Associação Brasileira das Indústrias de Fumo (ABIFUMO), 1998). Information from tobacco industry trade unions indicates that the industry's labour force decreased by 22 per cent in 1994, principally due to the introduction of mechanisation. Direct and indirect employment generated in the growing and processing sub-sectors of the industry are shown in Table 1.

Table 1. Number of direct and indirect employees in tobacco's cultivation and production, 1992-94

	Agriculture	Industry	Total
Direct	1 040 000	30 000	1 070 000
Indirect		1 465 000	1 465 000
Total	1 040 000	1 495 000	2 535 000

Source: AFUBRA (1995)

The Brazilian cigarette trade

The Brazilian cigarette trade is dominated by one company, Souza Cruz SA, controlled by the British American Tobacco Company (BAT). In 1994, Souza Cruz marketed 17 cigarettes brands in seven price categories; its share of total cigarette sales increased from 78 per cent in 1994 to 85.4 per cent in 1996 (Instituto Nielsen, 1996). Souza Cruz sells approximately 271 million cigarettes per day, and during 1994-95 was considered the leader in Brazilian agribusiness (Troccoli, 1994; 1995). In second place is Philip Morris of Brazil, which marketed 17 cigarette brands in 1994; its share of total cigarette sales in Brazil declined from 18 per cent in 1994 to 13.9 per cent in 1997. The remaining 5 per cent of cigarette sales in 1994 was distributed among other companies such as R.J. Reynolds, Sudan Tobacco Products Co., Cibrasa Tobacco, Alfredo Fantini Industry and Commerce, and Cigarros Americana.

Despite the overwhelming dominance of the Brazilian cigarette market by Souza Cruz, an intense struggle for market share is being fought between the BAT subsidiary and Philip Morris of Brazil, mainly through price cutting. In a more recent marketing strategy, Philip Morris introduced a 'kiddies-pack' containing 14 cigarettes, a way of selling cigarettes more cheaply which in effect targets children and lower-income adults.

Participation in the international tobacco trade

Brazil is one of the two leading exporters of un-manufactured tobacco in the world (see Figure 1), reserving one of the highest proportions of its tobacco crop (almost 50 per cent of total production during 1988-94) for export.

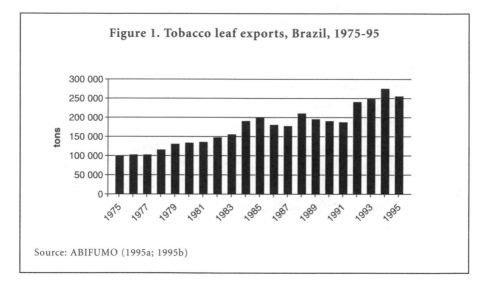

Figure 1. Tobacco leaf exports, Brazil, 1975-95

Source: ABIFUMO (1995a; 1995b)

The good quality and low price of the tobacco crop, made possible partly by the low costs of tobacco growing, assure the competitiveness of the Brazilian product. However, it is important to note that these low costs are obtained through the use of relatively cheap labour and low levels of mechanisation, reflected in comparatively low yields. Despite steady increases in the average yield of the tobacco crop from 1 156 kg per hectare during the 1970s to 1 400 kg/ha during the 1980s and 1 643 kg/ha in 1993-95, the average yield remained

34 per cent below the US and Zimbabwean averages (IBGE, 1994; US Department of Agriculture, 1995). The industry pays relatively little to producers for a kilogram of tobacco leaf, while each kilogram yields approximately 1 200 cigarettes. As the cigarette factories are highly automated, they employ little labour (30 000 directly employed workers, as opposed to total direct employment in the industry as a whole of 1 070 000). In addition, cigarette packs are light and easily stored and transported, leading to low transport and inventory costs and making this undertaking highly profitable.

The exportation of manufactured cigarettes is increasing, and they are not subject to the same excise taxes as the domestic product. In 1995 the Mercosur countries accounted for almost 12 per cent of the Brazilian tobacco companies' total revenues from exports (US Department of Agriculture, 1995). In 1996 and 1997 the Eastern European market expanded, constituting (together with other Latin American countries) the major importers of Brazilian cigarettes, mainly the international brands "Hollywood" and "Free" manufactured by Souza Cruz (US Department of Agriculture, 1997a).

Growth in cigarette production since 1985 has been associated with increasing cigarette exports, with little change in domestic consumption (Figure 2). The competitiveness of Brazilian tobacco leaf and cigarettes is evident in the industry's strong export performance during the last several years, despite initiatives in several countries which import tobacco and cigarettes to decrease smoking. The Brazilian share of world cigarette imports increased from 2 per cent in 1990 to 8 per cent in 1994 (Secretaria da Receita Federal (SRF), 1995; ABIFUMO, 1994; 1995a; 1995b). More recently, tobacco exports as a proportion of total Brazilian exports increased from 2.52 per cent in 1995 to 3.17 per cent in 1996.

Figure 2. Cigarette production and exports in Brazil, 1976-96

Source: ABIFUMO (1995a; 1995b); SRF (1995)

Cigarette consumption in Brazil

In Brazil, it has been estimated that 23.9 per cent of the population over the age of five smokes — a total of 30.6 million people. As in other countries (see

Chapters 3 and 4), a higher proportion of men than women smoke, and a high number of adolescents are starting to try cigarettes at an earlier age: 2.7 million Brazilian children and adolescents smoke. While smoking prevalence is higher in rural areas than in urban areas, no other significant regional differences can be seen (Ministério da Saúde, 1998).

Table 2. Brazilian cigarette production and exports, selected years 1976-96 (billion cigarettes)

Year	Production	Exports	Exports as % of production	Domestic consumption	Annual consumption growth (%)
1976	117.20	-	-	-	-
1980	143.16	0.462	0.3	142.7	-
1985	147.53	1.253	0.9	146.3	14.48
1990	173.28	9.889	5.7	164.1	0.86
1991	176.30	20.471	11.6	156.4	-4.69
1992	153.67	25.094	16.3	127.8	-18.29
1993	149.20	29.719	19.9	119.5	-6.49
1994	163.95	54.754	33.4	109.2	-8.62
1995	174.60	54.980	31.4	119.4	9.34
1996	182.50	63.330	34.7	119.2	-1.67

Source: ABIFUMO (1995a; 1995b); SRF (1995)

Statistics on domestic consumption of cigarettes are obtained by subtracting exports from total production, and given the steady rise in exports in recent years, domestic consumption appears to have decreased (see Table 2). However, this method probably underestimates domestic consumption, at least for the more recent years, because it does not take into consideration cigarettes that are smuggled into the country, nor false excise declarations. According to information from the industry, smuggling and excise falsifications could account for roughly 25 per cent of Brazil's total domestic consumption in 1997.

Notwithstanding the uncertainty introduced into statistics on domestic cigarette consumption by smuggling, it seems that Brazilians have been smoking less since 1990. Consumption varied during the period 1980-95, recording a 10 per cent increase between 1984 and 1991, although the overall tendency was towards a decline in domestic consumption (see Figure 3).

Descriptive analyses of cigarette consumption have shown that consumers of more expensive brands are less sensitive to price and income changes. On the other hand, consumers of cheaper cigarettes substitute brands in response to price and income changes and marketing strategies. Cigarette consumption in Brazil has varied with changes in the economy, in purchasing power (income), in cigarette prices (related mainly to changes in excise tax and marketing), and in public policies (laws, decrees, and norms that discourage smoking).

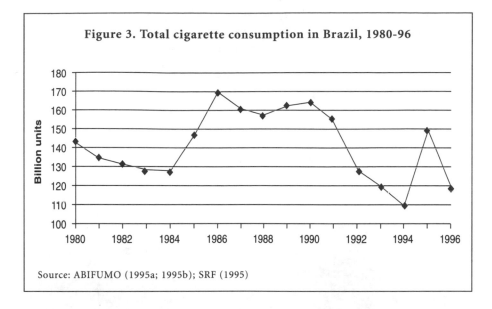

Figure 3. Total cigarette consumption in Brazil, 1980-96

Source: ABIFUMO (1995a; 1995b); SRF (1995)

Overall, the predictable inverse association between cigarette price and consumption (i.e. the lower the price the greater the consumption) held true until 1992 (see Figure 4). Thereafter, however, consumption data shows an atypical relationship, probably due to a fall in real incomes and increasing underestimation of domestic consumption by statistics due to cigarette smuggling and excise falsifications. According to more recent data, there was an increase in consumption from 1994 to 1995/96. This increase was apparently due to stabilisation of the economy, resulting in control of inflation and

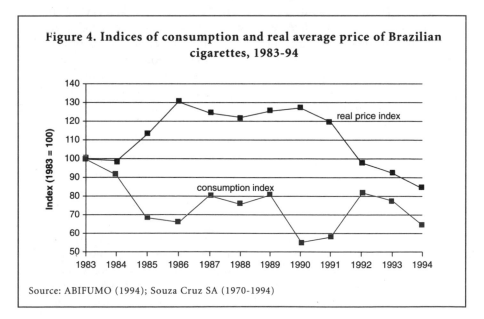

Figure 4. Indices of consumption and real average price of Brazilian cigarettes, 1983-94

Source: ABIFUMO (1994); Souza Cruz SA (1970-1994)

increasing real incomes, especially in the case of lower socio-economic groups. Nonetheless, in 1997, as the Brazilian tobacco industry has pointed out in their annual reports, a drop of 5.6 per cent in the volume of cigarette sales in the domestic market was observed.

Taxes and pricing of Brazilian cigarettes

Brazilian cigarettes are among the cheapest in the world: in 1995, the average price per pack of 20 category E cigarettes was U$1.07. Paradoxically, however, relative to other countries, tax is a high proportion of the price of Brazilian cigarettes, around 74 per cent (U$0.79) (Table 3).

Table 3. Cigarette taxes and retail prices, 1995

Country	Tax (% of retail price)	Price per pack of 20 (US$)
Denmark	83	5.40
Canada	53-70	2.34
United Kingdom	77	4.29
Brazil	74	1.07
USA	20-34	1.70
New Zealand	69	4.49
Australia	63	3.34
Taiwan	51	0.98
Japan	51	2.65

Source: ABIFUMO (1995a; 1995b)

Cigarettes are classified into 10 price categories (A to J), category A being the cheapest and category J the most expensive. Category A is also the one with the highest amount of tar, nicotine and carbon monoxide, according to chemical analysis (Ministério da Saúde, 1996) (see Table 4). Analysis of trends in the domestic market has shown that during 1993-97, consumption of category A cigarettes increased from 11.9 per cent to 49.8 per cent, with categories B, C and F having their consumption substantially reduced. Categories D and E maintained stable market shares.

There are several different types of cigarette tax, including ICMS which is a value-added tax. The taxes as a proportion of the factory price of cigarettes are given in Table 5. At the end of 1997, two states (Minas Gerais and Rio de Janeiro) increased the ICMS value-added tax from 25 per cent to 30 per cent, making the total tax in those states equivalent to 78.5 per cent of the average retail price.

Compared to other Latin American countries, Brazilian cigarette taxes are among the highest in Latin America (Table 6) — but this is not necessarily reflected in cigarette prices, which are higher still in the USA, Canada and several other countries (Tables 6 and 3). On the other hand, protectionist legislation introduced by the federal government (edict no. 613.484/69) has

Table 4. Market share, price, brand names and substance analysis of Brazilian cigarettes by category

Cate-gory	Market share (%)		Price (US$) RJ,MG (1998)	Brands (mg/cig)	Substance analysis, 1995			
	1993	'97			Nicotine (mg/cig)	Tar (mg/cig)	CO (µg/cig)	Ammonia
A	11.9	49.8	1.27	Derby Lights, Dallas.	1.4±0.1 1.06±0.09	17.1±1.25 16.12±0.18	16.11±1.10 16.01±1.27	14.96±0.34 14.02±0.34
B	18.8	1.8	1.45	Plaza, Belmont, Lark, Mustang.				
C	28.7	7.5	1.62	Hollywood, Luxor, Free, Continental, Ritz Slims, Palace, L&M Lights.	1.10±0.04 0.98±0.10	13.5±0.86 10.88±0.75	15.73±0.95 11.60±0.73	13.15±0.34 12.54±0.34
D	26.2	27.3	1.84	Marlboro, Hollywood Lights, Menthol box, L&M, Free box/ultra light/ones.	1.13±(0.05	14.96±0.26	15.34±0.89	13.24±0.34
E	11.2	11.7	2.10	Carlton, Free Slims, Galaxy, Parliament.				
F	3.2	1.9	2.54	Charm, Chancellor, John Player Special, Minister, Benson & Hedges.				
G	n.a.	n.a.	2.89	Capri				

Note: RJ = Rio de Janeiro state; MG = Minas Gerais state; n.a. = not applicable.
Source: ABIFUMO (1998); Ministério da Saúde (1996)

Table 5. Cigarette taxes as proportion of factory price, Brazil, 1997

Taxes	Tax as % of factory price	Total revenue (US$ million)
Industrial IPI	41.20	3 483
ICMS wholesale/retail	25.00	2 111
Stamp tax	4.04	341
COFINS	2.36	199
PIS	0.90	76
Total	73.50	6 210
Retail margin	8.50	713
Industry margin	18.00	1 529
Total	100.00	8 452

Source: Souza Cruz SA (1998)

eased the cash flow situation of the tobacco industry by extending the deadline of the IPI tax payment. This tax, previously collected after cigarettes had left the factory, is now collected after cigarettes are sold at the retailer. Total Brazilian cigarette tax revenue amounted to 5.4 per cent of total federal tax revenue and 3.6 per cent of total national tax revenue in 1997.

Table 6. Cigarette taxes — Mercosur, some Latin American countries, USA and Canada, 1997

Countries	Tax as % of retail price
Argentina	68.3
Brazil	73.5 (78.5 MG, RJ states)
Paraguay	13.5
Uruguay	66.5
Chile	70.6
Colombia	28.6
Costa Rica	35.7
El Salvador	43.9
Ecuador	55.2
Guatemala	53.3
Honduras	37.9
Mexico	47.8
Nicaragua	40.0
Panama	37.6
Dominican Republic	20.0
Venezuela	55.9
United States	20.0-34.0
Canada	53.0-70.0

Source: Souza Cruz SA (1998)

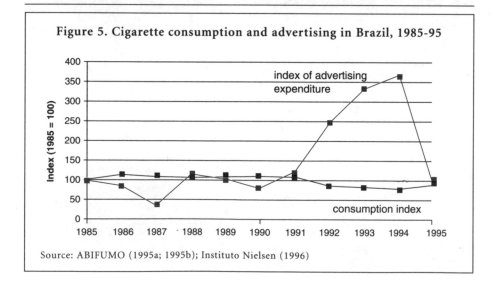

Figure 5. Cigarette consumption and advertising in Brazil, 1985-95

Source: ABIFUMO (1995a; 1995b); Instituto Nielsen (1996)

Advertising and cigarette consumption in Brazil

Apart from pricing, publicity also affects cigarette consumption. The tobacco industry tends to invest more in advertising during downswings in consumption, in order to reverse downward trends in sales. For example, a dramatic increase in cigarette advertising expenditure in Brazil occurred during 1991-95 (Figure 5), at a time when cigarette consumption was apparently declining significantly. The Brazilian tobacco industry has been for some years about the 16th biggest client of the local advertising industry, spending US$ 58.7 million in 1994, equivalent to 8.8 per cent of total advertising expenditure in Brazil of US$ 6.6 billion (Instituto Nielsen, 1996).

Cigarette consumption and changes in prices, incomes and policies

A review of the relevant economic literature and the available information on Brazilian cigarette consumption during the 1983-94 period led to the formulation of an econometric model of consumption (Becker, Grossman and Murphy, 1994), including measures of price and income elasticity for the market demands of two different groups of cigarette consumer: *rational demand* in the case of smokers with fixed preferences, and *myopic* or *narrow demand* on the part of adolescents and people with low levels of formal education and income.

This model is based on the premise that smoking, being a harmful activity, is the result of an evaluation of costs (dependence, damage to the person's own health and that of other people) and benefits (the pleasure of smoking). The myopic consumer is defined as someone with very little information about the long-term effects of smoking. They are, in other words, people with a naive outlook or with little schooling, such as children, the youth and the socio-economically disadvantaged. According to the literature, this group of myopic consumers should be the target of policies aimed at restricting tobacco consumption.

The remarks in the following sections are based on empirical analysis of the Brazilian cigarette market, and summarise the probable reactions of consumers to changes in the factors known to influence cigarette consumption.

(i) Changes in prices and income

The findings of the empirical analysis were compatible with the predictions of other, more theoretical, studies: estimates of price and income elasticities of demand showed that price increases may cause a reduction in the consumption of cigarettes, and that increases in consumer income expands their consumption.

There was little sensitivity to price variation in the short run (Table 7). For a person who smokes a pack of cigarettes per day, an increase of 10 per cent in the average price would result in a reduction in cigarette consumption of 80-136 cigarettes per year. The econometric model on which this conclusion is based was developed by Carvalho and Lobão as part of the economic study commissioned by INCA from the Fundação Getúlio Vargas.

Table 7. Econometric model of cigarette price elasticity

	Model 1	Model 2	
		Rational	Narrow
Prices:			
Short-run	-0.1118	-0.1407	-0.1962
Long-run	-0.7982	-0.4932	-0.4792
Income:			
Short-run		0.2277	0.3120
Long-run		0.7980	0.7621

Source: Chaloupka (1991); Becker, Grossman and Murphy (1994)

With regard to long-run price elasticity of demand, the same price increase of 10 per cent for the consumer suggested in the example above, would cause a consumption reduction of 344 cigarettes per year. 'Myopic' consumers (the youth and the less well-educated) were found to be more sensitive to price changes in the short-run than the rational group.

(ii) Change in public policies on tobacco consumption

It was noted that cigarette demand in Brazil underwent a structural change in price elasticity during the 3rd semester of 1990, when consumption clearly shifted to a lower level. This structural change is probably related to occupational health regulations introduced in 1990 requiring stricter controls on smoking. After that change, price elasticity of demand for both the short- and long-run increased, mainly in the 'myopic' or 'narrow' consumer group, where it almost doubled. These results suggest that changes in public policies on tobacco control influence the price elasticities of demand of both rational and 'myopic' consumers (Table 8).

Table 8. Change in price elasticity due to public policies

Year 1990	Rational consumers	Myopic consumers
Before 3rd semester:		
Short-run	-0.1407	-0.1962
Long-run	-0.4932	-0.4792
After 3rd semester:		
Short-run	-0.17	-0.35
Long-run	-0.58	-0.73

(iii) Change in price elasticity due to public policy before and after 1990

A simulation of the impact of public policy changes aimed at reducing cigarette consumption suggested a price elasticity of demand of -0.15 in the short-run, and -0.5 in the long-run.

(iv) Impact of 15 per cent price increase achieved via tax increase

Based on the above elasticities, increasing cigarette tax to 90 per cent of average retail price would increase tax revenues by 12-15.5 per cent (while reducing consumption by 1.5-3 per cent) in the short-run, and increase tax revenue 3-9 per cent (with a consumption reduction of 6-12 per cent) in the long run (Table 9).

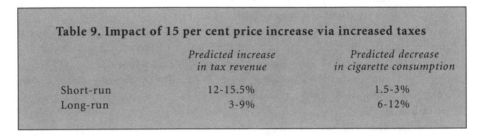

Table 9. Impact of 15 per cent price increase via increased taxes		
	Predicted increase in tax revenue	*Predicted decrease in cigarette consumption*
Short-run	12-15.5%	1.5-3%
Long-run	3-9%	6-12%

(v) Proposals to discourage tobacco consumption: impacts of public policies

The above analysis suggests that an efficient way to discourage tobacco consumption would be to increase the costs of smoking, either by using monetary measures, or by turning cigarette smoke into a major inconvenience. Firstly, with regard to increasing the final price of cigarettes to consumers by increasing cigarette taxes, the situation in Brazil at present is that:
- taxes account for 74 per cent of the retail price of cigarettes;
- despite high taxes, Brazilian cigarette prices are among the lowest in the world;
- all taxes have a greater burden on those with the least mobility: consumers addicted to tobacco, tobacco producers and cigarette manufacturers; and
- consumers that are tobacco-dependent must be the most affected in the long-run.
  Secondly, with regard to turning smoking into an inconvenience:
- the available statistics suggest that social norms influencing tobacco use are probably responsible for the changes in the structural demands for cigarettes; a practical example in Brazil was the fall in consumption observed a few months after the introduction of the warning labels on the cigarette packs in compliance with a 1995 government decree;
- these social norms make the consumer more sensitive to price variation, increasing the price elasticity of demand (with a lower impact among rational consumers and a greater impact among 'myopic' consumers).

(vi) Research proposals and needs in the economic area

Some research needs were identified after this data collection and analysis. Some strategies also have to be launched in order to achieve results in the economic area of tobacco control. Among them, some proposals are:

1. a study to analyse the effects of taxation on the tobacco production chain to evaluate the repercussions of cigarette price increases on tobacco growers, manufacturers, distributors and consumers;
2. a survey of the cigarette consumption profile in Brazil, to be included in the National Survey of Household Budgets;
3. finalisation of the tobacco cost-benefit analysis study;
4. to update, annually, the economic data on the tobacco industry;
5. to arrange a meeting with government representatives from the economic, planning and agricultural sectors to elaborate a policy proposal that takes into consideration the country's needs, at all levels;
6. to suggest the addition of mechanisms to register specific information about production, manufacture and commercialisation of tobacco products, in the data collection forms of the various government departments;
7. to collect data on stratification of cigarette consumption by state, based on the data captured in the administration of the ICMS (state value-added tax); and
8. to publish the economic study along with its conclusions and recommendations.

Conclusion: recommendations of the National Cancer Institute

As the agency in charge of national policy formulation on cancer and tobacco control in Brazil, the National Cancer Institute (INCA), in accordance with the evidence of the present study and as a WHO Collaborating Centre, advances the following recommendation for action:

- Formulate a comprehensive government tobacco control programme: the control of tobacco cannot be the exclusive responsibility of the Health Sector. It must be discussed with the commitment of the legislature and all relevant Ministries within the executive branch of government (including Finance, Agriculture, Justice, Education, and Labour).
- Increase taxes on cigarettes, in order to increase the cost of smoking to consumers.
- Work towards standardisation of cigarette prices and taxes in all Mercosur countries.
- Create mechanisms to restrict smuggling.
- Increase educational activities and campaigns, and prohibit tobacco advertising.
- Encourage tobacco farmers to switch to alternative crops.
- Intensify care for active and passive smokers.
- Earmark part of cigarette tax revenue for tobacco control activities.
- Formulate legislation to regulate nicotine, tar and carbon monoxide levels in cigarettes.

- Prohibit genetic and chemical manipulation of tobacco.
- Create mechanisms to inspect tobacco products throughout the entire production process.

References

Almeida, F.R de F. (1997), "Panorama internacional", *Agroanalysis*, August.

Associação Brasileira das Indústrias de Fumo (ABIFUMO) (1985-95), "Índices de consumo", ABIFUMO database.

Associação Brasileira das Indústrias de Fumo (ABIFUMO) (1994), *Relatório Perfil da Indústria do Fumo*, ABIFUMO.

Associação Brasileira das Indústrias de Fumo (ABIFUMO) (1995a), *Boletim Informativo*, ABIFUMO.

Associação Brasileira da Indústria do Fumo (ABIFUMO) (1995b), "Consumo Annual" in *Perfil da Indústria do Fumo*, ABIFUMO database.

Associação Brasileira das Indústrias de Fumo (ABIFUMO) (1998), *Boletim Informativo*, ABIFUMO database.

Associação dos Fumicultores Brasileiros (AFUBRA) (1995), *Relatório Anual*.

Becker, G.S., M. Grossman and K.M. Murphy (1994), "An empirical analysis of cigarette addiction", *American Economic Review*, 84:396-418.

Chaloupka, F.J. (1991), "Rational addictive behaviour and cigarette smoking", *Journal of Political Economy*, 99:722-42.

The Economist (1981), "Fumo em Folha: sua contribuição para o desenvolvimento sócio-econômico do terceiro mundo", Separata da Monografia.

Economist Intelligence Unit (1976), *Acordo Geral de Tarifas e Comércio*.

Federação dos Trabalhadores da Agricultura (FETAG) (1993), "Produção Gaúcha dos diferentes tipos de fumo", *Boletim Informativo*.

Instituto Brasileiro de Geografia Estatística (IBGE) (1994), *Anuário Estatístico*.

Instituto Nielsen (1996), "Investimento em Publicidade", in *Relatório da Fundação Getúlio Vargas/ Ministério da Saúde*.

Ministério da Fazenda (1994), *Participação do Fumo na Receita do Imposto sobre Produtos Industrializados (IPI)*, Receita Federal database.

Ministério da Saúde (1996), *Análise das substâncias conridas nos cigarros brasileiros*, Rio de Janeiro: Instituto Nacional de Câncer — Coordenação Nacional de Controle do Tabagismo e Prevenção do Câncer.

Ministério da Saúde (1998), *Falando sobre Tabagismo*, Rio de Janeiro: Instituto Nacional de Câncer — Coordenação Nacional de Controle do Tabagismo e Prevenção do Câncer.

SECEX (1996), *Mercadorias por países e portos*, Estatísticas da SECEX.

Secretaria da Receita Federal (SRF) (1995), *Consumo Anual de Relatório do Perfil da Indústria do Fumo*, SRF database.

Souza Cruz SA (1970-1994), *Preço Médio dos Cigarros*, Souza Cruz SA database.

Souza Cruz SA (1998), *Annual Balance Sheet*.

Troccoli I.R. (1994), "Comentário: A conjuntura do Agrobisness", *Agroanalysis*.

Troccoli I.R. (1995), "Comentário: A conjuntura do Agrobisness", *Agroanalysis*.

US Department of Agriculture (1995), *Tobacco World Markets and Trade*, Circular Series.

US Department of Agriculture (1997a), *Tobacco World Markets and Trade*, Circular Series.

Epilogue

Where Do We Go From Here?

Iraj Abedian and Prabhat Jha

This book represents a first attempt to outline the large set of issues involved in the economics of tobacco control. By its nature, the book asks as many questions as it answers, but it does offer a broad platform for subsequent global debates and research.

National tobacco control policies have inherent limitations. In an increasingly integrated world economic order, where trade barriers and border controls are diminishing, public policy in one country has trans-national repercussions. These "externality effects" could be both positive and negative and are of various types. Increased trade, for example, may produce pressures to lower entry barriers to manufactured goods. On the other hand, bans on advertising and promotion in one country may have an impact on neighbouring countries, while taxation in one country effects policies in neighbouring countries. Moreover, global knowledge on tobacco and its consequences for physical and economic health is increasing. The profound impact of tobacco on health may harm human capital development, and such information may influence both popular beliefs and public policy choices. In other words, it is unlikely that most countries can set their own tobacco control policies without consideration of the global framework. Depending on the prevailing global framework, the presence of public policy externalities dictates that countries follow different policies in order to maximise their self-interest.

It is therefore instructive to consider policy options within a 'game-theoretic' framework. In principle, the game may be played in two settings: one is when the global framework is co-ordinated and enforced; the other is within an unco-ordinated international framework. Appropriate national policies would vary under each of these conditions. The notion of 'appropriateness' in economic terms relates to the concept of optimality of a policy mix. Herein lie potential differences between the economic and the public health communities . For some in the public health community, an optimal (but arguably unachievable) tobacco control policy might be an unqualified elimination of tobacco consumption altogether, through demand and supply reduction. This, it may be argued, leads to the avoidance of social welfare losses caused by smoking; as a corollary, then, social welfare is maximised. For some economists, by contrast, an optimal policy mix may take on other meanings, depending on the goals of the policy.

Optimal policy, at one level, may be interpreted as the mix of tobacco control measures that offer, at the margin, equivalent cost-effectiveness. At another level, an optimal policy mix may refer to a package of policies focused on demand and supply aspects of tobacco given a particular economic structure. Optimality in this sense would tend to emphasise demand reduction as the most effective means of reducing consumption, but would need to take into account the size and trade patterns of the tobacco industry in a country. In this respect supply considerations may divide countries into the categories 'self-sufficient', 'net-importers', and 'net-exporters'. The majority of countries are 'net-importers'; meaning their local consumption exceeds their domestic production. Only a handful of countries such as Brazil, Malawi, Zimbabwe and the USA are 'net-exporters'. Given that the tobacco industry is profitable world-wide and based in every country, the *perceived* impact of the tobacco industry may also enter into supply considerations, or at least into the political economy of tobacco control.

The concept of an optimal policy mix towards tobacco control is as (if not more) relevant at the global level. Clearly, a mix of world health, investment, trade, and policing policies is needed to ensure effectiveness in this regard. Within a game-theoretic framework, unless the global backdrop is made clear and consistent, it is difficult to define a common optimal policy mix at the national level. At present there are no international goals for reducing consumption, in the way there is for example on ozone emissions. For several reasons, as discussed in this book, there is no consensus among economists on what constitutes, if anything, optimal consumption. There is some movement towards a Framework Convention for Tobacco Control that may permit countries to adopt policies more closely linked to an optimal global policy. In the absence of an integrated and binding global protocol, however, it is only rational for each country to look after its own self-interest. The global outcome, as is well described in the game theory, is clearly sub-optimal. However, individual countries may well arrive at an optimal policy mix with above-average 'gains'. As a corollary, there would be countries with substantial 'losses'. The definition of such gains or losses could vary, for example with long-term health or short-term job losses.

At the national level, tobacco control policies continue to revolve around policy instruments such as taxes, advertising (both for and against tobacco consumption), and property rights. The efficacy of taxes depends mainly on the 'price elasticity' of smokers and their income levels. As such, in developing countries, taxes are a far more effective tool for reducing tobacco consumption. However, some key questions remain to be further explored. For instance: How does price elasticity differ among the various income groups? What is the 'smuggling elasticity' of tax increases, and how does this vary by country?

Counter-advertising and complete bans on all forms of tobacco advertising and promotion constitute the two key policy instruments for information dissemination with regard to smoking. Both these issues are problematic. Banning tobacco advertising is often an emotive issue. It leads to a number of wider issues ranging from promoting a legal product to the boundaries of government interventions. An array of issues remains to be further researched. The link between advertising and consumption itself has to be further explored. A closely related issue is the informational content of cigarette advertising. Whereas regulation of advertising so far has focused on issues regarding health warnings, there is much room to concentrate on the misinformation contained in tobacco advertising. In this case, the principle of advertising is left intact, but the content thereof is subject to regulation.

A further aspect of smoking is the assignment of property rights. In most societies, by default and by historical practice the constitutional initiative has been given to smokers. Non-smokers consequently have had to lobby to acquire the right to clean air, and thus bear the cost of acquiring the right to clean air. Clearly, an explicit re-assignment of property rights is needed, and is important for a number of reasons. Firstly, it would make it possible that the non-pecuniary cost of smoking is born by the smoker who is the primary 'beneficiary' of the consumption (based on the assumption that the smoker derives some satisfaction from his/her smoking). For example, banning smoking in public buildings forces the smoker to go out of the building for smoking; this is generally a relatively high non-pecuniary price. Clearly, different individuals would have a different 'price-elasticity' with respect to this non-pecuniary component of the cost of smoking. Secondly, by re-assigning the relevant property rights, much of the glamour commonly attached to smoking would be dissipated. This has substantial long-term effects on perceptions, particularly those of children and youth. On the whole, therefore, much research remains to be done on property rights and smoking.

Considerable variation exists from country to country (or even within countries, as in India and China) in the epidemiological status of the tobacco epidemic, economic systems, taxation collection, and institutional capacity. Thus a need exists for local analysis of the costs and benefits of tobacco consumption, and for tailored economic evaluation of tobacco control policies. Such efforts, building on the South African model, have begun in several low- and middle-income countries, such as Sri Lanka. A forthcoming World Bank report on tobacco control policies will emphasise the importance of taxation and will draw on newer country-level analyses, including data that has emerged from the US debate on the tobacco industry. More recently, the World Health Organisation has announced that tobacco control will be a priority for its programming.

These efforts bode well for future analytical contributions to the debate on the economics of tobacco control. As the global research on the economics of tobacco control gathers momentum, and country experience accumulates, much more detail needs to be known about the fine-tuning of public policy towards tobacco control. The contents of this book would need to be revised accordingly.

Yet, such research need not delay immediate action at country level. Measures to reduce demand have been shown to be effective in developed countries, and adult smoking rates in the UK and many other Western countries have decreased by half or more over the last 20 years. The European Union will ban advertising and promotion over the next decade. The final resolution of the conference in South Africa on *The Economics of Tobacco: Towards an Optimal Policy Mix* called on governments world-wide to introduce immediate tax increases above the rate of inflation, and to ban advertising and promotion of tobacco products. Such actions would lead to significant decreases in the global tobacco epidemic, which if left unchecked will almost certainly kill about 100 million adults world-wide over the next 20 years, half of them in middle-age.

Subject Index

Note: b = box; f = figure; fn = footnote; t = table

353

Bibliographical Index

Note: b = box; f = figure; fn = footnote; t = table